Papers on

# BIOLOGICAL
# MEMBRANE
# STRUCTURE

# Papers on
# BIOLOGICAL
# MEMBRANE
# STRUCTURE

*Selected by*

**DANIEL BRANTON**
*University of California, Berkeley*

**RODERIC B. PARK**
*University of California, Berkeley*

Little, Brown and Company   BOSTON

LIBRARY OF CONGRESS CATALOG CARD NO. 68–14620

FIRST PRINTING

Published simultaneously in Canada
by Little, Brown & Company (Canada) Limited

PRINTED IN THE UNITED STATES OF AMERICA

# FOREWORD

Biologists now agree that membranes are a ubiquitous cell structure. Plasma membranes surround the living cell substance of both prokaryotic and eukaryotic cells. In eukaryotic cells there is further elaboration of specialized internal membranes which form the boundaries of many intracellular organelles. It is not the ubiquity of membranes, however, which is most interesting to the biologist, but the unsolved problems of membrane structure and function. Eventually, the details of membrane molecular architecture must be related to such functions as ion accumulation, selective permeability, quantum conversion in photosynthesis, oxidative phosphorylation, and nerve conduction. These are but some of the membrane-associated phenomena we do not understand. Our lack of understanding results in part from some unique aspects of membrane chemistry. First, the membrane is a highly structured environment and some reactions which occur within it behave as solid state rather than solution phenomena. Second, except for myelin, red blood cells, and the internal membranes of mitochondria and chloroplasts, the chemical composition of membranes is largely unknown. This is because it is hard to accumulate large amounts of membrane of a specific kind and because, until recently, lipids were difficult to analyze once they were obtained. Finally, membrane proteins themselves are notoriously hard to handle because of their insolubility in water. It may be somewhat surprising then that so many detailed and diverse models of membrane structure have been published. The diversity of these models undoubtedly reflects the growing evidence that membrane structure and composition vary considerably in relation to membrane function.

New observations in membrane research have often not precluded the validity of older ones, and many of the "classical" papers remain cogent and useful to the contemporary worker who must reconcile his results with earlier observations. It is the purpose of this collection to present some of these early papers as well as some of the more recent ones which form the basis of our present concepts of membrane structure.

We have divided our collection of papers into three sections. Section I includes the earlier models of membrane structure that were developed in an attempt to explain permeability and surface properties. The second section includes papers in which direct observation of membrane structure, using X-ray diffraction and electron microscopy, began to take precedence over functional explanations as a basis for constructing models of membrane structure. Finally, in Section III, papers are presented which attempt to correlate both functional and structural observations on membranes into a consistent model of membrane architecture for a given membrane type.

We thank the authors and holders of copyrights for permitting us to reprint the papers in the collection. In particular we express our appreciation to those who loaned us rare reprints and original photographs for reproduction.

Mrs. H. E. Mueller and Mr. A. O. A. Pfeifhofer provided generous help with some of the translations and we are most grateful to them as well as to Mrs. Eleanor Crump for her extraordinarily patient help in assemblying the collection.

DANIEL BRANTON
RODERIC B. PARK
*Berkeley, October 1967*

# CONTENTS

# CONTENTS

*Pagination of the papers in this collection is indicated by the bold-face number centered at the bottom of the page. Other page numbers appearing on certain papers refer to original publication.*

# INTRODUCTION

## PART I. MEMBRANE PERMEABILITY AND SURFACE PROPERTIES

Early observations with the light microscope demonstrated that organisms were composed of cells with discrete boundaries. These boundaries appeared to differ for plant and animal cells, however, in that plant cells were generally bounded by a rather inflexible cell wall, while animal cells possessed a much less obvious and more flexible boundary. For a long time it was believed that the plant cell wall was the cell boundary and thus differed in a fundamental way from animal cells; in fact, the older German literature used the word cell membrane to designate the plant cell wall. But, once plant cells were observed in hypertonic medium, the similarity between plant and animal cell boundaries became more apparent. Under these conditions plant cells plasmolyzed and a cell boundary similar to that of animal cells separated from the cell wall. Plasmolysis not only revealed the essential similarity of plant and animal cell boundaries, but also provided one of the earliest experimental techniques for studying their characteristics.

The nature of the protoplasmic boundary in plant and animal cells has fascinated biologists for over a hundred years. Although all present-day students of cell surfaces readily accept the plasma membrane as the physical manifestation of the boundary between the protoplasm and the external medium, this total acceptance came about in relatively recent times. The experimental evidence for a plasma membrane can be traced to observations on the plasmolysis of plant cells in which the cell boundary was shown to have differential permeability. Using this method, Pfeffer (50) demonstrated the differential permeability of the cytoplasm, and DeVries (14) showed that isolated plant vacuoles also behaved as osmometers.

While these experiments established the presence of a differentially permeable layer around and within cells, they did not exclude the possibility that the membrane was merely a layer of cytoplasm organized by its contact with the external medium. That the membrane was a phase of definite extent, different from the cytoplasm, was most elegantly demonstrated by Janet Plowe (51)* in 1930. Her experiments on isolated plant protoplasts proved conclusively that the plasma membrane existed as a structural entity separate from the remainder of the cytoplasm. Interestingly, she makes no mention of Overton's relevant paper which had been published thirty years previously.

* An asterisk means the paper is included in this text.

**1**

Before any direct analyses of individual or isolated membranes were attempted, the chemical composition of the plasma membrane was inferred from its permeability properties. In 1899, Overton (47)* summarized the results of his experiments on the permeability of plant plasma membranes. Because these experiments showed that nonpolar substances, such as diethyl ether, penetrate cells very rapidly, he suggested that a lipoid film, possibly containing lecithin and cholesterol, might cover the outer layer of protoplasm. This suggestion was remarkably correct as far as it went, but it failed to account for the rapid penetration of polar substances, such as water, into cells. Later workers attempted to resolve this deficiency by proposing the existence of a membrane which contained both polar and nonpolar paths for solute entry.

One of the first direct analyses of cell membranes was carried out by Gorter and Grendel (27)* on ghosts from plasmolyzed blood cells. The area covered by a monolayer of the lipids extracted from these membranes was determined in the newly developed Langmuir trough. This monomolecular area was found to be twice that of the membrane surfaces from which the lipids had been extracted, and for this reason Gorter and Grendel proposed that "Chromocytes are covered by a layer of fatty substances that is two molecules thick." The research reported in this paper appears to be the experimental origin of membrane models which use an extended (smectic) lipid bilayer as a principal feature. Although Gorter and Grendel's experiments have been criticized on the grounds that the lipid extraction was incomplete and that the area calculation was too small, these two errors apparently compensated each other, since a reinvestigation of red blood cell lipids, using an improved Gorter and Grendel type of experiment, confirmed the original conclusion (3).

While studies of membrane composition continued, the physical properties of membranes were also investigated. Surface tension measurements, in particular, provided information which was difficult to reconcile with the supposed lipid composition of the membrane. The first speculations concerning surface tensions at cell surfaces were aimed to a greater extent at solving the process of cell movement and pseudopodia formation, rather than examining the detailed structure of membrane surfaces. Gad (25), in 1878, showed that drops of a number of biological oils (storage triglycerides such as olive and cod liver oils) produced pseudopodia when exposed to basic solutions. This can be explained by the fact that saponification of the fats takes place at the surface of the fat droplet, yielding fatty acid salts that produce local changes in the surface tension. A diagram, from Gad's paper, of a cod liver oil drop in basic solution is shown in Figure 1.

Further studies were made, the results of which could be explained in terms of local changes in surface tension of oil drops under investigation. When Overton's permeability studies also suggested the presence of a lipoid film at the cell surface, the relevance of these oil drop experiments was greatly enhanced. However, one important piece of evidence was lacking for the theory that membranes were primarily lipoidal in nature, namely, measurements of

2

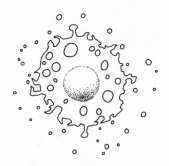

FIGURE 1. The microscopic appearance of a drop of cod liver oil suspended in a 0.06% $Na_2CO_3$ solution. After Gad (25). The irregular shape of the drop is caused by local changes in surface tension due to hydrolysis of the cod liver oil.

interfacial tensions actually present at cell surfaces. No concerted effort was made to obtain these data until the work of Harvey and his colleagues in the 1930's. [See the review by Harvey in 1954 (29)]. These accurate studies were made possible by the development of adequate instruments and the selection of suitable biological material. One instrument was the du Noüy tensimeter (16) which, with the appropriate corrections, could accurately measure interfacial tensions. This instrument records the force required to pull a horizontally placed wire loop through an interface between two liquids. From these data one can then calculate the force per unit length of wire surface (i.e., twice the circumference of the loop), which is a direct measure of surface tension. By using this technique, it was found that interfacial tensions between olive oil or castor oil and water were typically 15–16 dynes/cm. A second instrument vital to these studies was the microscope centrifuge (28) in which suitable cells, generally *Arbacia* eggs, could be observed in a centrifugal field. If the suspending medium had approximately the same density as the egg, the heavy portions (yolk platelets, nucleus, mitochondria) and light portions (oil droplets) of the egg separated under the influence of the field and exerted a distending force on the egg membrane (see Figure 2). From the density and volumes of these portions of the egg, the distending force could be calculated. The distance in centimeters around the distended egg could be measured, and the force/length (surface tension) of the cell membrane could be calculated. In these calculations it was always assumed first that the resistance to deformation was totally due to the plasma membrane and not to restraining forces within the cytoplasm, and second that the membrane was inelastic in behavior. Although neither of these conditions was strictly met, they probably did not introduce serious errors (29). The centrifuge microscope could also be used to measure the force required to distort an oil drop in the presence of various surrounding media, and thus calculate the interfacial tension between the oil drop and the external medium. Using the centrifuge microscope, Harvey obtained surface tensions ranging from 0.2 to 3.0 dynes/cm for *Arbacia*, *Amoeba dubia*, rabbit macrophages, and frog leukocytes. Danielli and Harvey (13)* showed that these tensions were of a much lower value than the interfacial tensions between immiscible lipoids such as mackerel oil and sea water (7 dynes/cm). It was therefore necessary to abandon the 19th century hypothesis that cell movements could be explained by local lowering of

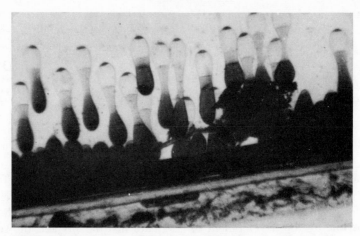

FIGURE 2. Centrifuged, unfertilized *Arbacia punctulata* eggs on a microscope centrifuge slide showing various stages as an egg breaks apart into two halves. Centrifugal direction down. The order of stratification in the eggs is oil (top), nucleus, clear layer, mitochondria, yolk, pigment (bottom). Many heavy half eggs are shown at the bottom of the slide. From the work of E. B. and E. N. Harvey (28).

surface tensions. Similar results were obtained when Danielli and Harvey (13)* and Harvey and Shapiro (31) measured surface tensions of oil drops in mackerel eggs. These oil drops in eggs or egg extracts again had surface tensions of only 0.8 dynes/cm rather than the 15 dynes/cm which would be expected for an oil-water interface. Some surface-active substance was apparently lowering the interfacial tensions of the oil drop. Danielli and Harvey concluded from ammonium sulphate precipitation experiments that the substance in egg cytoplasm which lowered the interfacial tension was protein. It was then possible to explain the low surface tension of the oil drop by assuming that the drop was composed of oriented lipids whose polar ends faced the water and were covered with a layer of protein. This model is shown in Figure 3A (see page 6).

The similarity between cell surface tensions and surface tensions of oil-protein complexes provided the basic material from which Danielli and Davson constructed their plasma membrane model. This model (see Figure 3B) is formed from two surfaces resembling those found on an oil drop covered with a layer of protein (see Figure 3A). The lipids are oriented with their polar ends toward the water and are covered with a layer of protein. The nonpolar region between the two lipid layers is unspecified in thickness. In this sense the model is similar to an oil drop forcibly flattened in an aqueous protein solution so that the two sides of the drop are almost appressed. The original Danielli-Davson model was developed further over the next twenty years to include polar pores and to establish the amount of lipid material on the membrane, thereby defining the membrane thickness. The most recent model appeared in 1954 (Figure 3C) and was soon followed by Robertson's unit membrane model in 1959 (see Section II).

The arguments supporting this often-quoted model gloss over one very important point. The composition of mackerel oil, squirrel hake oil, and whiting oil (Harvey and Shapiro) is certainly not that of membrane lipid. Fish oils are triglycerides while membrane lipids contain highly polar groups as in phospho-, galacto- and sulfolipids. Triglycerides are at best very poor detergents, retaining their immiscibility with water under almost all conditions. The very fact that they can exist as a separate liquid phase in cells and do not dissolve in existing membranes is an indication of their incompatibility with membrane lipids. Polar lipids on the other hand are effective detergents. Danielli (11) showed in 1937, several years after the Danielli-Davson membrane model was proposed, that polar lipids, and phospholipids in particular, were very effective in lowering interfacial tension between water and bromobenzene. The interfacial tension dropped from 40 dynes/cm to 14 dynes/cm upon addition of 1 percent lecithin to the two-phase system. Fatty acids lowered the interfacial tension to that of cell membranes when titrated to a basic pH. One can guess that this should also have been the case for lecithin, although these data are not reported. Would Danielli and Davson have proposed the same model had these data on polar lipids as agents for lowering surface tension been available two years earlier? Granted the fact that membrane surfaces are polar and the interior of membranes mostly nonpolar, the unique assignment of either proteins or lipids to a given region of the membrane cannot be based on the simple assumption that proteins are polar and lipids are nonpolar. Danielli's data (11) demonstrate clearly that lipid molecules possess both polar and nonpolar regions and the same property has been shown by Criddle *et al.*, for membrane proteins (10).

## PART II. MEMBRANE STRUCTURE EXAMINED BY PROBING RADIATION

During the next thirty years the application of refined physical techniques to the study of membrane structure led to an elaboration of the molecular model of the membrane suggested by Danielli and Davson. Among the more important of these techniques were polarization microscopy, X-ray diffraction analysis, and electron microscopy. The first two techniques provided unique information about the molecular order and dimensions of biological structures such as nerve myelin, while the last provided the first direct, detailed image of membranes and demonstrated that the polarization microscope and X-ray diffraction analyses of nerve myelin were relevant if not crucial to an understanding of certain membrane structures.

Extensive light and polarization microscope studies of myelin were undertaken during the late 19th and early 20th centuries, not because of any particular knowledge relating myelin to cell membranes but because of general interest in the anatomy and physiology of the nervous system. Polarization microscopy demonstrated that nerve tissue was strongly birefringent (66) and

Oil Phase

Aqueous Phase

Fig. 3A

Exterior

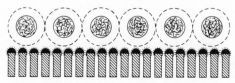

Lipoid

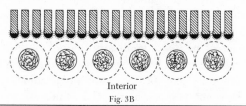

Interior

Fig. 3B

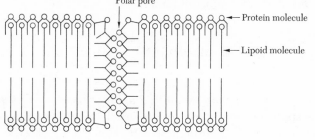

Fig. 3C

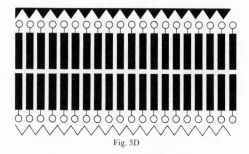

Fig. 3D

6

the high degree of molecular organization indicated by these findings attracted considerable attention.

The polarization microscope could be a useful tool for studying myelin because of its ability to measure the interaction of polarized light with small (less than a wavelength of light), organized, structural or molecular arrays within cells or tissues. Such organized arrays are generally anisotropic and can transmit light vibrating in one plane at a different velocity from light vibrating perpendicular to this plane. When polarized light vibrating in one plane enters a birefringent structure it behaves as though resolved into two rays which follow similar paths but vibrate in mutually perpendicular planes and travel at different rates. Because they travel at different rates the two rays emerge from the birefringent material out of phase (one ray is considered to be retarded) and the resultant light is elliptically polarized. In the polarization microscope the light entering the specimen is polarized by a polarizer and the rays of elliptically polarized light which exit from the specimen are examined through the analyzer. The direction of vibration of the fast- and slow-moving light components in an anisotropic material may be identified by using a crystal of known birefringent properties. When this crystal, generally known as a compensator, is placed in the optical path and rotated in the plane normal to the beam, it will alternately add to the effect of the specimen or subtract from it. By using the known optical properties of the compensator, the unknown optical properties of the specimen may be deduced.

For many biological materials, such as myelin, there exists a unique axis, the optical axis, with respect to which the structure (molecules or molecular aggregates) is arranged symmetrically. Such materials are called uniaxial. The velocity of light traveling along this axis (i.e., vibrating perpendicular to this axis) is the same whatever the azimuth in which the vibrations occur. This axis is normally chosen as a reference axis.

The refractive index (ratio of the velocity of light in vacuum to its velocity in the substance) for any component vibrating perpendicular to the optic axis is designated as the "ordinary" refractive index ($\omega$). The refractive index for the component vibrating in the plane perpendicular to the plane of vibration of the ordinary component is designated as the "extraordinary" refractive in-

FIGURE 3A. Molecular structure of an oil, aqueous egg content interface. Hydrated protein molecules on bottom and oil molecules on top. Adapted from J. F. Danielli and E. N. Harvey in the *Journal of Cellular Physiology*, 5:491, 1935, with permission of J. F. Danielli and the publisher.

FIGURE 3B. A model for cell membrane structure adapted from J. F. Danielli and Hugh Davson in the *Journal of Cellular Physiology*, 5:498, 1935, with permission of J. F. Danielli and the publisher. A lipid layer of undefined thickness is covered on each side by globular proteins.

FIGURE 3C. A refinement of the original Danielli and Davson model — adapted from Danielli, *Collston Papers*, 7:8, 1954, with permission of the author. This model is of defined thickness, shows pore structures and is a bimolecular lipid leaflet stabilized by absorbed protein monolayers.

FIGURE 3D. The molecular structure of the unit membrane adapted from J. D. Robertson in the *Biochemicaι Society Symposium*, 16:29, 1959, with permission of the author and the Biochemical Society. This model is also a refinement of the original Danielli and Davson model in which thickness is defined and the protein exists on the exterior of the membrane as spread monolayers.

dex ($\epsilon$). If $\epsilon$ is greater than $\omega$, the material is said to show positive birefringence; when $\epsilon$ is less than $\omega$ the birefringence is termed negative. The sign of the double refraction is a very important datum in reconstructing an unknown structure, since the relative values of the indices of refraction ($\omega$ and $\epsilon$) can be related in a predictable fashion to the orientation of molecules within an organized structure. For example, the index of refraction for light traveling through a crystalline array of long-chain fatty acids will be greater for the component vibrating parallel to the length of the fatty acid molecules than for the component vibrating perpendicular to this length. Where the molecules constituting a structure are themselves anisotropically oriented, the birefringence of the structure is termed intrinsic. Thus intrinsic birefringence is found in systems where the bonds within or between molecules have a regular asymmetry. A second type of birefringence, termed form birefringence, is due to the regular orientation of molecular aggregates separated from each other by phase boundaries. Form birefringence is found in composite structures in which the individual structural unit, e.g., a membrane, is small when compared with the wavelength of light, but large when compared with the molecules of which it is composed. Although both intrinsic and form birefringence are due to the morphological properties of the object, the former is due to a crystalline array of asymmetric molecules, whereas the latter is caused by the regular distribution of supramolecular structures. Operationally the two may be distinguished because form birefringence (and not intrinsic birefringence) varies as a function of the refractive index of the mounting liquid between the supramolecular aggregates. By using immersion media of different refractive indices, one can construct a curve of birefringence plotted against the index of refraction. At the position of minimum anisotropy, any residual birefringence is considered intrinsic.

Although several investigators before him had described the optical properties of nerves, it remained for W. J. Schmidt (55)* to derive a reasonable model of myelin which accounted for both its strong positive intrinsic birefringence and its weak negative form birefringence. Schmidt postulated that monomolecular layers of lipid molecules oriented in the sheath with their longitudinal axes running radially, alternated with layers of protein lamellae oriented parallel to the surface of the sheath. Some aspects of Schmidt's model proved incorrect, particularly the idea that each protein layer consisted of many individual discrete lamellar aggregates. But the general molecular orientation that he attributed to the constituent lipids and proteins was confirmed by others (4, 56), and strongly supported by the X-ray diffraction studies of F. O. Schmitt and his co-workers.

As in the case of Schmidt, F. O. Schmitt *et al.*'s study of nerve myelin (57)* was not intended as an investigation of membrane organization, but rather as an investigation of molecular organization in the tissue which provided the physical substratum for impulse propagation. Because of the extremely regular arrangement of component molecules and supramolecular aggregates in myelin, significant morphological conclusions could be derived from analysis by means of X-ray diffraction.

X-ray diffraction techniques can be used for an analysis of biological systems because wavelengths of X rays are of the order of 1 Å, i.e., small when compared with the sizes of the lipid and protein molecules of membranes. In essence, the technique consists of passing a beam of collimated X rays through the material to be analyzed and placing beyond this a photographic plate to record the diffraction pattern. The X ray passing through the material will be diffracted and give rise to an interference pattern on the photographic plate. According to Bragg's law, dimensions of regular repeating units within the material can be calculated from measured distances and angles in the resultant interference pattern. The larger the spacings within the material the smaller will be the distances between the spots or bands and the center of the diffraction pattern (see Figure 4). Thus the image which forms close to this center, i.e., the low-angle diffraction pattern, must be studied if the relatively large spacings (from ca. 20–500 Å) found in many biological materials are to be analyzed.

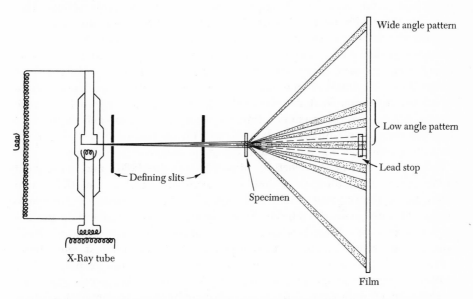

FIGURE 4. Diagram of an X-ray diffraction arrangement for biological specimens. The position of the wide angle and small angle pattern on the film is indicated.

Although X-ray diffraction methods had previously been applied to the study of nerve myelin structure, Schmitt, Bear, and Clark (57)[*] were the first to examine the low-angle diffraction pattern and discover the unexpectedly large, ca. 170 Å, spacing in fresh myelinated frog nerves. As a result, Schmitt and his co-workers were able to suggest the dimensions of the basic repeating structures which W. J. Schmidt had postulated for the myelin sheath. Subsequent diffraction data and further analysis led Schmitt, Bear, and Palmer (58) to the conclusion that the myelin sheath is composed of smectic lipid layers wrapped concentrically about the axon, with proteins intercalated between the lipid layers. Thus, F. O. Schmitt's models, derived from X-ray diffraction analysis, provided powerful confirmation of W. J. Schmidt's model derived from birefringence methods.

Cogent as were these arguments concerning the molecular architecture and repeat dimensions within the myelin sheath, it is all the more surprising to note that no conclusions relating these dimensions to those of the biological membrane could be or were drawn by Schmitt, Bear, and Clark in their 1941 article. Not until the 1950's (see below) was it demonstrated that the myelin sheath was directly derived and continuous with the cytoplasmic membrane.

In the meanwhile, efforts had been made in Schmitt's laboratory to investigate the thickness and ultrastructure of cellular membranes by using the analytical leptoscope. This method consists in comparing the intensity of light reflected from an unknown object, e.g., a hemolized erythrocyte envelope, with that reflected from a known thickness standard. The thickness of the object is equal to that of the calibrated standard which matches it in intensity, provided correction is made for any difference in the refractive index of the object and comparison film. Using this technique, Waugh and Schmitt (63) were able to provide measurements of the rabbit erythrocyte, and they found the thickness of the membrane to be within a range of ca. 120–230 Å. One of the biggest difficulties in evaluating these measurements is that they depend in part on the method used to obtain and wash the erythrocyte envelope. This indicated that the thickness measured included a variable and unknown quantity of nonmembrane material. Nevertheless, the leptoscope provided some reasonable limits on the maximum thickness of the membrane and might have provided even more important data on the ultrastructure of cellular membranes had it not been neglected in favor of the electron microscope.

The introduction of the electron microscope in the 1930's and subsequent improvements in it during the following years provided a tool that could form images of structures which had previously been considered "submicroscopic." Because refined methods of preparing biological materials for the electron microscope lagged behind the development of the microscope itself, some of the earliest electron micrographs of biological interest were those of chloroplasts (37) and red cell membranes (65), which could be prepared by simply placing the washed membranes on an electron microscope grid. The development of improved methods of handling biological specimens evolved along two principal lines. The first consisted of metal shadowing, in which a small amount of metal was vaporized in a vacuum and deposited obliquely on a preparation. The technique provided some of the best early electron micrographs of biological specimens, including protein aggregates, viruses, cell walls, and isolated cellular organelles, such as chloroplasts. A second line of development involved improvements in sectioning techniques so that ultrathin sections showing well-preserved cellular fine structure permitted examination of cell organelles and membranes *in situ*. In terms of membrane research one of the early achievements in this latter technique was the direct observation of the regular concentric layered arrangement of the myelin sheath (17) that had been suggested by the polarized microscope and X-ray diffraction analyses twenty years previously. A few years later such thin sections provided Geren (26) with convincing evidence that the layered myelin sheath membranes were continuous with the surrounding Schwann cell membrane (see diagram in Robertson, [53]*) and led her to suggest that sheath membranes and cell membranes may be similar in molecular composition and arrangement.

Subsequently, Fernández-Morán and Finean (18)* provided a detailed correlation of the electron microscope image and low-angle X-ray diffraction pattern of the myelin sheath in which some of the structural parameters of the sheath could be related to the localization of its chemical components. This study was among the first to explicitly regard myelin as a model system for the study of cell membranes, and it established the framework upon which more detailed X-ray diffraction and electron microscope analyses developed.

While Fernández-Morán and Finean were primarily concerned with the spacings revealed by the *positions* of their X-ray diffraction maxima, even more useful information was obtained when Finean (20) took into account the *magnitudes* or intensities of the X-ray diffraction maxima. Finean attempted to relate these intensities to the density of electrons, and hence to the position of atoms and molecules within the repeating structures making up the membrane of the myelin sheath. The analysis made by Finean is diagrammed in Figure 5. Although the results shown in this figure presented only the most reasonable of several mathematically viable solutions, they provided some of

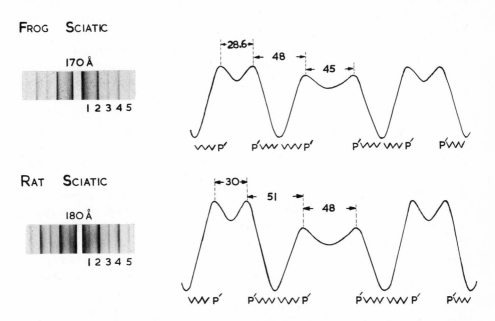

FIGURE 5. Composite illustration showing the low angle diffraction patterns of frog and rat sciatic nerve myelin together with calculated electron-density distribution curves. The interpeak distances are indicated in Å units, and the postulated position of lipid layers with their phosphate groups (P) and hydro-carbon chains ( VVV ) are shown with reference to the electron density curves. From Finean (20), by permission of the author and the American Heart Association, Inc.

the most convincing evidence that the myelin membrane has its lipid constituents sandwiched between layers of protein.

As new preparatory techniques leading to greatly improved tissue sectioning methods for electron microscopy were developed, many different cell membranes and membranous cellular organelles were examined. But disagreements about the appearance and dimensions of these membranes in the electron microscope raised serious doubts concerning the existence of a common membrane structure in all cells and cellular organelles. When Robertson (53),* however, summarized a large body of evidence obtained with the electron microscope, he came to the conclusion that indeed there was a common structure at the surface of a wide variety of cells. Using a new fixative procedure involving $KMnO_4$, he was able to observe a similar three-layered unit, approximately 75 Å thick, at the surface of a number of different cell types as well as in many different cellular organelles. This unit appeared as two dense lines about 20 Å wide separated by a lighter space of 35 Å. Extending these observations to the membranes of the myelin sheath, Robertson was able to relate this unique and apparently consistent triple-layered structure to the molecular models which had been provided by Danielli and Davson, Schmidt, Schmitt, and Finean. Thus Robertson equated the dense lines of the triple-layered membrane structure to the proteins and polar groups of the membranes, and the lighter interzone spaces to their nonpolar groups. This interpretation received support from the experiments Stoekenius (61) performed with phospholipids dispersed in water to form synthetic myelin figures. Comparison of heavy metal soaps (uranyl linolenate) and phospholipid brain extracts demonstrated that the dark bands in myelin figures marked the position of hydrophilic ends of the lipid molecules, just as Robertson had suggested that the dark bands indicated the position of hydrophilic portions of cellular membranes.

Robertson proposed a model of the membrane which he called a "unit membrane." Though very similar to its antecedent, the Danielli-Davson model, Robertson's ideas served to clarify and unify a diverse body of information and emphasize the relationship between the work of the 1930's and the new observations made with the electron microscope. His concept of the membrane was widely adopted by many workers. By referring to the biological membrane as a unit, he emphasized not only that all three parts of the triple-layered 75 Å structure seen in the electron microscope were part of one membrane, but also that all membranes had a similarity of molecular arrangement and origin.

So convincing was the train of arguments which led to Robertson's notion of the unit membrane that Danielli was inspired to make the following statement at the Biochemical Society Symposium in 1962: "It now seems to be agreed that its [the plasma membrane] basic structure is that which I suggested in 1934, and it is highly probable that the same structure is present in many other intercellular membranes. So far as it is possible to predict at the present time, it is unlikely that this general picture will be substantially disturbed, and the focus of attention is likely to shift to other fields."

However, several observations had already been made which did indeed appear to disturb this general picture. Hillier and Hoffman (33, 34) had studied the structure of the membrane of erythrocytes by using shadowing techniques which revealed a mosaic structure. They suggested that the erythrocyte envelope was composed of plaques situated on the outside of a fibrous network joined together by lipids.

Using a similar approach, Frey-Wyssling and Steinmann (23)* examined the structural features of the closed flattened sacs which constituted the internal membrane system of the plant chloroplast. Frey-Wyssling and Steinmann (22) had previously noted that these chloroplast membranes failed to show any substantial intrinsic birefringence as would be expected if they contained highly oriented lipid bilayers as in myelin. When these membranes were examined in the electron microscope a repeating granular structure was disclosed, leading Frey-Wyssling and Steinmann to propose that the membranes were composed of an array of micellar or globular subunits. Thus both polarization and electron microscope studies of chloroplast membranes suggested the possibility of a membrane whose molecular organization might be different from that suggested by the unit membrane concept.

## PART III. FUNCTIONAL AND STRUCTURAL DIVERSITY

In spite of these observations in other membrane systems, the combined polarized light, X-ray diffraction, and electron microscope examination of myelin demonstrated so reasonably that its composition could be attributed to bimolecular leaflets of lipid interposed with protein that Robertson's interpretation of these data in terms of Danielli and Davson's model of membrane structure dominated the thinking of many electron microscopists during the early 1960's. The idea of a common structure for all biological membranes had great appeal. However, it was not surprising that a few biologists viewed this reductive hypothesis with doubt. In the first place, the extraordinary compositional diversity of membranes had been documented in several systems, not only in respect to the protein-lipid ratio (Table 1) but also in respect to the

TABLE 1. PERCENT LIPID AND PROTEIN OF PLANT AND ANIMAL MEMBRANES

| Membranes | % Lipid | % Protein |
|---|---|---|
| Myelin (46) | 80 | 20 |
| Chloroplast lamellae (49) | 50 | 50 |
| Erythrocyte (15) | 40 | 60 |
| Mitochondrial inner membranes (21) | 25 | 75 |

diversity of lipid components (Table 2). Could such diversity be reconciled with a universal lipid protein sandwich? In the second place, the functional diversity of membranes had indicated that permeability phenomena, with which Danielli and Davson had initially been concerned, were not the only

TABLE 2. LIPID COMPOSITION OF PLANT AND ANIMAL MEMBRANES

| Lipids | Myelin[1] | Chloroplast[2] | Erythrocyte[1] | Mitochondria[1] |
|---|---|---|---|---|
| Phospholipid | 32% | 10% | 55% | 95% |
| Cholesterol | 25 | 0 | 25 | 5 |
| Sphingolipids | 31 | 0 | 18 | 0 |
| Glycolipids (excluding sphingolipids) | 0 | 41 | 0 | 0 |
| Others (including sulfolipids, pigments, and unknown) | 12 | 50 | 2 | 0 |

[1] Adapted from review by Korn (40).
[2] Adapted from review by Park and Biggins (48).

membrane-associated activities. Could energy transfer and quantum conversion in photosynthesis, photophosphorylation and oxidative phosphorylation, nerve conduction, as well as selective permeability and ion accumulation all be explained in terms of a membrane model based primarily on myelin, a structure functioning as an insulator and known for its metabolic inactivity? Finally, the evidence demonstrating the applicability of the unit membrane model to a diversity of membrane systems was weak. It depended primarily on the electron microscope observation that myelin, and the Schwann cell membrane with which it is continuous, resembled other biological membranes after chemical fixation, especially with $KMnO_4$. But could far-reaching conclusions be derived solely from similarities of electron microscope image following chemical fixation in powerful oxidizing agents (such as $KMnO_4$) whose chemical interaction with cell components probably alters many naturally occurring protein-lipid relations?

Such questions reflected a growing awareness of the biochemical diversity among different membrane systems. This cannot be illustrated by any single research paper but is easily understood by comparison of data from several such papers, as illustrated in Table 2. The Table clearly shows substantial differences in lipid composition of myelin, mitochondrial, chloroplast, and erythrocyte membranes. Of even greater interest is the variation in the protein-to-lipid ratios shown in Table 1. According to the unit membrane theory the lipid content of a membrane should form a bimolecular leaflet whose surface area is equal to the surface area of the membrane. It is difficult to reconcile the variable lipid content, documented in Table 1, with the assumption that in all membranes a simple lipid bilayer is sandwiched between protein.

The biochemical diversity of membranes probably accounts for the association of unique functions with certain cellular organelles (quantum conversion and photosynthetic phosphorylation in chloroplast lamellae, oxidative phosphorylation in mitochondrial membranes, etc.). This association of structure and function has been examined most extensively in chloroplast and mitochondrial membranes and is dealt with in papers by Fernández-Morán et al. (19),* and Park and Pon (49).* In both papers, techniques were used that differed from the $KMnO_4$ fixation and sectioning methods used by Robertson (53),* and the results provided evidence that membranes may be composed of subunits. Arguments were made in both papers for a relationship between these morphological units and known physiological units. It appears from recent investigations (35, 36) that the initial assignment of definite function to the subunits may have been premature, but the approach used in these papers served to frame meaningful questions about the relation between membrane structure and function.

Evidence of the subunit structure of chloroplast lamellae and other membranes has been considerably extended since the early observations presented by Park and Pon (49).* An example of more recent studies on these membranes is presented in Figure 6, in which the paracrystalline particle array

FIGURE 6. Shadowed preparation of a spinach chloroplast lamella showing the micellar nature of this membrane. The paracrystalline array of quantasome subunits shown here is the least common quantasome arrangement, linear and random arrays being more common. From Park and Biggins (48), reprinted by permission from *Science;* copyright 1964 by the American Association for the Advancement of Science.

(185 Å × 155 Å) of a spinach chloroplast is evident. In Figure 7, a section through a $KMnO_4$ fixed spinach chloroplast again reveals substructure in the membrane. This micrograph shows that the 75 Å thick $KMnO_4$ fixed membrane consisting of a simple triple layer, though commonly observed, is far from universal. Such subunits and bridges between the two opaque bands of the triple-layer structure have been observed by several workers in a variety of membranes (24, 54, 60, 64). Furthermore, careful measurements of adjacent

**15**

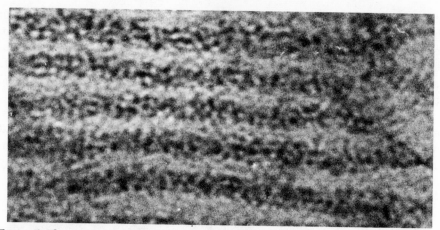

FIGURE 7. Thin section of chloroplast lamellae showing globular substructure in these photosynthetic membranes. From Weier *et al.* (64), reprinted with permission of the Academic Press, Inc.

membranes in a single cell have revealed substantial differences in membrane width or thickness (59). These observations demonstrate that if the universality implicit in the unit membrane concept depended on electron micrographs showing similarities in all biological membranes, more detailed observations failed to substantiate these resemblances.

In both the negative stained and shadowed preparations of the papers by Fernández-Morán *et al.*, and Park and Pon, the possibility of drying artifacts arising during specimen preparation could not be ruled out. This and related objections to the use of harsh chemical fixatives were circumvented by the technique of freeze-etching (45). Initially devised to avoid the use of any chemical fixative, embedding material, or stain, freeze-etching also provided extensive face views of the cellular membranes (5, 44). This is a result of the fact that the freeze-etching procedure involves fracture of a frozen specimen. This fracture naturally follows sharp discontinuities or planes of weakness, many of which are associated with the cellular membranes. Initially it was believed that these planes of weakness would occur along the surfaces of membranes, but, as Branton demonstrated (6),* they occur inside the membrane. This internal fracture appears to be due in part to the surface properties of most membranes and in part to the relative weakness of the internal hydrophobic bonding in the membrane compared with the ice matrix.

The discovery that frozen membranes may be fractured to expose inner membrane faces provided a new approach to the study of membrane structure. Although the manner in which membranes split in freeze-etching was in part consistent with a lamellar membrane structure, small particles averaging about 85 Å in diameter were seen in many freeze-etched membranes and their presence strongly supported the possibility of globular subunits within the biological membrane. Subsequent examination of a broad spectrum of cellular structures by freeze-etching (7, 8, 52) revealed a consistent diversity in different membranes. Two examples taken from recent publications will suffice to illustrate the range of morphological diversity revealed in freeze-etched membranes of different origins. At one extreme are the extraordinarily smooth membrane faces seen in myelin sheath (Figure 8); at the opposite extreme are the highly particulate membranes of chloroplast lamellae (Figure 9). Thus freeze-etching, together with the earlier indications provided by polarization microscopy of myelin (see Schmidt [55]*) and of chloroplast lamellae (22), provided evidence that a range of substructural complexity could exist within the framework of the biological membrane.

What theoretical considerations can be used in interpreting the morphological diversity revealed in these electron microscopy studies? Until about 1960 it was generally believed that a lamellar structure was the most widespread form in which lipoproteins or lipids could exist. Then, as a result of work by Luzzati and co-workers (42), Stoeckenius (62), Lucy and Glauert (41), and Bangham and Horne (2), it became evident that lipid-water systems are polymorphic assemblages in which small variations in temperature and concentration may induce drastic changes.

Such considerations led to theoretical proposals of membrane structure in which the classical bimolecular lipid protein sandwich was discarded in favor of more dynamic models. One of these, suggested by Kavanau (38),* gives special emphasis to the transformations possible in the lipid constituents of membranes. As such, it attempts to elucidate a large number of membrane functions in terms of a model which—though far more complex than suggested by the unit membrane concept—still is consistent with the older polarized light, X-ray diffraction, and electron microscope data.

Much less is known about the composition and conformation of the proteins than about the lipids of membranes. Danielli and Davson's initial model of the membrane indicated a layer of globular proteins on the surface of the lipid bilayer. But, as a result of further studies of protein films at oil-water interfaces, Danielli concluded that "on coming into contact with an oil-water interface, [the proteins] unroll into thin sheets in a reversible manner . . ." (30). The work of Schmitt (56) also suggested that the spacings in the myelin sheath were such as to exclude the possibility of any but unrolled or spread proteins on the lipid bilayers. For this reason it has been customary to ascribe some sort of spread, pleated sheet conformation to the protein, and Kavanau, for example, postulates that it "consists of unfolded and uncoiled fabric proteins in an extended $\beta$-conformation, possibly resembling a pleated sheet with average spacing between the backbones of about 4.7–4.9 Å" (39). However, Maddy and Malcolm's recent work (43) using infrared spectroscopy shows that an extensive array of the protein in the $\beta$-conformation adjacent to the lipid is no longer justifiable. As Maddy and Malcolm point out, "This removes a rather stable and perhaps intractable element from certain models, a trend in tune with recent concepts of the dynamic interrelation between different micellar states . . ." of the membrane.

Using a theoretical approach, Hechter explored this question of protein conformation and (32)* he developed a dynamic model of membranes in which the fundamental protein matrix consisted of hexamer and pentamer subunits associated with a conventional mixed lipid bilayer. But, in Hechter's model, the order in this lipid bilayer depends upon hexagonal ice-like water particles

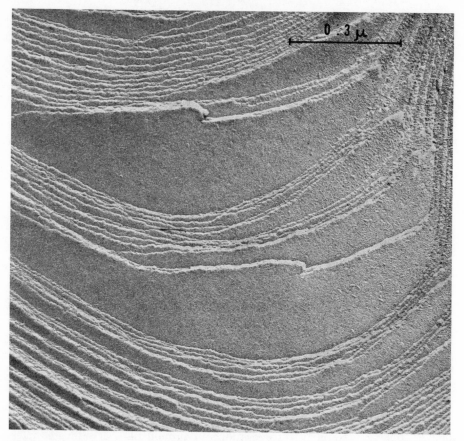

FIGURE 8. Membrane faces of frog myelin prepared by freeze-etching. Note the smoothness of these faces in comparison to those of chloroplast lamellae in Figure 9. From Branton (7), reprinted with permission of the Academic Press, Inc.

in alignment with the surfaces of the protein, and the interaction of these proteins with surrounding water molecules are, in turn, used to explain many membrane activities.

Although many of the conceptual details presented in Kavanau's and Hechter's papers may be incorrect, it is significant that both authors attribute to the biological membrane a complexity which refutes any notion of a spatially or temporally uniform structure. These two authors rightfully emphasize the pitfalls inherent in simple schematic diagrams, but their divergent approaches exemplify the wide latitude of disagreement concerning even the most basic membrane phenomena. While our actual knowledge of membrane structure is vastly greater than it was fifty years ago, our knowledge of how membranes work has not greatly increased. It is becoming obvious, however, that attempts to assign each membrane molecule a unique place in the membrane matrix are futile; it is improbable that such static models can ever explain the dynamics of membrane activity. Just as we now find structural diversity among various

FIGURE 9. Membrane faces of spinach chloroplast lamellae prepared by the same freeze-etch technique used for Figure 8. These membranes clearly show globular substructure. From the work of Branton and Park (8), reprinted with permission of the Academic Press, Inc.

membranes, we may also find that structure within a single membrane varies with time. This temporal variation may help to explain membrane function, and a promising approach to understanding the relationship between membrane structure and function may result from analyses of membranes trapped in various functional states.

In a sense, our knowledge of membrane-associated phenomena today stands where our knowledge of the gene stood in 1944. At that time, as a result of Avery, MacLeod, and McCarty's work (1), and during the next two decades, as a result of the subsequent developments in molecular genetics, the chemical and structural attributes of the genetic material were identified and related to its functional capacity. Today we know which chemical components compose membranes, we have some boundary conditions which delimit their structure, and we can assign certain functional attributes to certain of these membranes. On the other hand, we do not have details about the configuration of the membrane components or their relation to each other, we cannot ascribe unique functional attributes to individual membrane components, and we do not have a molecular understanding of such fundamental membrane functions as ion accumulation or energy transduction. Clearly the years ahead hold promise for exciting advances in the study of membrane structure and membrane-associated phenomena.

## BIBLIOGRAPHY

In the list of references that follows, a number in boldface type indicates that the paper is reprinted in this collection.

1. Avery, O. T., MacLeod, C. M., and McCarty, M. Studies on the chemical nature of the substance inducing transformation of pneumococcal types. Induction of transformation by a desoxyribonucleic acid fraction isolated from pneumococcus type III. *J. Exptl. Med.*, 79: 137–157, 1944.
2. Bangham, A. D., and Horne, R. W. Negative staining of phospholipids and their structural modification by surface-active agents as observed in the electron microscope. *J. Mol. Biol.*, 8: 660–668, 1964.
3. Bar, R. S., Deamer, D. W., and Cornwell, D. G. Surface area of human erythrocyte lipids: reinvestigation of experiments on plasma membrane. *Science*, 153: 1010–1012, 1966.
4. Bear, Richard S., and Schmitt, Francis O. The optics of nerve myelin. *J. Opt. Soc. Am.*, 26: 206–212, 1936.
5. Branton, D., and Moor, H. Fine structure in freeze-etched *Allium cepa* L. root tips. *J. Ultrastructure Res.*, 11: 401–411, 1964.
6. Branton, D. Fracture faces of frozen membranes. *Proc. Nat. Acad. Sci.*, 55:5: 1048–1056, 1966.
7. Branton, D. Fracture faces of frozen myelin. *Exptl. Cell. Res.*, 45: 703–707, 1967.
8. Branton, D., and Park, R. Subunits in chloroplast lamellae. *J. Ultrastructure Res.*, 19: 283–303, 1967.
9. Chance, B., and Nishimura, M. On the mechanism of chlorophyll-cytochrome interaction: The temperature insensitivity of light induced cytochrome oxidation in *Chromatium*. *Proc. Nat. Acad. Sci.*, 46: 19–24, 1960.
10. Criddle, R. S., Bock, R. M., Green, D. E., and Tisdale, H. Physical characteristics of proteins of the electron transfer system and interpretation of the structure of the mitochondrion. *Biochemistry*, 1: 827–842, 1962.
11. Danielli, J. F. The relations between surface pH, ion concentration and interfacial tension. *Proc. Roy. Soc. (London)*, B 122: 155–174, 1937.
12. Danielli, J. F., and Davson, H. A contribution to the theory of permeability of thin films. *J. Cell. Comp. Physiol.*, 5: 495–508, 1935.
13. Danielli, J. F., and Harvey, E. N. The tension at the surface of mackerel egg oil, with remarks on the nature of the cell surface. *J. Cell. Comp. Physiol.*, 5: 483–494, 1935.
14. DeVries, H. Plasmolytische Studien über die Wand der Vacuolen. *Jahrb. Wiss. Bot.*, 16: 465–598, 1885.
15. Dodge, J. T., Mitchell, C., and Hanahan, D. J. The preparation and chemical characteristics of hemoglobin-free ghosts of human erythrocytes. *Arch. Biochem. Biophys.*, 100: 119–130, 1963.
16. du Noüy, P. L. An interfacial tensiometer for universal use. *J. Gen. Physiol.*, 7: 625–631, 1925.
17. Fernández-Morán, H. Electron microscope observations on the structure of the myelinated nerve fiber sheath. *Exptl. Cell. Res.*, 1: 143–149, 1950.
18. Fernández-Morán, H., and Finean, J. B. Electron microscope and low-angle X-ray diffraction studies of the nerve myelin sheath. *J. Cell. Biol.*, 3: 725–748, 1957.

19. Fernández-Morán, H., Oda, T., Blair, P. V., and Green, D. E. A macromolecular repeating unit of mitochondrial structure and function. *J. Cell. Biol.*, *22:* 63–100, 1964.

20. Finean, J. B. The nature and stability of the plasma membrane. *Circulation, 26:* 1151–1162, 1962.

21. Fleischer, S., Klouwen, H., and Brierley, G. Studies of the electron transfer system. XXXVIII. Lipid composition of purified enzyme preparations derived from beef heart mitochondria. *J. Biol. Chem.*, *236:* 2936–2941, 1961.

22. Frey-Wyssling, A., and Steinmann, E. Die Schichtendoppelbrechung grosser Chloroplasten. *Biochim. Biophys. Acta, 2:* 254–259, 1948.

23. Frey-Wyssling, A., and Steinmann, E. Ergebnisse der Feinbauanalyse der Chloroplasten. *Vierteljhrsh. Naturforsch. Ges. (Zürich), 98:* 20–29, 1953.

24. Fuhs, G. W. Spherical subunits in photosynthetic membranes of two Cyanophyceae and the bacterium *Rhodospirillum rubrum*. *Archiv für Mikrobiologie, 54:* 253–265, 1966.

25. Gad, J. Zur Lehr von der Fettresorption. *Archiv für Physiologie, 1878:* 181–205, 1878.

26. Geren, B. B. The formation from the Schwann cell surface of myelin in the peripheral nerves of chick embryos. *Exptl. Cell. Res., 7:* 558–562, 1954.

27. Gorter, E., and Grendel, F. On bimolecular layers of lipoid on the chromocytes of the blood. *J. Exptl. Med., 41:* 439–443, 1925.

28. Harvey, E. N. The microscope-centrifuge and some of its applications. *J. Franklin Inst., 214:* 1–23, 1932.

29. Harvey, E. N. Tension at the cell surface. *Protoplasmatologia 2, E5:* 1–30, 1954.

30. Harvey, E. N., and Danielli, J. F. Properties of the cell surface. *Biological Reviews of the Cambridge Philosophical Society, 13:* 319–341, 1938.

31. Harvey, E. N., and Shapiro, H. The interfacial tension between oil and protoplasm within the living cells. *J. Cell. Comp. Physiol., 5:* 255–267, 1934.

32. Hechter, O. The role of water structure in the molecular organization of cell membranes. *Fed. Am. Soc. Exptl. Biol. Proc., 24:* 2: 2–3, 1965.

33. Hillier, J., and Hoffman, J. F. On the ultrastructure of the plasma membrane as determined by the electron microscope. *J. Cell. Comp. Physiol., 43:* 203–247, 1953.

34. Hoffman, J. F. On the reproducibility in the observed ultrastructure of the normal mammalian red cell plasma membrane. *J. Cell. Comp. Physiol., 47:* 261–287, 1956.

35. Izawa, S., and Good, N. E. The number of sites sensitive to 3-(3,4-dichlorophenyl)-1,1-dimethylurea, 3-(4-chlorophenyl)-1,1-dimethylurea, and 2-chloro-4-(2-propylamino)-6-ethylamino-s-triazine in isolated chloroplasts. *Biochim. Biophys. Acta, 102:* 20–37, 1965.

36. Kagawa, Y., and Racker, E. Partial resolution of the enzymes catalyzing oxidative phosphorylation. X. Correlation of morphology and function in submitochondrial particles. *J. Biol. Chem., 241:* 2475–2482, 1966.

37. Kausche, G. A., and Ruska, H. Über den Nachweis von Molekülen des Tabakmosaikvirus in den Chloroplasten viruskranker Pflanzen. *Naturwissenschaften, 28:* 303–304, 1940.

38. Kavanau, J. L. Membrane structure and function. *Fed. Am. Soc. Exptl. Biol. Proc., 25:* 3: 1096–1107, 1966.

39. Kavanau, J. L. "Structure and Function in Biological Membranes." Holden-Day, Inc., San Francisco, 1965.

40. Korn, E. D. Structure of biological membranes. *Science, 153:* 1491–1498, 1966.

41. Lucy, J. A., and Glauert, A. M. Structure and assembly of macromolecular lipid complexes composed of globular micelles. *J. Mol. Biol., 8:* 727–748, 1964.

42. Luzzati, V., and Husson, F. The structure of the liquid-crystalline phases of lipid-water systems. *J. Cell. Biol., 12:* 207–219, 1962.
43. Maddy, A. H., and Malcolm, B. R. Protein conformations in the plasma membrane. *Science, 150:* 1616–1617, 1965.
44. Moor, H., and Mühlethaler, K. Fine structure in frozen-etched yeast cells. *J. Cell. Biol., 17:* 609–628, 1963.
45. Moor, H., Mühlethaler, K., Waldner, H., and Frey-Wyssling, A. A new freezing-ultramicrotome. *J. Biophys. Biochem. Cytol., 10:* 1–13, 1961.
46. O'Brien, J. S. Stability of the myelin membrane. *Science, 147:* 1099–1107, 1965.
47. Overton, E. Ueber die allgemeinen osmotischen Eigenschaften der Zelle, ihre vermutlichen Ursachen und ihre Bedeutung für die Physiologie. *Vierteljhrsh. Naturforsch. Ges. (Zürich), 44:* 88–135, 1899.
48. Park, R. B., and Biggins, J. Quantasomes: size and composition. *Science, 144:* 1009–1011, 1964.
49. Park, R. B., and Pon, N. G. Correlation of structure with function in *Spinacea oleracea* chloroplasts. *J. Mol. Biol., 3:* 1–10, 1961.
50. Pfeffer, W. "The Physiology of Plants" (translated by A. J. Ewart). Clarendon Press, Oxford, 1897.
51. Plowe, J. Q. Membranes in the plant cell. I. Morphological membranes at protoplasmic surfaces. *Protoplasma, 12:* 196–221, 1931.
52. Remsen, C. C. The fine structure of frozen-etched *Bacillus cereus* spores. *Archiv für Mikrobiologie, 54:* 266–275, 1966.
53. Robertson, J. D. The ultrastructure of cell membranes and their derivatives. *Biochem. Soc. Symp., 16:* 3–43, 1959.
54. Robertson, J. D. Unit membranes: a review with recent new studies of experimental alterations and a new subunit structure in synaptic membranes. In "Cellular Membranes in Development," M. Locke, ed. Academic Press, New York, 1964.
55. Schmidt, W. J. Doppelbrechung und Feinbau der markensheide der nervenfasern. *Z. f. Zellforsch. mikr. Anat., 23:* 657–676, 1936.
56. Schmitt, F. O. Nerve ultrastructure as revealed by X-ray diffraction and polarized light studies. *Cold Spring Harbor Symp. Quant. Biol., 4:* 7–12, 1936.
57. Schmitt, F. O., Bear, R. S., and Clark, G. L. X-ray diffraction studies on nerve. *Radiology, 25:* 131–151, 1935.
58. Schmitt, F. O., Bear, R. S., and Palmer, K. X-ray diffraction studies on the structure of the nerve myelin sheath. *J. Cell. Comp. Physiol., 18:* 31–41, 1941.
59. Sjostrand, F. S. A new ultrastructure element of the membranes in mitochondria and of some cytoplasmic membranes. *J. Ultrastructure Res., 9:* 340–361, 1963.
60. Sjostrand, F. S., and Elfvin, L. G. The granular structure of mitochondrial membranes and of cytomembranes as demonstrated in frozen-dried tissue. *J. Ultrastructure Res., 10:* 263–292, 1964.
61. Stoeckenius, W. Osmium tetroxide fixation of lipids. *Proc. Eur. Conf. on Electron Microscopy, 2:* 716–720, 1960.
62. Stoeckenius, W. Some electron microscopical observations on liquid-crystalline phases in lipid-water systems. *J. Cell. Biol., 12:* 221–229, 1962.
63. Waugh, D. F., and Schmitt, F. O. Investigations of the thickness and ultrastructure of cellular membranes by the analytical leptoscope. *Cold Spring Harbor Symp. Quant. Biol., 8:* 233–241, 1940.
64. Weier, T. E., Engelbrecht, A. H. P., Harrison, A., and Risley, E. B. Subunits in the membranes of chloroplast of *Phaseolus vulgaris, Pisum sativum,* and *Aspidistra* sp. *J. Ultrastructure Res., 13:* 92–111, 1965.
65. Wolpers, C. Zur Feinstruktur der Erythrocytenmembran. *Naturwissenschaften, 29:* 416–424, 1941.
66. Wynn, W. H. The minute structure of the medullary sheath of nerve-fibres. *J. Anat., 34:* 381–397, 1900.

# MEMBRANES IN THE PLANT CELL

## I. MORPHOLOGICAL MEMBRANES AT PROTOPLASMIC SURFACES

JANET Q. PLOWE

With 11 Text-figures

Received for publication, September 8, 1930

## INTRODUCTION

The question of the existence and function of plasma membranes is of concern to the physiologist both from a practical and from a theoretical point of view. It is of practical interest because, in attempting to analyze the action of chemicals on the living organism, it is essential to know whether substances in the external medium necessarily come into direct contact with all internal constituents of the cell which they affect, or whether action on an external regulatory layer alone may be responsible for changes in other parts of the cell which the chemicals never reach. It is of theoretical interest because, if it can be shown that the existence and function of plasma membranes is essential to the life of the protoplast, it follows that it is as incorrect to think of protoplasm as a living substance apart from its organization into protoplasts as it would be to think of proteins, or water, or carbohydrates as living unless organized into protoplasm.

In that case, the protoplast, rather than protoplasm, becomes "the physical basis of life"

The concept of specialized, differentially permeable layers in the cell is so convenient in the explanation of cell phenomena that it has widespread acceptance. The statement is made in a current text on plant physiology, with no implication of uncertainty, that "The nucleus, plastids, etc., as well as the cytoplasm, have surface membranes on the inner and outer surfaces which permit certain substances to pass through while

Reprinted by permission of Janet Q. Goodrich from *Protoplasma*, **12**, 196–221 (1931).

keeping others from doing so. The cell is able to carry on many different processes at the same time, owing to these various membranes which surround the different structures in it" (RABER 1928, p. 13).

The view that membranes surround nucleus, vacuole, and protoplast is generally accepted by cytologists (SHARP 1926, p. 57; WILSON 1925, pp. 54—55, 85). Yet the membrane theory is not only disputed by those who propose, instead, an explanation of self-regulatory ability based on the behavior of a colloidal system rather than on a complex cell structure, but it is granted by its adherents that the experimental evidence on which it rests is inadequate. HÖBER, who has contributed both experimental work and theoretical consideration in support of the theory, states that ,,Einen einwandfreien direkten Nachweis der Plasmahaut gibt es danach bisher überhaupt nicht" (1926).

The question calls for further investigation, not only on its own merits, but because an answer is of importance in physiological work along other lines.

## PREVIOUS INVESTIGATIONS

In the last century, DE VRIES (1885) isolated the layer of cytoplasm surrounding the plant vacuole by rapid plasmolysis. He made a study of the permeability and physical properties of this layer, which he called the tonoplast. He appears to have looked upon the isolated tonoplast as living, since it might divide, but probably the division he saw resulted from surface tension forces alone. More significant, perhaps, is the fact that the differential permeability of the tonoplast so closely parallels that of the entire living protoplast that it seems unlikely that the tonoplast originates as an artifact.

PFEFFER (1897) demonstrated that the outer surface of a plant protoplast retained differential permeability for dyes when killed with acid, although, when the surface layer was ruptured, the dyes penetrated and stained the cytoplasm.

In view of our present knowledge of the radical changes in physical properties undergone by dying protoplasm, both these pioneer contributions to the physiological morphology of the cell must be considered an uncertain basis for conclusions regarding plasma membranes in the living protoplast.

Comparatively little of the recent investigation of physical properties of protoplasm has been directed toward the question of differentiation of surface layers. Microscopic observation ordinarily fails to reveal such a layer at either cytoplasm-wall or cytoplasm-sap interface, in the plasmolyzed or unplasmolyzed cell; however PRICE (1914) using dark field illumination, was able to detect the presence of an outer layer distinct from the remainder of the plasmolyzed *Spirogyra, Mougeotia,* or *Cucurbita* protoplast. In the first, the layer contains fine particles in rapid motion; the second shows no movement, suggesting that it is in the gel condition; in the third, the layer is homogeneous. In *Spirogyra* a similar layer surrounds the vacuole. PRICE also notes that the strands which persist between plasmolyzed protoplast and wall in *Cucurbita* are like the material composing the outer layer, from which their origin is clearly discernible in some cases.

KÜSTER (1910) describes the appearance of a fine membrane in cells of *Allium* treated with acid on death from rapid deplasmolysis; this later collapses against the plasma mass. He reports (1926) that when a protoplast divides on plasmolysis, a thin strand of tonoplast may persist, running through the strand of cytoplasm connecting the two portions of the protoplast. The strand of tonoplast becomes evident on "foamy degeneration" of the cytoplasm. In another paper (1927) he describes the occurence of naked vacuolar membranes in the sap of ripe solanaceous berries, where they could hardly be considered to result from the use of reagents.

GICKLHORN and WEBER (1927) report that when mesophyll cells are placed in conductivity water or in isotonic solutions, the vacuole, surrounded by a thin layer of protoplasm, may contract, although the remainder of the protoplasm remains next to the cell wall. When these cells are placed in stronger solutions, the protoplast undergoes normal plasmolysis and the vacuole contracts further. The thin layer about the vacuole may be a distinct osmotic membrane.

On the basis of measurable potential differences between vacuolar sap and the external artificial sap in which cells of *Valonia* are immersed, OSTERHOUT, DAMON, and JACQUES (1927) conclude that the inner and outer layers of the protoplast differ.

## THE MICROMANIPULATION METHOD

Some time ago PFEFFER (1897) remarked that the question of the presence of differentially permeable membranes "Would be definitely answered . . . if it were found that substances commonly present or artificially introduced, diffused through the central mass of the plasma, but did not appear in the vacuole or in the water outside." PFEFFER's idea can now be carried out, using fine glass pipettes and needles in connection with a micromanipulation device.

The original term, "microdissection", should be abandoned, for dissection implies dismemberment of a dead organism, and micromanipulative methods are now associated with the study of the internal physiology of the living cell. It is by such means that the internal conductivity, the internal hydrogen ion concentration, and the internal oxidation-reduction potential of active, living cells are now being investigated.

Less work with micromanipulation apparatus has been done on plant cells than on animal cells, because the layer of protoplasm in the plant cell is relatively thin and the cell wall offers an obstacle to the insertion and free movement of needles or pipettes.

KITE (1913 a, b; 1915) who was the first to publish extensive reports of micromanipulation experiments, attempted to investigate the consistency of cytoplasm and nucleus and the relative permeability of the internal and external cytoplasmic layers in plant as well as in animal cells. It is unfortunate that in many instances he made no distinction between dead and living protoplasm. This lack of discrimination causes uncertainty in interpreting his accounts.

SEIFRIZ (1921) employed such plant material as *Vaucheria*, pollen tubes, and bread mould in investigations of the physical properties of protoplasm, working chiefly on expressed cytoplasm.

CHAMBERS and SANDS (1923) used the pollen mother cells of *Tradescantia*, in some cases piercing the cell wall and in older cells removing the wall before dissection. They directed their attention towards mitotic structures. Here again the distinction between dead and living structure was not always carefully drawn.

SCARTH (1927) contributed the first account of investigation of the interior of a plant cell indisputably alive and in normal condition. His material included *Tradescantia, Elodea, Symphoricarpos,* and *Spirogyra.* He used needles with horizontal tips, piercing the end walls of the cells. Lateral and vertical movement were made possible by the extreme flexibility of the needles. SCARTH was chiefly interested in the internal structural organization of cytoplasm and nucleus.

SEIFRIZ and HÖFLER (1927) subsequently described a method by which the interference of the cell wall could be done away with and living, plasmolyzed protoplasts reached with the needle as freely as in animal cells. This method, to be described later, gives admirable material for investigation of the protoplast. Not only is the needle or pipette free to move in any direction, but the outer layer of the cytoplasm is not in contact with the cell wall.

## IS A CELL UNDERGOING MICROMANIPULATION A NORMAL CELL?

It is justifiable to ask whether the behavior of a protoplast into which microneedles or micropipettes are inserted can give us any information about the nature of the protoplast under normal conditions. Those who have opportunity to watch the process of micromanipulation can hardly fail to be reassured by the astounding indifference of the protoplast to the insertion and movement of needles and to injection. Others may be enabled to judge to what extent protoplasts subjected to micromanipulation retain normal behavior by consideration of the following illustrations.

TAYLOR and WHITAKER (1927) find that streaming may continue in *Nitella* for more than ten days after microelectrodes are inserted into the protoplast. TAYLOR and FARBER (1924) investigating the function of the micronucleus in *Euplotes,* show that, after the micronucleus has been removed with a micropipette, the organism continues its existence as an individual, but fails to divide. The micronucleus can, however, be removed and immediately reinjected without interfering with reproduction.

SEIFRIZ (1929 a) finds that an injected nickel particle may be carried along in streaming myxomycete protoplasm. CHAMBERS, POLLACK, and HILLER (1927) state that *Amoeba proteus* and *Amoeba dubia* injected with phenol red may retain normal behavior for forty-eight hours. POLLACK (1928) finds that amoebae injected with alizarin sulfonate recover normal movement more quickly if calcium salts are injected.

Such instances are evidence that interference with normal function does not necessarily follow the insertion of microneedles into the living protoplast, or the injection into it of material from a micropipette.

## LOCAL, REVERSIBLE INJURY IN THE PROTOPLAST

Protoplasts, like organisms, may be subject to reversible injury. Temporary changes in properties accompanying reversible injury have been made familiar by the work of OSTERHOUT (1922). A second question therefore arises: Is it not likely that the movement of microneedles or the force of an injection produces local alterations in the protoplast and renders results inaccurate, even though death of the protoplast does not follow? The possibility of such transitory local injury changes within the protoplast is suggested by workers with micromanipulation. Survival of the cell is not a satisfactory guarantee, for them, that the behavior of the protoplast has been normal throughout the investigation. Such signs as cessation or increase of Brownian movement, aggregation of granules, swelling, must constantly be watched for. The appearance of acidity may be used in detecting local injury. CHAMBERS and POLLACK (1927) and CHAMBERS, POLLACK, and HILLER (1927) have shown that the reaction of the protoplasm of certain animal cells changes from its normal level (pH 6.7—7.5) to as low as pH 5.3 on fatal injury. REZNIKOFF and POLLACK (1929) state that, although a churning motion with a needle or pipette causes a distinct temporary local acidity in the cytoplasm of *Amoeba dubia*, the ordinary quiet insertion of a needle, or even the injection of NaCl or KCl solution, causes no change in reaction.

## PROTOPLASMIC STREAMING IN PLANT CELLS AS A CHECK ON NORMAL CONDITION

Changes in protoplasmic streaming offer, in many plant cells, a sensitive indicator of changes in the condition of the protoplasm. While protoplasm in cells which normally show streaming may cease streaming without having undergone appreciable injury, it is also true that known injury is regularly accompanied by changes in the manner of streaming or by complete cessation. If we disregard all results in which streaming is affected, we may feel reasonably sure that the behavior of the protoplasm in other respects will not be abnormal.

SCARTH has reported that a strand of cytoplasm traversing the vacuole may continue streaming while stretched by a microneedle. TAYLOR's experience with *Nitella* and SEIFRIZ' with mycomycetes were cited above. To these may be added the following facts from the present work. When a needle is pushed into the protoplast of an onion cell, carrying a layer of cytoplasm with it, streaming will take place in the layer about the needle in a wholly normal manner. Strands may form running from the needle to the wall. The nucleus may move out along the needle to its tip. Further, if the needle is thrust through the protoplast until it touches the protoplast-vacuolar surface on the opposite side, then partially withdrawn, a strand of protoplasm will be pulled out from that surface into the vacuole, and in this strand, too, normal streaming will occur. Or, if the needle is withdrawn from the plasmolyzed protoplast, pulling a strand of protoplasm out after it, streaming will occur in this strand both towards and away from the protoplast. A protoplast may be pinched in two with the needle, and yet streaming in the two portions continue undisturbed. An opening may be made through the protoplast which brings the vacuole into communication with the external solution, and yet streaming continue uninterrupted.

These results encourage us to believe that, with careful manipulation, it is possible to carry on intracellular investigations of plant protoplasts as well as of animal protoplasts in which the protoplasm under observation is normal insofar as any organism, organ. or tissue can be considered normal while under experimental conditions.

## MICROMANIPULATIVE STUDIES OF THE PRESENCE OF MEMBRANES

Evidence from microdissection is generally in support of the presence of differentiated layers at protoplasmic surfaces. CHAMBERS (1917) states that *Paramoecia* and marine over can recover from dissection only if a new film, or series of films, is formed, cutting off the injured region.

CHAMBERS and RÉNYI (1925) report that tearing of the surface is fatal to somatic cells from various animal tissues, although a puncture of the surface may be survived. SEIFRIZ (1921) finds that vacuolar membranes from bread mould may persist and gel when the cytoplasm disintegrates. When a resting myxomycete plasmodium is torn, the last part to tear is always the outer border. An Amoeba, partially severed, may be drawn together again by the contraction of a thin remaining strand derived from the outer border. These results indicate the presence of physical differentiation in the outer layers of the protoplast. He describes (1927) removing the surrounding cytoplasm from the vacuolar membrane of the plasmolyzed onion cell. For the nucleate erythrocyte of *Cryptobranchus*, SEIFRIZ (1926) describes an outer „wall" about 0.8 $\mu$ in thickness, which is moderately elastic.

Membranes surrounding the contractile vacuole in protozoa are of interest in view of LLOYD's report that vacuoles in the gamete of *Spirogyra* may function as contractile vacuoles (1928). KITE (1913 b) describes the wall of the contractile vacuole in Amoeba as of high consistency and adhesiveness, and the contractile vacuole walls of *Paramoecium* as of greater density than the endoplasm. HOWLAND (1923) finds the wall of the contractile vacuole of *Amoeba verrucosa* and *Paramoecium caudatum* rigid enough to indent, rather than pierce, with a blunt needle. TAYLOR (1923) states that the contractile and subsidiary vacuoles in *Euplotes* may be moved about by needles, showing a wall of high consistency, and that shreddy remains of the walls of the subsidiary vacuoles may sometimes persist after the vacuoles have fused.

The evidence from unfixed material supports the idea of a nuclear membrane credited by cytologists. KITE (1913 a, b) describes definite nuclear membranes for marine ova, *Amoeba proteus*, and the epidermal cells of *Necturus*, although, he disagrees with the idea that most protoplasmic surfaces possess membranes. CHAMBERS (1917) describes a definite nuclear membrane, which collapses and wrinkles when the nuclear fluid is withdrawn with a pipette, in the marine ova he has studied. SEIFRIZ (1921) reports dissecting off the degenerate membrane from the dead nucleus of *Amoeba*. SCARTH (1927) believes that the membrane of the nuclei in the plant cells on which he has worked is fluid in the living condition.

# THE INADEQUACY OF PRESENT EVIDENCE FOR THE EXISTENCE OF MEMBRANES AT PROTOPLASMIC SURFACES

Evidence from many different sources suggests a definite differentiation of the layers of protoplasm in the living cell which are in contact with cell wall, cell sap, and with the nucleus, or, in the last case, possibly differentiation of the surface layer of the nucleus itself. Certain points render this evidence insufficient for concluding that such differentiation regularly occurs in the living plant cell. It is still uncertain to what extent the organization of the protoplast in the walled, vacuolate plant cell parallels that in the animal cell. With the exception of PRICE's darkfield studies, evidence for plant material is not based on living protoplasts.

The following report is offered as a contribution to our knowledge of differentiation of surface layers in the living, normal plant protoplast.

## TERMINOLOGY

In discussing the literature, the terminology of the papers under consideration was largely followed, but considerable confusion exists. DE VRIES called the layer surrounding the vacuole the tonoplast and that at the outer surface of the protoplast, the ectoplast. PFEFFER referred to the two as plasma membranes. From the first, some difficulty has arisen from the occasional use of the word "membrane" as synonymous with cell wall. Now the common use of the word "membrane" alone to designate an *osmotic* membrane makes it a physiological rather than a purely structural term.

DE VRIES' "tonoplast" presents fewer difficulties. It is this term which the present writer has used to denote a distinct layer of cytoplasm about the vacuole.

"Ectoplast", however, is widely used in a wholly different sense. In a myxomycete plasmodium or in a protozoan, the ectoplast or ecto-plasm is a thick layer of cytoplasm which is certainly not the outer "plasma membrane" in either a structural or a physiological sense. MAST (1924) has given us the term "plasmalemma" for the thin external layer which is the "membrane" if an osmotic function exists. This term seems free from the difficulties presented by both "ectoplast" and "plasma membrane". It has seemed permissible, therefore, to extend its use to the botanical world, and to employ it to denote a distinct, differentiated layer on the outer surface of the plant protoplast.

Since plasmalemma and tonoplast are themselves cytoplasmic structures, we cannot refer to the layer of protoplasm between them simply as cytoplasm. It obviously is not ectoplasm. Endoplasm, on the other hand, would include the tonoplast. No term in use at present adequately distinguishes this portion of the cytoplasm. A new one seems necessary to avoid confusion. *Mesoplasm* is proposed as indicative of its position in relation to the other layers.

Plasmalemma and tonoplast, then, will be used hereafter to denote differentiated layers at the interfaces between protoplasm and wall and protoplasm and sap, respectively, and mesoplasm for that portion of the cytoplasm which lies between these layers.

## METHODS AND MATERIAL

CHAMBERS (1924) describes micromanipulation methods in general, and SCARTH (1927) and SEIFRIZ (1927) describe the application of these methods to plant cells.

The material used for the greater part of this work was the inner (morphologically, the upper) epidermis of bulb scales of Bermuda onions, results obtained with other cells being so designated. This, when stripped off, gives a layer only one cell in thickness, save where occasionally a patch of large, colorless mesophyll cells clings to it. This provides exceptionally favorable material for microdissection. Sections of the stripped epidermis may be mounted in a hanging drop of tap water in the micromanipulation moist chamber, and the cells entered by horizontal needles which pierce the end walls. This is the method Scarth has used with other plant cells in his work. More conveniently, one may employ the method described by Seifriz and Höfler. Strips of epidermis are plasmolyzed in 18 percent (0.56 M.) sucrose. This reduces the protoplast to about one half its original volume. The protoplasts are well rounded away from the end walls after about twenty minutes in the plasmolyzing solution. A strip is then cut with a sharp razor, transversely to the long axis of the leaf, on a glass slide. The blade passes between the end wall and the protoplast in many cells, leaving the protoplast untouched and uninjured. This section of epidermis is mounted in a hanging drop of plasmolyzing solution on a cover slip which forms the roof of the micromanipulation moist chamber, the open ends of the cells pointing towards the open end of the moist chamber. If desired, the material may be held in place by a blunt needle with a vertical tip. A dissection needle with a horizontal tip now has access to the protoplasts through the open ends of the cells, without touching the cell wall. There is no limitation on the movement of the needle, and one obstacle to succesful use of these methods on plant material is thus done away with.

This method was used for the greater part of this work, but unplasmolyzed cells were also studied, to eliminate any introduction of error as a result of plasmolysis. The method can be used for thicker tissues by plasmolyzing thin sections, then cutting the sections transversely after plasmolysis.

## DISTINCT BEHAVIOR OF MESOPLASM AND PLASMALEMMA IN PROTOPLASMIC STRANDS

Definite indication of the existence of an outer layer distinct from the rest of the cytoplasm is obtained when a strand is pulled out from the surface of the plasmolyzed protoplast by the microneedle. At first both mesoplasm and plasmalemma follow the needle and cannot be distinguished from one another. For a short time, material from the protoplast will continue to flow into the strand as the needle is drawn back, then this flow will cease, and the material composing the strand elongates as the needle moves. The length to which the mesoplasm can be elongated is not very great. When this limit is reached the mesoplasm rounds into droplets, while the plasmalemma persists as a slender thread connecting the droplets and forming a layer over each droplet (Fig. 1). If the needle is drawn still further back, the thread stretches and the balls are carried farther apart. If the needle is moved towards the protoplast again, the strand contracts and the balls reapproach one another. They maintain their globular form until actually in contact. If the globules and the connecting thread were composed of the same material, we should expect to see the same shapes shown as the globules reapproach one another which were shown as they separated and rounded up, just as

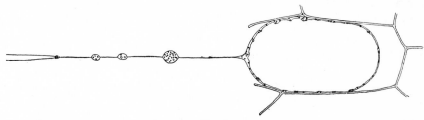

Fig. 1

an elongated soap bubble passes through the same forms when allowed to shorten as it did when elongated. But no sign of fusion of the droplets appears, until they are actually in contact with one another. Similarly, a globule reapproaching the protoplast itself must actually come into contact with the mass from which it arose before it loses its spherical shape and starts to flow back into the plasma mass, even though the two are connected at all stages by a thread of plasmalemma.

It has been known for some time (CHODAT 1911) that when mesoplasm is included in strands persisting between protoplast and wall on plasmolysis, the cytoplasm rounds into balls on a thin thread which appears to arise from the outer layer of the protoplast. The behavior of the protoplasm on micromanipulation is evidently another manifestation of the same tendency. The conclusion that the outer layer and the inner cytoplasm are distinct seems inescapable. When a drop of homogeneous fluid is elongated until surface forces cause it to separate into droplets, these droplets are wholly free from one another; no connecting thread will remain. A highly viscous fluid such as tar or molasses may be pulled out into a long, slender thread, but there will not be droplets on this thread. The layer forming the thread and the layer forming the balls must be distinct.

## PLASMALEMMA IN THE DEAD PROTOPLAST

The smooth surface of a dead, swollen protoplast can actually be torn away by the microneedle (Fig. 2) allówing the mesoplasm to flow out into the surrounding medium as a shreddy, granular mass which does not mix with the water. This brittle external layer is the structure which PFEFFER ruptured in acid-killed cells by deplasmolysis, allowing dyes to penetrate through the cracks so formed into the mesoplasm. It seems to retain some of the differential permeability of its living condition, but otherwise is very different from the fluid, extensile living layer from which it arose.

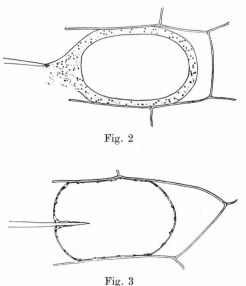

Fig. 2

Fig. 3

Swelling of the protoplasm follows the death of unplasmolyzed as well as plasmolyzed cells. Since the protoplast of an unplasmolyzed cell is in contact with the wall, it is impossible to determine whether the dead plasmalemma can be torn away from the mesoplasm, but if a needle is pushed throug hthe wall until it pierces the outer layer but not the tonoplast, the swollen protoplast will collapse until the tonoplast lies almost flat against the wall. Apparently the dead plasmalemma held back the fluid which distended the mesoplasm, and its puncture allowed the fluid to escape.

It is no easy matter to puncture or tear the plasmalemma of the living protoplast. Even a very sharp needle carries a layer of protoplasm with it as it enters the cell; the needle invaginates, rather than pierces, the protoplast (Fig. 3); the plasmalemma lies next the needle, and the mesoplasm and tonoplast are also indented and carried in. When the needle is pushed through the protoplast until it traverses the vacuole and passes through the opposite side, the second protoplast wall stretches

and covers the advancing needle like a tent. It is evident from the movement of the granular mesoplasm that material for this cone and for the
layer covering the needle is supplied by flow from other regions, but if
the needle is pushed through far enough, particularly if it is moved
rapidly, this flow will be inadequate and a strain will result which may find
relief in one of several different ways. The plasmalemma may be ruptured,
resulting in death of the cell. The protoplast may be completely punctured
at the point at which the needle enters and at the opposite side where
the needle tip stretches it into the form of a cone. In this case the severed
edges of the layer about the needle come into contact with the edges
of the puncture in the cone and
fuse. The protoplast resumes it
normal contours, but a tube of
protoplasm now surrounds the
needle which joins the protoplast at both ends (see Fig. 4).
Perhaps the situation may be
more clearly visualized by
analogy with invertebrate em-
bryology. The needle first
invaginated the protoplast,
resulting in a gastrula stage,

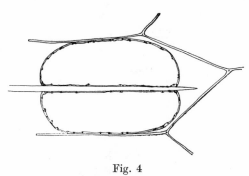

Fig. 4

the end of the "archenteron" was then brought into contact with the
opposite wall of the gastrula, and an opening, the "stomadaeum", was
formed. The vacuole corresponds in position to the coelom, and is at
all stages completely shut off from the outside solution. This interpretation
of the state of affairs can be corroborated when the needle is moved
backwards and forwards. Material from the needle flows into the wall
of the protoplast, and material at the other end of the needle flows from
the wall of the protoplast onto the needle. In addition to these two possibilities, the strain produced by the needle may have a third result.

## PUNCTURE OF THE VACUOLE AND CONTRACTION OF THE PROTOPLAST

Sometimes the layers of protoplasm about the needle remain intact
while those on the opposite side of the protoplast, stretched by the needle,
are ruptured. The opening enlarges rapidly, forming a gaping aperture.
The cell sap is in direct contact with the external solution, and in the
case of cells whose sap contains colored pigment, its outward diffusion

can be followed.  The hole grows slowly after its initial rapid formation, and as it enlarges the protoplasm flows together until finally only a ball of protoplasm remains, containing a nucleus but no central vacuole (Fig. 5).  What is now the outer layer of this mass consists in part of the layer originally in contact with the cell sap.  The cytoplasm is normal, the streaming of the granules continues, and no swelling or appearance of Brownian movement results.

An enlarging puncture of this sort not infrequently arises at the point at which the needle first enters the protoplast, or more rarely,

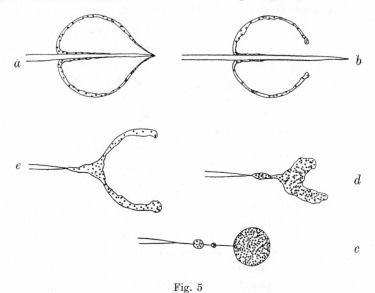

Fig. 5

at a point remote from the needle as a result of the tension produced. The last case is more common among cells which have stood for some time in plasmolyzing solution.  This suggests that the internal structure of the protoplast undergoes gradual readjustment to its new form, and loses in extensibility.  Enlarging punctures, not resulting in death of the cell, also occur at times in unplasmolyzed cells.

## ELASTICITY AS A CAUSE OF PROTOPLASMIC CONTRACTION

The fact that the hole formed enlarges so slowly after its first appearance suggests that its enlargement and the contraction of the protoplasm may be due to elastic forces rather than surface forces.  It is hard to see why the rate of enlargement should change so abruptly if it were the result of surface tension. Elastic substances, however, often show lag in recovery, returning rapidly partway to their original form, then completing the return very slowly.

There are other points in the behavior of the protoplast which are more readily explained on the assumption of elasticity than of surface tension alone. When a strand is pulled out from the surface of the protoplast and stretched farther and farther, it will finally break, and contract very rapidly, almost snapping back, and usually crumpling as it recoils (SCARTH, 1927, has described similar behavior of internal cytoplasmic strands when broken.) These strands lag in the final stages of their contraction. The return of the final lagging portion to the plasma mass can be accelerated by pressing on the adjacent portion of the protoplast.

## ELASTICITY IN THE PLASMALEMMA

If a strand is pulled out from the protoplast but not elongated to the point at which the mesoplasm separates into balls, the heavy granular mass will at first flow back into the protoplast when the needle reapproaches it almost as fast as the needle itself moves, but at the last will flow more slowly, so that a portion persists for a time as a round protrusion on the surface of the protoplast. This will also flow back into the main mass in time, and can be made to flow back instantly by pressing with the needle on an adjoining portion of the protoplast. Now, such pressure indents the surface of the protoplast, making its curvature more sharp. When one liquid droplet flows into another as a result of surface tension forces, the speed of flow will increase as the difference between the curvature of the two droplets increases. Hence, the effect of such pressure should be to retard the flow, were it caused by surface tension. Again there is a strong suggestion that it is elastic forces, probably in the plasmalemma, that cause the flow. If the elasticity were resident in the mesoplasm, strands of varying thickness should flow with equal rapidity, whereas thicker strands flow more slowly than those in which the proportion of mesoplasm to plasmalemma is lower, and thin strands arising from the plasmalemma alone and carrying balls of mesoplasm move most rapidly of all.

## ELASTICITY IN THE CYTOPLASM

The behavior of the mesoplasm suggests that it, too, possesses elasticity in a low degree. It will be noted that when a strand is pulled out from the protoplast, some lines of granules appear to snap and flow back towards the protoplast before others on either side of them do. This and similar phenomena when the needle is moved through the protoplast are explicable if we think of the mesoplasm as based on a continuous, labile, elastic framework. Some fibrils in such a framework might be under greater tension than other, and break and contract sooner. Such a structure has been suggested by SEIFRIZ (1924, 1929) and supported by SCARTH (1927).

## TEARING THE LIVING PLASMALEMMA

The layer of protoplasm in the plasmolyzed or unplasmolyzed cell is so thin that it is difficult to demonstrate that tearing the outer surface has wholly different effects from piercing the entire thickness of the protoplast. But if one of the contracted protoplasmic balls resulting from a widening puncture of the protoplast is used, it can be seen that the needle may pierce the entire thickness of such a ball without injury, while if the outer surface

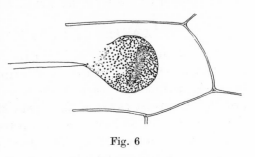

Fig. 6

is town with a rapid motion, the mesoplasm swells and ceases streaming, the swelling commencing at the ragged edge of the tear (Fig. 6).

## WHAT IS THE SIGNIFICANCE OF STRANDS PERSISTING BETWEEN PROTOPLAST AND WALL AFTER PLASMOLYSIS?

KÜSTER (1910) has noted that portions of a protoplast separated by plasmolysis frequently do not fuse on deplasmolysis. This fact is occasionally cited as evidence for the existence of a distinct external layer on the protoplast. This is questionable, for two soap bubbles may likewise fail to fuse when brought into contact, and the two portions of the protoplast, filled with and surrounded by liquid, are more analogous to soap bubbles than to liquid droplets. The behavior of isolated portions of protoplasts brought into contact with one another could be further followed here. If the solution in which plasmolyzed, sectioned material is mounted is diluted, the protoplasts will move toward the open end of the outer cells as they swell, until they partially protrude or are even set free in the surrounding medium. A partially protruding protoplast can be pinched in two with the needle, much as a soap bubble can be divided, but in this case a thin strand of plasmalemma connects the two portions (Fig. 7). One portion is anucleate, yet streaming in it will continue in exactly the same manner as in protoplasts containing the nucleus, even after the connecting thread is broken. A ball of protoplasm thus separated will not fuse when brought again into contact with the other portion of the same protoplast or with another protoplast, which confirms KÜSTER's observation. However, when the two balls of protoplasm are separated again, a newly formed plasmalemma thread will connect them. These threads suggest plasmodesmae. It is already known that plasmodesmae must arise secondarily, since they occur between cells of different genetic origin in graft hybrids (HUME 1913), but whether or not there is true

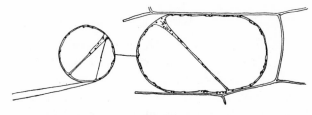

Fig. 7

cytoplasmic continuity in plasmodesmae is still an open question. The threads seen here originate from a secondary contact of protoplasm, and apparently involve no true fusion of mesoplasm.

Strands running from a plasmolyzed protoplast to the cell wall are sometimes thought to arise from plasmodesmae. Others suggest that their presence indicates the continuity of substance between wall and membrane which CRANNER (1919) has supported. The greater number of the strands disappear after prolonged plasmolysis. The few that remain can be broken by careful manipulation. But whenever a free protoplast is brought into contact with the wall, a new strand will form at the new point of contact. In order to remove the protoplast this new strand must be broken, and in breaking the first a new contact is apt to be made and another strand formed, and so on. These newly formed strands fasten the protoplast to the wall as securely as those persisting from plasmolysis. In one case a plasmolyzed protoplast, lying in a cell which had both end walls removed, was rolled over and over by two needles from one end of the cell to the other, all previously existing strands thus being broken. The plasmolyzing solution was then made more concentrated, and on further contraction of the protoplast it was evident that numerous new strands now connected it with this new region of the wall.  When we also consider the fact that the strands between needle and protoplast are fully as persistent as those between protoplast and wall, it seems that the strands are more likely the result of the glutinosity of the plasmalemma than of continuity of substance between wall and protoplast, or of the presence of plasmodesmae.

## THE TONOPLAST

The tonoplast is the most striking of the differentiated protoplasmic layers in that it can be completely isolated and still retain many of the properties shown in the living cell.

### DISTINCTNESS OF THE TONOPLAST IN THE LIVING CELL

The best indication of a distinction between tonoplast and mesoplasm in the normal cell is obtained when a needle draws out a strand from the wall of the vacuole.  Frequently the granular material in such a strand will round up into balls on a hyaline, tonoplast thread, much as the mesoplasm rounds into balls on an external plasmalemma thread when a strand is pulled out from the outer surface.  The fact that this does not invariably occur is probably due to the fact that an internal strand cannot be elongated to any great extent, whereas a thread pulled out from the external surface can be elongated to several times the length of the protoplast, if necessary, in order to reach the limit of extensibility of the mesoplasm.

On the death of the cell, the material composing the transvacuolar strands, as well as the remainder of the cytoplasm, swells.  The mesoplasm in the strands flows together to form globules on a thin, hyaline thread.  Threads which originally contained no granular material do not swell visibly, and show no rounding into droplets.  Apparently the material composing the tonoplast swells little, if any, on death.

### ISOLATION OF THE TONOPLAST

The tonoplast will often remain intact when a sudden, tearing motion of the needle ruptures the plasmalemma.  The mesoplasm swells and contracts, slipping back over the surface of the tonoplast (Fig. 8). Plasmalemma and mesoplasm can be completely removed by the needle, leaving the tonoplast free, as a transparent bag filled with cell sap.  The tonoplast is clear, colorless, hyaline, apparently quite fluid and only slightly sticky. The isolated vacuole swells in a diluted medium and shrinks in a concentrated one. If it contains colored sap (as in cells of the beet, occasional cells of *Elodea* and onion) it is evident that the pigment is retained. If placed in a colored solution, the dye does not penetrate. Since this layer retains its differential permeability, it seems not unlikely that its physical condition may also closely approach that of the same layer in the normal cell. When the tonoplast is elongated by the needle, it breaks or separates, like an elongated soap bubble, into small globules containing cell sap. Only short strands can be pulled from its surface. Torn, it flows together into a transparent mass. In the isolated tonoplast we have a striking instance of a fluid membrane possessing differential permeability approaching that of the living protoplast.

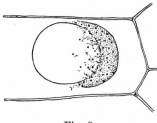

Fig. 8

Separation of the tonoplast on death also occurs in cells mounted in tap water, so its isolation cannot be attributed to the plasmolyzing agent. In non-plasmolyzed cells cut by the razor in sectioning, the tonoplast forms a layer distinct from the swollen mesoplasm, and can easily be separated with the needle. The separation of tonoplast from mesoplasm can be followed as an unplasmolyzed protoplast swells as a result of injury with the needle. Starting at the point of injury, the tonoplast appears to blister off in a manner recalling the separation of the fertilization membrane from an echinoderm egg. At times, the tonoplast is not, at first, distinct from the swollen mesoplasm, but becomes distinguishable later as the mesoplasm shrinks away and collapses against the plasmalemma and wall. The tonoplast isolated from unplasmolyzed cells behaves on manipulation just as does the same layer from plasmolyzed cells.

The number of different ways in which separation of the tonoplast can be brought about is striking. If plasmolysis or deplasmolysis is very rapid the tonoplast may separate from the rest of the cytoplasm. If the protoplast is cut by the razor, the tonoplast may separate while the rest of the cytoplasm swells and flows together. If an injection or the insertion of a needle produces too great a strain in the cytoplasm, the outer layers may be ruptured or swell, and the tonoplast persist. If the nucleus is injured, the tonoplast will remain distinct while the rest of the protoplasm undergoes marked changes. Certainly a layer which appears in both plasmolyzed and unplasmolyzed cells, whether death occurs slowly or suddenly, whether death is caused by mechanical injury or by toxic products of nuclear injury, which is invariably distinct from the remainder of the protoplasm and which always possesses the same properties, must represent a layer distinct from the remainder of the protoplast in the living condition. Taking into consideration the difference in behavior of the granular and hyaline material when a strand is pulled out into the vacuole from the vacuole wall, it seems certain that the living protoplast possesses a differentiated layer about the vacuole. . . .

## CONFIRMING RESULTS FROM OTHER CELLS

Leaf cells of *Elodea*, cortical parenchyma cells of beet and carrot roots, mesophyll cells from the cabbage leaf, cortical parenchyma cells from stems of young seedlings of *Lupinus albus*, and root hairs of *Trianea* were used as material to supplement the work on onion cells.

Separation of the tonoplast as a result of mechanical injury was seen in the first four named, and in the last, but did not occur in the cells of *Lupinus*.

The formation of balls of mesoplasm on a thread of plasmalemma was seen very clearly in *Elodea*, both in strands persisting between protoplast and wall after plasmolysis and in strands pulled from the outer surface of the protoplast with the needle. In *Trianaea* root hairs, such balls could be seen on strands persisting after plasmolysis and also when strands were pulled out with the microneedle from the surface of living, extruded cytoplasm. Balls appeared regularly on strands pulled out from the protoplast of the carrot cells, but the smallness of the protoplast and the thinness of the layer of cytoplasm make it impossible to say with certainty, as can be said in the other cases, that a part of the vacuole was not carried out into the strand pulled out from the protoplast, and that its separation into smaller vacuoles was not the cause of the formation of balls.

The failure of such balls to form in cabbage, beet, and lupine cells is connected with the fact that the strands pulled from the surface of these protoplasts are short, ordinarily breaking and starting to contract before they have exceeded the length of the protoplast.

In all the cells, contraction of the strand after breaking resembles contraction of an elastic body rather than flow of a true fluid, being much more rapid in the first than in the last stages. Contraction is always accelerated by pressure on the protoplast.

Cells of several types showed that puncture of the entire thickness of the protoplast, followed by contraction of the protoplasm into a ball, was not fatal. This could be seen most clearly in *Elodea*.

In no case did liberated cytoplasm mix with water. Its behavior can be followed best in the hairs of *Trianaea*. Here cytoplasm which is forced out violently swells at first, and some particles enter into Brownian movement. The mass may look as if it were composed of discrete particles, but when a needle is thrust into it and retracted, the entire mass is pulled out after the needle, finally breaking and contracting. Evidently a continuous structure persists, even though not visible. The swollen protoplasm shrinks and darkens soon after liberation. It then behaves like a fairly rigid body when pushed about with the needle.

## CONCLUSIONS

*The internal and external surface layers of the protoplasm, of onion cells indistinguishable microscopically or ultramicroscopically, are nevertheless distinct from the rest of the cytoplasm.* The corroborative evidence from other cells suggests that a distinct plasmalemma and tonoplast, ordinarily too thin to be detected optically, are regular features of the organization of the plant protoplast.

*The plasmalemma is protective in function.* This is shown by the fact that it is fatal to tear this surface layer, although the cell is not ordinarily injured by prolonged probing. The fact that the protoplast may be punctured as a whole, opening the vacuole to the outside soloutin, without fatal effects, suggests that the tonoplast affords protection to the mesoplasm similar to that given by the plasmalemma.

*The plasmalemma is highly elastic. Elasticity is less marked, but detectable, in the mesoplasm. . . .* The protoplasm thus behaves as though based upon the continous structural framework of a gel, rather than upon a continuous aqueous phase like that of an emulsion or suspension. This is in agreement with the familiar fact that rapid change in configuration of the protoplast (plasmolysis, deplasmolysis, pressure) is ordinarily fatal even though the same result, produced by gradual steps, can be brought about without injury.

Plasmalemma and tonoplast are elastic fluids. Noting the extensibility of the plasmalemma, the ease with which it accommodates itself to changes in configuration, the fact that the greater part of a protoplast may flow through a minute opening without injury, a new explanation suggests itself for the phenomena first noted by NÄGELI (1855) and repeatedly confirmed and cited since. It has generally been considered, in agreement with his account, that the fact that exuded or expressed protoplasm from root hairs, pollen tubes, *Vaucheria*, etc., behaves as if surrounded by a membrane wholly similar to that of the intact protoplast is an indication that the protoplasmic membrane is "autonomous", or that the formation of surface membranes by protoplasm is a result of surface forces at the protoplasm-water interface. Is it not likely that in these cases we are *not* dealing with the reformation of a membrane by naked mesoplasm, but that plasmalemma as well as mesoplasm is forced out, and that the mesoplasm is covered, at all stages, by the fluid plasmalemma? The droplets which fail to "re-form" a membrane are then those which consist of mesoplasm with no covering plasmalemma.

## SUMMARY

1. Existing evidence for the formation of morphological membranes at protoplasmic surfaces in the living plant protoplast is reviewed and judged inadequate.

2. Cases from the literature and from the author's work are cited to show that micromanipulation may be employed in the investigation of this problem without perceptible disturbance of the normal condition of the protoplast.

3. Investigation of plasmolyzed and unplasmolyzed protoplasts with the microneedle indicates:

    a) That there is an external layer, or plasmalemma, surrounding the protoplast, which, while fluid, is more elastic and more extensile than the remainder of the cytoplasm.

    b) That a similar, but less elastic layer, the tonoplast, surrounds the vacuole.

c) That the mesoplasm is much less extensile than the tonoplast and plasmalemma between which it lies. . . .

Department of Botany, University of Pennsylvania, Philadelphia, Pa.

## LITERATURE CITED

CHAMBERS, R., 1917. Microdissection studies. I. The visible structure of cell protoplasm and death changes. Amer. Journ. Physiol. **43**, 1—12.

— 1924. The physical structure of protoplasm as determined by microdissection and injection. Cowdry, *General Cytology*, University of Chicago Press.

— & H. POLLACK, 1927. Micrurgical studies in cell physiology. IV. Colorimetric determination of the nuclear and cytoplasmic pH in the starfish egg. Journ. Gen. Physiol. **10**, 739—755.

— — & S. HILLER, 1927. The protoplasmic pH of living cells. Proc. Soc. Exp. Biol. & Med. **24**, 760—761.

— & G. S. RENYI, 1925. The structure of cells in tissues as revealed by microdissection. I. The physical relationships of the cells in epithelia. Amer. Journ. Anat. **35**, 385—402.

— & H. C. SANDS, 1923. A dissection of the chromosomes in the pollen mother cells of *Tradescantia virginica* L. Journ. Gen. Physiol. **5**, 815—820.

CHODAT, R., 1911. Principes de botanique. J. B. Baillière et fils, Paris.

CRANNER, B. HANSTEEN, 1919. Beiträge zur Physiologie der Zellwand und der plasmatischen Grenzschichten. Ber. Deutsch. Bot. Ges. **37**, 380—391.

GICKLHORN, J., & F. WEBER, 1927. Über Vakuolenkontraktion und Plasmolyseform. Protoplasma **1**, 427—432.

HÖBER, R., 1926. Physikalische Chemie der Zelle und der Gewebe. W. Engelmann, Leipzig.

HOWLAND, R. B., 1923. Studies on the contractile vacuole of *Amoeba verrucosa* and *Paramoecium caudatum*. Proc. Soc. Exp. Biol. and Med. **20**, 470—471.

HUME, M., 1913. On the presence of connecting threads in graft hybrids. New Phytol. **12**, 216—221.

KITE, G. L., 1913 a. The relative permeability of the surface and interior portions of the cytoplasm of animal and plant cells. Biol. Bull. Marine Biol. Lab. **25**, 1—7.

— 1913 b. Studies on the physical properties of protoplasm. I. The physical properties of the protoplasm of certain animal and plant cells. Amer. Journ. Physiol. **32** 146—164.

— 1915. Studies on the permeability of the internal cytoplasm of animal and plant cells. Amer. Journ. Physiol. **37**, 282—299.

Küster, E., 1910. Über Veränderung der Plasmaoberfläche bei Plasmolyse. Zeitschr. Bot. 2, 689—717.

— 1926. Beiträge zur Kenntnis der Plasmolyse. Protoplasma 1, 73—104.

— 1927. Über die Gewinnung nackter Protoplasten. Protoplasma 3, 223—234.

Lloyd, F. E., 1928. The contractile vacuole. Biol. Rev. 3, 329—358.

Mast, S. O., 1924. Structure and locomotion in Amoeba proteus. Anat. Rec. 29, 88.

Nägeli C., 1855. Pflanzenphysiologische Untersuchungen.

Osterhout, W. J. V., 1922. Injury, recovery, and death in relation to conductivity and permeability. J. B. Lippincott, Philadelphia.

— E. B. Damon & A. G. Jacques, 1927. Dissimilarity of inner and outer surfaces in Valonia. Journ. Gen. Physiol. 11, 193—205.

Pfeffer, W., 1897. The physiology of plants. (Tr. A. J. Ewart) Clarendon Press, Oxford.

Pollack, H., 1928. Micrurgical studies in cell physiology. VI. Calcium ions in living protoplasm. Journ. Gen. Physiol. 11, 539—545.

Price, S. R., 1914. Some studies on the structure of the plant cell by the method of dark ground illumination. Ann. Bot. 28, 601—632.

Raber, O., 1928. Principles of plant physiology. Macmillan Co., New York.

Reznikoff, P., & H. Pollack, 1929. Intracellular hydrion concentration studies. II. The effect of injection of acids and salts on the cytoplasmic pH of Amoeba dubia. Biol. Bull. Marine Biol. Lab. 56, 377—382.

Scarth, G. W., 1927. The structural organization of plant protoplasm in the light of micrurgy. Protoplasma 2, 189—205.

Seifriz, W., 1921. Observations on some physical properties of protoplasm by aid of microdissection. Ann. Bot. 35, 269—296.

— 1924. The structure of protoplasm and of inorganic gels: an analogy. Brit. Journ. Exp. Biol. 1, 431—443.

— 1926. The physical properties of erythrocytes. Protoplasma 1, 345—365.

— 1927. New material for microdissection. Protoplasma 3, 191—196.

— 1929. The structure of protoplasm. Biol. Rev. 4, 76—102.

— 1929 a. Protoplasmic structure. Proc. Int. Cong. Plant Sci. 1, 251—258.

Sharp, L. W., 1926. An introduction to cytology. McGraw Hill, New York.

Taylor, C. V., 1923. The contractile vacuole in Euplotes: an example of the sol-gel reversibility of cytoplasm. Journ. Exp. Zool. 37, 259—290.·

— & W. P. Farber, 1924. Fatal effects of the removal of the micronucleus in Euplotes. Univ. Calif. Pub. Zool. 26, 131—144.

— & D. M. Whitaker, 1927. Potentiometric determinations in the protoplasm and cell sap of Nitella. Protoplasma 3, 1—6.

Vries, H. de, 1885. Plasmolytische Studien über die Wand der Vakuolen. Jahrb. Wiss. Bot. 16, 465—598.

Wilson, E. B., 1925. The cell in development and heredity. Macmillan, New York.

# THE PROBABLE ORIGIN AND PHYSIOLOGICAL
# SIGNIFICANCE OF CELLULAR OSMOTIC
# PROPERTIES

E. Overton

Preliminary statement: . . . This lecture was given by the author on October 31, 1898, before the Science Foundation in Zurich, and was to a certain extent a review of some parts of an extensive study that I have carried out for many years. I have already published two articles in this journal on certain parts of this subject in the years 1895 (about the osmotic properties of the living plant and animal cell, Volume XL) and 1896 (about the osmotic properties of the cell in its importance for toxicology, etc., Volume XLI, anniversary publication). . . .

. . . I have been carrying out investigations on the general osmotic properties of plant and animal cells for more than nine years. After having performed some 10,000 experiments with more than 500 different chemical compounds I should have reached a satisfactory general view about them.

The results of these investigations could be summarized in a few words, but I would like first to say something about the methods of investigation. For clearer presentation I shall try to deal with only a few concrete experimental objects.

One of the most important and clearest methods for determining the osmotic properties of the living cell is the osmometric one. Extremely good objects for experiments with this method are, for example, root hairs of *Hydrocharis morsus ranae.*

A cut and healthy root of *Hydrocharis,* grown at an average temperature of about 20°C,[1] placed in a 7 percent solution of sucrose, will show either no plasmolysis or a very weak plasmolysis of the root hair. However, if the root is submerged in a 7.5 percent solution of sucrose, a uniform plasmolysis takes place within 10 seconds in the tips of medium-to-long root hairs; i.e., at the tip of the root hair the protoplasm becomes separated from the cell wall of the root hair. If the root is kept submerged in this sucrose solution without a change in concentration (through evaporation), the degree of plasmolysis remains nearly unchanged for 24 hours. The protoplasmic streaming in the hair, which can be seen extremely well in *Hydrocharis,* continues with only a slight

[1] The osmotic pressure of the cellular fluid of the root hair of *Hydrocharis* varies with conditions under which it is grown; and it is especially dependent upon the temperature under which growth takes place. More information about this subject may be found in the more extensive work.

The English translation of Ueber die allgemeinen osmotischen Eigenschaften der Zelle, ihre vermutlichen Ursachen und ihre Bedeutung für die Physiologie from *Vierteljahrschrift der Naturforschende Gesselschaft* (Zürich), **44,** 88–135 (1899) was prepared expressly for inclusion in this volume by R. B. Park.

45

change in intensity. If the root is put into clean distilled water it shows a spontaneous disappearance of the plasmolyzed condition, which returns instantly as soon as the root is returned to the 7.5 percent sucrose solution.

The concentration at which plasmolysis occurs can be more accurately determined in *Hydrocharis* by recognizing plasmolysis in all root hairs in a certain zone with a 7.1 percent sucrose solution — a high degree of carefulness assumed — which will vanish upon transfer to a 7.0 percent sucrose solution and will reappear when the root is returned to the 7.1 percent solution. Although this experiment will not give the maximum precision which may be obtained for determinations of the critical plasmolytic concentration, experiments designed to determine the limiting concentration for plasmolysis to more than one part per thousand are time-consuming and complicated and have proved to be of no practical value for the determination of the osmotic properties of the cell.

Equal plasmolysis of the root hair takes place in a 7.5 percent sucrose solution, or any other solution of a compound or a mixture of several compounds if the osmotic pressure of the solution equals that of a 7.5 percent sucrose solution, provided that the compounds are not harmful to the protoplast at the concentrations used, and that they do not penetrate appreciably into the protoplast.

Whether a compound is harmful or not at a certain concentration can easily be determined for the selected experimental sample (as well as with many others) by watching the protoplasmic streaming — it should soon cease or at least become modified under harmful influence.

In case a compound enters the protoplast without damaging it appreciably, its solution may or may not cause plasmolysis. After some time plasmolysis will disappear, depending on how quickly the compound penetrates, provided the concentration equaled or exceeded that of a 7.5 percent sucrose solution.

The extraordinary rate at which certain compounds enter the protoplast may be seen in experiments using methyl alcohol and ethyl alcohol.

A root of *Hydrocharis,* after having been brought from a 7 percent to a 7.5 percent sucrose solution, and showing plasmolysis within 10 seconds or even less, does not show plasmolysis, for even 5 seconds, if instead of a 7.5 percent sucrose solution a solution of 7 percent sucrose and 3 w/v percent methyl alcohol or 3 w/v percent ethyl alcohol is used, in spite of this solution being isoosmotic to a sucrose solution of 35 percent or 28 percent.[2] An equilibration of the concentrations between the alcohols in the cellular fluid and the surrounding solution to an absolute difference in concentration of about 0.5 parts per thousand of alcohol must have occurred within 10 seconds.

Most plant cells may be subjected to solutions containing 3 w/v percent of methyl or ethyl alcohol for a long time without suffering damage.

[2] The osmotic pressure increases in concentrated sucrose solutions more rapidly than the concentration. The osmotic pressures of such solutions cannot be accurately calculated at this time. The mentioned sucrose solutions, which are supposed to equal a 7 percent sucrose solution plus 3 w/v percent methyl or ethyl alcohol, are only an approximation.

Other aqueous solutions of all primary alcohols, aldehydes, ketones, aldoximes, ketoximes, mono-, di-, and trihalogen hydrocarbons, nitroalkyls, alkylcyanides, neutral esters of inorganic and organic acids (the latter only in case of not having more than one hydroxyl group) and of numerous other organic compounds penetrate at approximately the same rate as these two alcohols.

The secondary alcohols penetrate somewhat slower. Particularly the lower members of the group penetrate rather slowly compared with the higher members of this group. The glycols and amides of monovalent acids enter the living protoplasts at approximately equal rates, but again the higher members are somewhat faster than the lower members, as far as experiments have shown.

Glycerin deosmizes slowly, but erythritol is much slower in entering the cell; urea and thiourea lie between these two with regard to how fast they enter the cell.

The amounts of six carbon alcohols, hexoses, amino acids, neutral salts of organic acids, and various other compounds which enter the living protoplast are scarcely perceptible.

The osmotic behavior of the living protoplast has been compared with that of a precipitation membrane;[3] moreover, the end layers of the protoplast have been interpreted as precipitation membranes, a hypothesis which I favored for a long time. For the last three years I have increasingly doubted this hypothesis and have more and more suspected that the peculiar osmotic properties of the living protoplasts are due to a *"selective solubility,"* a presumption that has become nearly a certainty as time moved along.

At a very early stage it struck my attention that compounds soluble in ether, fatty oils, and similar solvents, or more easily soluble in ether than in water (this is the most important thing) enter the protoplast very fast. However, the protoplast is not noticeably, or very slowly, permeable to compounds that dissolve easily in water, but are insoluble or very slightly soluble in ethyl ether or fatty oil.

In following this effect it turned out that, starting off with a compound that enters the protoplast very slowly and carrying out substitutions on the molecule which increase the solubility in ether, fatty oil, etc., the rate of penetration into the living protoplast had increased.

I give a few examples:

Carbamid (urea), as already cited, penetrates the living protoplast very slowly. Substituting one of the H atoms by a methyl or ethyl group increases the solubility in ether and decreases the solubility in water: the rate of penetration into the living protoplast increased greatly.

Substituting two H atoms of urea by methyl or ethyl groups, or one atom by a methyl group and the other one by an acetyl group, the resulting compound penetrates the protoplast rather quickly. Finally, substituting three H atoms of urea by methyl or ethyl groups allows the resulting compound to penetrate through the protoplast almost immediately. Phenylurea is slightly less per-

[3] [Such as the copper ferrocyanide membrane. See Sachs, J. V. "Lectures on the Physiology of Plants." Clarendon Press, Oxford, 1887, p. 213.—Ed. note.]

meable to the living protoplast than the foregoing compound. With phenylurea $\left(CO\diagdown\begin{array}{c}NH_2\\NH\cdot C_6H_5\end{array}\right)$ the equilibrium between the concentrations of the cellular fluid and external fluid had taken place essentially after about two minutes (in the case of easily permeable cell walls).

The same behavior is shown by corresponding compounds of thiourea.

Another example is shown by substituting products of glycerin. Substituting one hydroxyl group by one halogen allows the resulting monohalogen hydrin to penetrate very quickly through the protoplast; substituting two hydroxyl groups by halogen atoms gives a compound which penetrates the protoplast instantly. The same effect is shown by the compound resulting from substitution of a hydrogen atom on two hydroxyl groups of glycerin by one methyl or ethyl group.

Though I did not have the opportunity to investigate the compounds in question, it can be predicted, with a high degree of probability, that the compound resulting from substituting the hydrogen of two hydroxyl groups in hexoses by a $CH_2$ group will penetrate approximately as fast as erythritol, and a compound formed by substituting the hydrogen of four hydroxyl groups in hexoses by two $CH_2$ groups will enter the living cell quite quickly. The compounds in question have been — as it is known — synthesized and written about in recent years, particularly by Tollens and his students. Using a special method it could be demonstrated that all alkaloids in a free state rapidly penetrate the living protoplast, whereas their salts penetrate slowly provided they are not dissociated by hydrolysis. It is well known that free alkaloids, unlike their salts, are mostly soluble in ether, fatty oils, and similar solvents. It turned out when determining the permeability conditions of living protoplasts to aniline[4] dyes, that while very dilute solutions of basic aniline dyes are instantly taken up by the living protoplast, the corresponding sulfo-acidic salts are not accepted at all by most of the cells. In this connection the dyes that dissolve in ethyl alcohol, i.e., aniline blue, nigrosin, indulin, etc., are extremely well accepted by the living protoplast while the sulfo-acidic salts of aniline blue, nigrosin, indulin, etc., that dissolve in water are not accepted by the protoplast. Now, the salts of the basic aniline dyes are strongly dissociated in the very dilute aqueous solutions that must be used in experiments; the free bases of dyes are, however, readily dissolved by ether, oil, etc. The sulfo-acidic salts of aniline dyes in contrast are insoluble in ether, fatty oils, etc.

[4] From his marvelous abstracts: Pfeffer has already demonstrated the penetration of many basic aniline dyes in the paper on uptake of aniline dyes by living cells (Experiments of the Botanical Institute Tubingen, Volume II, pages 179–331). He also found that nigrosin and aniline blue (he investigated only the water-soluble dyes — i.e., the sulfo-acidic salts — of the foregoing dyes) do not enter the living cells. Pfeffer maintains, however, that methyl orange (a sulfo-acidic compound) is absorbed, which I can confirm for in many root hairs active absorption takes place. Chemically pure methyl orange, however, is not absorbed by work of the living cells, except its (extremely slightly soluble) precursor substance dimethylamidoazobenzene. I have tested a very large number of aniline dyes for their properties of penetrating into living cells of plants and animals and have found the previous statement to be true.

In addition I have been able to find methods that demonstrate the extremely fast penetration of aqueous solutions of benzene, xylene, and similar compounds, that are only very slightly soluble in water and can generally not be investigated by osmotometric methods (aqueous solutions of benzene are just at the limit of these methods).

Furthermore, it is very remarkable that mercuric chloride which, unlike most salts, is very soluble in ether, oil, lanolin, and so forth, kills protoplasts instantly even in very diluted solutions, while most of the salts of the heavy metals react much slower and often cause plasmolysis, before the life of the cell ceases. Likewise the extremely fast-reacting fixatives, iodine, osmic acid, and picric acid, are fat soluble. The fixative potassium bichromate, frequently used by the zoologists for some time, is insoluble in oils and reacts very slowly. For example, a *Nitella* submerged in a 4 percent K-bichromate solution shows plasmolysis, but the protoplasmic streaming may still last for a full hour. Only after gradual damage of the plasma membrane by the acidic solution occurs will the salt penetrate into the protoplast.

By means of these and other results that I cannot discuss now, it seems to me very probable that the general osmotic properties of the cell are due to the end layers of the protoplast, which are impregnated by a substance whose dissolving properties for various compounds may well match those of a fatty oil. Then again there is a very different question, what this substance may be.

This substance hardly will be a normal fatty oil, because, for example, filaments of algae may be kept for days in about a two parts per thousand solution of secondary sodium carbonate ($Na_2CO_3$) without damage; this solution should gradually saponify the impregnating substance if it was a fatty oil.

The conditions in warm blooded animals are even more unfavorable for the existence of a fatty oil as an impregnating substance. Not only does blood give a strong alkaline reaction, but the higher temperature of blood (around 42°C in birds, for example) would speed up the process of saponification. Furthermore, it is a fact that blood vessels, which have nearly the same osmotic properties as intact living plant cells, do not seem to produce fatty oils.

After long and thorough contemplation I am tempted more and more to suppose that *cholesterol* or a cholesterol derivative (perhaps a cholesterol ester) or a mixture of such compounds is the impregnating substance. It is very likely that lecithins and in certain cases fatty oil, too, are involved. Cholesterol would possibly protect somehow against saponification.

By means of the experiments done by Hoppe Seyler, Prof. Schultze, and others, it has become very probable that cholesterol (the word used to describe a series of compounds, i.e., including also the various phytostearins) exists in all living plant and animal cells. Until recently no particular function had been ascribed to cholesterol. The molecule is chemically very inert and after being produced is only slightly metabolized. It must seem at once very probable that this compound, so commonly found in all living cells, plays an important role. The chemical affinity would only substantiate the purpose that

I ascribe to cholesterol in this article.[5] However, it is improbable that cholesterol is the only impregnating substance. I believe that this impregnating substance is kept in liquid form or as a paste by addition of another compound. By means of a slight alteration of the composition of this impregnation mixture, smaller variations of the osmotic properties of these cells, which occasionally occur in animal cells, would be easily explained.

One could possibly raise questions about how we explain the easy permeability of most protoplasts to water with this kind of impregnation of the protoplasmic membrane. To this I have to answer that various esters, mixtures of cholesterol with other fatlike bodies, etc., can absorb substantial amounts of water: I would like to remind you, for example, of lanolin (a cholesterol ester, a mixture of such esters) that can absorb double its weight in water, and of the cholesterol-lecithin mixture that exists in the ligaments of the nerve fibers. But also the mixture of ester-like compounds, contained in the cuticle of plants and the suberin lamellae of cork cells, absorb a definite, though small, amount of water. It is commonly known that the real fatty oils can absorb some water; if they did not have this property their ability to become rancid could not be explained.

If my opinions about the causes of the peculiar osmotic properties of the living cell should essentially match reality, one must naturally assume that the impregnating substances of the protoplasmic membrane exist in some form (i.e., as an emulsion or as another body) in the rest of the cytoplasm. Therefore the cytoplasm too has the property, at least in many protoplasts, of immediately forming a "plasma membrane" with the same osmotic properties as the maternal protoplasmic membranes, as a result of bringing the cytoplasm in touch with distilled water or an aqueous solution, as derived from the experiments of Pfeffer.

The reason protoplasts lose their characteristic osmotic properties on dying, or at least a few hours or days after their death, is not very easily explained; it is probably connected with the coagulation of the albuminous substances in the protoplasts occurring at death, which leads on one hand to stress and the resulting formation of cracks in the boundaries of the protoplasts, and on the other hand eliminates the free movement of the cholesterol-containing bodies present perhaps in a suspension in the cytoplasm. I have dealt with these questions very little and realize that in this regard and other directions, too, there is much left to be explained.

Leaving this rather hypothetical field, I turn to a discussion about conditions in animal tissue. Up to this point I was talking primarily about the osmotic properties of plant protoplast; the same experimentally determined rules can be applied as a norm to animal cells as well. Some special cells, however, deviate from this norm more or less, because they carry out special functions. However, this deviation is not a very substantial one.

[5] The possibility of cholesterol having other functions than those assumed here is not denied; thinking about the enormous amounts of cholesterols that are contained in the marrow of nerve fibers, one must be tempted to assume that cholesterol serves other functions too.

On examination of the osmotic properties of the animal cells, one must apply various methods, depending on the nature of the cells under investigation. At this time I cannot discuss in detail all the methods involved, and it better suits my purpose to make some general remarks about the animal cells.

It is well known that only a few animal cells have rigid walls such as those of plant cells, and apart from Butschli's hypothesis of the foam structure of all protoplasts, the number of animal cells with one or more plasma fluid spaces is very limited. The chorda cells, for example, contain a large central space for plasma fluid, as do the bulbous cartilage cells (tongue cartilage cells) of *Prosobranchia* and the bulbous connective tissue cells. One or more vacuoles are found (apart from protozoa) in endoderm cells of some tunicates, sometimes even a part of the cells of certain tumors (pathological anatomy refers to them as hydropic cells) and some further species of cells.

Plasmolysis may be induced in some of the foregoing animal cell species the same way as in plant cells. Thus, I have been able to cause plasmolysis in chorda cells of tadpoles and in some fishes in various stages of development. However, it is generally not possible to determine the limiting plasmolytic concentration of a solution (this applies to many plant cells as well) and, therefore, a method of investigation equivalent to that used for plant cells may be applied to these cells only on a very limited scale.

In almost all animal cells the protoplasm contains no or ill-defined cell fluid cavities. But still these protoplasts in general lose water when brought into solutions of a higher osmotic pressure than those of the cell fluid of the organisms, provided the dissolved substances do not act toxically and do not interact with the imbibition fluid of the protoplasm. This water loss of the protoplasts can be directly recognized in many animal cells by the volume decrease of the cell or by other characteristic changes accompanying water loss. If, on the contrary, tissue cells of vertebrates, for example, were brought into a solution with lower osmotic pressure (partial osmotic pressure of substances not penetrating into protoplasts) than those of the body fluids, they accept water, which leads to an increase in volume and other characteristic phenomena.

This holds, with only some restrictions, for certain cells that are because of their specific function in the organism barely susceptible, within certain limits, to the osmotic pressure of the surrounding solution.

For a clear understanding of the conditions in most animal cells, two points must be considered. First, one must remember these cells contain dissolved salts as well as various organic compounds in the imbibition fluid of their protoplasm. We know that salts and other compounds dissolved in highly swollen gel — protoplasm must be regarded as such — exert an osmotic pressure similar to that in ordinary aqueous solution. In many cases the osmotic pressure is almost the same no matter whether a certain amount of the dissolved substance is suspended in pure water or in an equal volume of gel. This results, as shown in experiments by Graham, Voigtländer and others, in diffusion of many compounds in a gel proceeding as fast as in pure water. The reasons for diffusion are, however, differences of the osmotic pressure (of the partial osmotic pressure) of a compound at various points of the solution; the velocity of diffusion for a given substance is proportional to the slope of the osmotic pressure at two given points of the solution.

The friction in a gel cannot be less than that of pure water and, therefore, where the diffusion in a gel proceeds as fast as in water, the osmotic pressure of a dissolved substance in a gel must be at least the same as that of the same quantity of substance dissolved in an equal volume of water. In those cases, however, where the gel has an ability to store a dissolved compound (as for many dyes, but some other compounds as well), a given amount of this compound dissolved in the gel will yield a smaller osmotic pressure than when dissolved in the same volume of water. It might well be possible that the total osmotic pressure of the compound dissolved in the imbibition water of the protoplasm, by similar reasons, is smaller than for the same compounds at equal concentration in the same volume of pure water.

In addition to the osmotic pressure exerted by the compounds dissolved in the imbibition fluid of the protoplasm, a certain swelling pressure appears in the protoplasm, and these two pressure variables increase in unequal proportion on diffusion of water from the living protoplast. The swelling pressure increases at a faster rate than the osmotic pressure upon water diffusion. Similar conditions are found in the cells of the apical meristem of plants before appearance of the vacuoles, and in the protoplasm of the mature plant cells as well. On account of the unusually small volume of the protoplasm of mature plant cells compared with the volume of cellular fluid, the swelling pressure of the protoplasm is disregarded during plasmolysis experiments. . . .

(Editors' note: The remainder of this paper is concerned with pharmacological effects and penetration of anesthetics into cells.)

# ON BIMOLECULAR LAYERS OF LIPOIDS ON THE CHROMO-
# CYTES OF THE BLOOD.

By E. GORTER, M.D., AND F. GRENDEL.

(*From the Laboratory of Pediatrics of the University of Leiden, Leiden, Holland.*)

(Received for publication, December 15, 1924.)

We propose to demonstrate in this paper that the chromocytes of different animals are covered by a layer of lipoids just two molecules thick. If chromocytes are taken from an artery or vein, and are separated from the plasma by several washings with saline solution, and after that extracted with pure acetone in large amounts, one obtains a quantity of lipoids that is exactly sufficient to cover the total surface of the chromocytes in a layer that is two molecules thick. Subsequent extractions with ether or benzene yield only small traces of lipoid substances.

We therefore suppose that every chromocyte is surrounded by a layer of lipoids, of which the polar groups are directed to the inside and to the outside, in much the same way as Bragg (1) supposes the molecules to be orientated in a "crystal" of a fatty acid, and as the molecules of a soap bubble are according to Perrin (2). On the boundary of two phases, one being the watery solution of hemoglobin, and the other the plasma, such an orientation seems *a priori* to be the most probable one. Any other explanation that does not take account of this constant relation between the surface of the chromocytes and the content of lipoids seems very difficult to sustain.

## Technique.

1. All the glassware (centrifuge tubes, pipettes, funnels, filters, beakers, extraction apparatus) were made fat-free by concentrated sulfuric acid to which potassium dichromate had been added.

2. The reagents (water, benzene, acetone, ether, etc.) were twice distilled in an all glass distillation apparatus. The salt was ignited before use in a quartz crucible.

3. The blood was taken directly from an artery or a vein. The vessel was laid free and a needle twice boiled in doubly distilled water to which first 1 per cent

soda, and then 0.5 per cent potassium oxalate had been added, was introduced into it.  The first stream of blood was discarded to avoid the possibility of error from contamination with the fat of the subcutaneous tissue.  The next portion was then permitted to flow into a small stoppered weighing bottle, containing 0.5 per cent potassium oxalate.  In the case of the goat and the sheep the jugular vein was directly punctured through the skin but in this case the stream of blood was permitted to flow for some time, so as to wash the needle clean of all contaminating fatty substances before a measured quantity was received in our glass vessel.  In human subjects the same procedure of puncturing the vein through the skin was followed.

4. After mixing, 10 cc. (or in later experiments 1 cc.) of blood were pipetted into a centrifuge tube of 60 cc. and three or four times washed with 50 cc. salt solution (0.9 per cent) in the usual way.

5. The extraction was performed with acetone during 48 or 72 hours.  Large quantities were used.

After several extractions, the acetone was filtered into a glass beaker and the liquid evaporated on a water bath.  This procedure was the most difficult part of the operation because loss was very liable to occur at this time.  The residue was finally taken up in benzene and filtered into a measuring flask of 50 cc., when 10 cc. of the blood had been used, or in a tube marked at 2.5 or 5 cc., when 0.5 or 1 cc. had been taken.  Just before each determination the liquid was made up to the mark with benzene.

### Determination of the Surface Occupied by the Lipoids Spread Out in a Monomolecular Layer on Water.

Langmuir (3) has demonstrated that fats and fatty acids spread in a monomolecular layer when they have been dissolved in benzene and a few drops of the solution are placed on a large surface of water. Adam (4) has slightly modified the apparatus originally described by Langmuir.  We have made use of Adam's modification.  The benzene solution was delivered out of a calibrated 0.1 cc. pipette.

Now, it has been shown that the molecules of a fatty substance spreading on a water surface do not exert any pressure in a direction parallel to the surface before the condition is arrived at that they form precisely a monomolecular film, in which latter they come to be arranged in a vertical position.  In the Langmuir-Adam apparatus the water surface chosen is so large that sufficient room is provided to the molecules so that they are not in close contact with each other, By the displacement of a strip of copper on which a balance is mounted one is able to determine the precise moment at which the molecules begin to exert a pressure in a horizontal plane, and by placing different weights on the pan of the balance, it is possible to compensate and to measure this pressure.  The reduction of the size of the surface is obtained by moving a glass strip covered with a thin layer of paraffin oil over the edges of the copper tray, which are covered as well with paraffin oil. As soon as the molecules are in close contact in a layer exactly one molecule thick, the balance moves out of the equilibrium position. By placing small weights on the balance one is able to compress the layer without much further reduction of the size of the surface, till suddenly by increasing the weight the layer is disturbed and equilibrium of the balance is no longer obtained. The dimensions of the surface are measured with a ruler.

We always began with the determination of the surface contamination. By placing 50 mg. in the pan of the balance and moving the glass strip from a distance of about 30 cm. we were able to determine that it hardly ever exceeded 0.5 cm. at room temperature.

From a pipette 0.1 cc. of the benzene solution of the lipoids of the chromocytes was blown onto the surface of the water in the tray and by moving the glass strip the point was noted at which the balance began to move, 50 mg. being the weight in the pan. The pressure exerted on each cm. of the layer was 2 dynes per 50 mg. weight in the pan.

## Determination of the Number and the Dimensions of the Chromocytes.

The number of chromocytes was determined by filling the *mélangeur* as soon as possible from the weighing bottle containing the blood, and by counting in the counting chamber of Bürker the cells in 80 small squares, each measuring 1/4,000 c.mm. The surface of the chromocytes was evaluated from blood smears on slides, coloured by Pappenheim's panoptical dye. With the aid of a drawing prism of Zeiss 40 to 50 chromocytes were drawn on millimeter paper. By taking account of the magnifying power of the microscope one was able to measure the dimensions of the cells in a horizontal and a vertical direction.

The surface of the cells was derived from these numbers by making use of Knoll's (5) formula that in chromocytes having the form of a disc (a form that is taken by all chromocytes that are spread on glass) the surface is $2D^2$ ($D$ being the diameter).

The total surface of the chromocytes from 1 to 10 cc. blood was easily obtained by multiplying the number of cells by their surface.

### SUMMARY OF RESULTS.

We have examined the blood of man and of the rabbit, dog, guinea pig, sheep, and goat. There exists a great difference in the size of the red blood cells of these animals, but the total surfaces of the chromocytes from 0.1 cc. blood do not show a similarly great divergence, because animals having very small cells (goat and sheep) have much greater quantities of these cells in their blood than animals with blood cells of larger dimensions (dog and rabbit).

TABLE I.

| | Animal. | Amount of blood used for the analysis. | No. of chromocytes per c.mm. | Surface of one chromocyte. | Total surface of the chromocytes (a). | Surface occupied by all the lipoids of the chromocytes (b). | Factor a:b. |
|---|---|---|---|---|---|---|---|
| | | gm. | | sq. μ | sq. m. | sq.m. | |
| 1 | Dog A | 40 | 8,000,000 | 98 | 31.3 | 62 | 2 |
| 2 | | 10 | 6,890,000 | 90 | 6.2 | 12.2 | 2 |
| 3 | Sheep 1 | 10 | 9,900,000 | 29.8 | 2.95 | 6.2 | 2.1 |
| 4 | | 9 | 9,900,000 | 29.8 | 2.65 | 5.8 | 2.2 |
| 5 | Rabbit A | 10 | 5,900,000 | 92.5 | 5.46 | 9.9 | 1.8 |
| 6 | | 10 | 5,900,000 | 92.5 | 5.46 | 8.8 | 1.6 |
| 7 | | 0.5 | 5,900,000 | 92.5 | 0.27 | 0.54 | 2 |
| 8 | " B | 1 | 6,600,000 | 74.4 | 0.49 | 0.96 | 2 |
| 9 | | 10 | 6,600,000 | 74.4 | 4.9 | 9.8 | 2 |
| 10 | | 10 | 6,600,000 | 74.4 | 4.9 | 9.8 | 2 |
| 11 | Guinea Pig A | 1 | 5,850,000 | 89.8 | 0.52 | 1.02 | 2 |
| 12 | | 1 | 5,850,000 | 89.8 | 0.52 | 0.97 | 1.9 |
| 13 | Goat 1 | 1 | 16,500,000 | 20.1 | 0.33 | 0.66 | 2 |
| 14 | | 1 | 16,500,000 | 20.1 | 0.33 | 0.69 | 2.1 |
| 15 | | 10 | 19,300,000 | 17.8 | 3.34 | 6.1 | 1.8 |
| 16 | | 10 | 19,300,000 | 17.8 | 3.34 | 6.8 | 2 |
| 17 | | 1 | 19,300,000 | 17.8 | 0.33 | 0.63 | 1.9 |
| 18 | Man. | 1 | 4,740,000 | 99.4 | 0.47 | 0.92 | 2 |
| 19 | | 1 | 4,740,000 | 99.4 | 0.47 | 0.89 | 1.9 |

We give all the results of our experiments, omitting only those in which we were unable to avoid losses in the procedure of evaporation of the acetone.

It is clear that all our results fit in well with the supposition that the chromocytes are covered by a layer of fatty substances that is two molecules thick.

### BIBLIOGRAPHY.

1. Bragg, W. H., and Bragg, W. L., X rays and crystal structure, New York, 4th edition, revised and enlarged, 1924.
2. Perrin, J., *Ann. phys.*, 1918, x, series 9, 160.
3. Langmuir, I., *J. Am. Chem. Soc.*, 1917, xxxix, 1848.
4. Adam, N. K., *Proc. Roy. Soc. London, Series A*, 1921, xcix, 336; 1922, ci, 452, 516.
5. Knoll, W., *Arch. ges. Physiol.*, 1923, cxcviii, 367.

# THE TENSION AT THE SURFACE OF MACKEREL EGG OIL, WITH REMARKS ON THE NATURE OF THE CELL SURFACE

JAMES FREDERIC DANIELLI AND E. NEWTON HARVEY

*Physiological Laboratory, Princeton University and Marine Biological Laboratory, Woods Hole, Massachusetts*

FIVE FIGURES

By application of the method of flattened sessile drops and the use of the microscope-centrifuge, Harvey and Shapiro ('34) were able to measure the tension at the surface of the single oil drop which is present in the egg of the mackerel. These measurements, made on the living egg at various stages in its development, yielded a mean value of 0.6 dyne per centimeter at the interface between the oil and the protoplasm. This is an unusually low value, much lower than has been found in any non-living oil water system at the same hydrogen ion concentration as the living egg; only in the case of systems which are much more acid (oil and amine) or much more alkaline (oil and soap) had such low tensions been recorded (e.g., Peters, '31). Harvey and Shapiro ('34) also measured the tension at the surface of mackerel body oil, using buffer solutions of different pH, and obtained a value of approximately 9 dynes at the same pH as the interior of the egg. It was thus made evident that either the egg oil contains some very surface active substance which is not present in the body oil, or else there is some substance in the protoplasm which has a very great surface activity (i.e., is capable of greatly reducing the tension at the surface of the oil).

The immediate object of the work described here was the investigation of the physical basis of this low interfacial tension.

Reprinted by permission of James F. Danielli and The Wistar Institute of Anatomy and Biology from the *Journal of Cellular Physiology*, Vol. 5, No. 4 (February 1935), pp. 483–494.

## EXPERIMENTAL

To obtain oil, mackerel eggs not more than 8 hours from the fish (usually only 2 or 3 hours) were drained on filter paper. Sometimes the eggs were washed with distilled water before draining, sometimes only with sea water. Small amounts of sea water did not affect the results appreciably. The eggs were then broken up so that their contents could escape from the tough envelopes. Three methods of breaking were used, freezing in a refrigerator, freezing with dry ice, or mechanical crushing at room temperatures. No difference was observed in the behavior of the products obtained by these three methods. The crushed eggs were then centrifuged in 20 cc. tubes at medium speeds. Under these conditions, the oil readily separated in a layer at the top of the tubes while the egg envelopes sank to the bottom, leaving a large middle layer of slightly opalescent cell contents. The two liquid layers were separated, and the oil washed several times with distilled water. Tests made on several samples of oil showed that this washing of the oil did not remove from it anything of importance (i.e., any surface active substances) for the experiments described in this paper. All distilled water used was distilled from a specially cleaned Pyrex glass vessel and condenser so as to avoid contamination by grease, and was periodically checked by measuring its surface tension. All glassware was cleaned with chromic acid and soaked out with distilled water.

The oil was viscous, of a pinkish orange color, and a denser lighter-hued crystalline fraction deposited when kept sealed in nitrogen at room temperatures. Before the deposition of crystals the oil was quite clear and transparent to the eye. When allowed to stand in an open vessel the color changed to a pale lemon tint after about 2 days' exposure, a waxy layer separated at the surface, and the viscosity appeared to have increased. Oil was used before any visible change had occurred.

The interfacial tensions recorded in the following sections were all measured with the interfacial tensimeter of du Nouy

('25). This instrument had been carefully checked against a Harkins ('26) drop-weight apparatus using a number of different oil-water interfaces. The deviations between the two sets of readings were found to be not greater than 5 per cent, the tensimeter values always lower than the drop weight values. The experiments described here are not subject to an error greater than 10 per cent, and in most cases the error is probably much less than 10 per cent.

## The interface oil—aqueous solution

1. The tension at the interface between the aqueous egg material and the egg oil was found to be 0.8 dyne. This value had already been attained 30 seconds after bringing the oil into contact with the aqueous layer, and remained constant. In one case measurements were made at intervals over a period of 7 days; by the end of this time, both the oil and the aqueous material were badly decomposed, but there was no change in the interfacial tension. If mackerel body oil was substituted for the egg oil, the same value of 0.8 dyne was obtained. This value is substantially the same as that found by Harvey and Shapiro for the egg oil while in the intact living egg. The same figure was obtained for oil-egg material extracted both from fertilized and unfertilized eggs, and also for eggs killed by ether treatment immediately after stripping the female.

2. An attempt was made to measure the tension at the interface between egg oil and sea water. This was difficult, for proteins from the aqueous cell contents adhered to the oil very tenaciously. It is doubtful whether any one of the specimens was completely free of protein. With the cleanest specimen, values of about 7 dynes were recorded; a similar value was obtained with a phosphate buffer of pH 6.8, the pH of Fundulus eggs, as determined by Chambers ('32). No particular importance can be attached to this measurement as an absolute value, but it agrees well with the 9 dynes/cm. obtained by Harvey and Shapiro for mackerel body oil in contact with buffer. Its significance lies in the fact that the figure is much higher than that obtained in the presence of the fluid contents of the egg, so that there is no evidence in favor of

the view that the low value of 0.8 dyne in contact with egg extract is due to some peculiarity of the oil.

3. To test the surface activity of the aqueous cell contents it was necessary to measure the tension at an interface formed with an oil which has no surface activity. Brom-benzene was chosen, as it is easily purified by distillation under reduced pressure, and it is very convenient to have an oil which is heavier than water. The tension at the interface between brom-benzene and distilled water is 39 dynes.

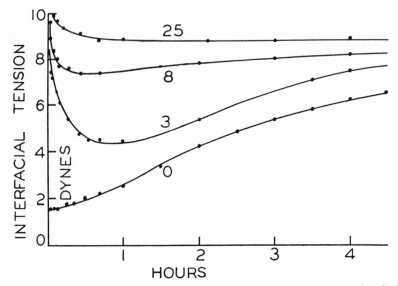

Fig. 1  Effect of shaking brom-benzene with aqueous egg contents for 0, 3, 8 and 25 minutes. After shaking, the interfacial tension is plotted as a function of time. For details see text.

The lower curve of figure 1 shows the change with time of the tension at the interface between brom-benzene and the aqueous egg material. The interfacial tension in dynes is plotted vertically, time in hours horizontally. It will be seen from the curve that when the oil and the egg material were first brought into contact the tension was quite low, only just over a dyne, and that with the passage of time very marked increase occurs, the tension tending to a limiting value of 8.5 dynes which is practically attained at the end of 40 hours. Accompanying this increase in interfacial tension there is a heavy flocculation of material from the originally almost clear fluid. Evidence will be presented shortly which indicates that this material is protein. Evidently some change in the nature of the protein occurs on the surface of the brom-benzene which makes the protein insoluble and reduces its surface activity, so that it is replaced in the surface by fresh unchanged protein, which in its turn suffers a change and is replaced. For lack of a more definite name, this change in solubility of the protein at the interface will be referred to in the future as denaturation. The final value of 8.5 dynes probably corresponds to the degree to which the denatured protein is able to lower the interfacial tension, and this value is only reached when the whole of the available protein has changed. A similar change in interfacial tension, and denaturation of protein, was observed when the hydrocarbon Nujol was substituted for brom-benzene.

There was one possible alternative to the view that the change in solubility of the protein took place at the surface of the oil, namely, that some reaction with brom-benzene was taking place in the bulk of the aqueous layer, due to its being saturated with brom-benzene. If this view were correct, there would be no increase in the rate of denaturation on increasing the ratio of oil-water surface to volume. To test out this view, equal volumes of brom-benzene and aqueous egg material were vigorously shaken up for various periods of time. Under these conditions, the oil forms a fine emulsion and the ratio of surface to volume is very much increased. When the allotted time had elapsed, the oil droplets were removed from the suspension by centrifuging. The oil had a density of 1.5, so that at moderate speeds the removal is almost instantaneous. The aqueous layer after centrifuging was then placed in contact with a fresh quantity of brom-benzene, and the interfacial tension measured, just as in the case of the untreated aqueous material. The curves obtained after 3, 8 and 25 minutes' shaking are also shown on figure 1. It is obvious from these curves that the relative increase of surface does indeed produce a great increase in the rate of denaturation. It can thus safely be concluded that the denaturation is taking place at the oil-water interface. Additional experiments showed that a protein-like egg white does not denature (precipitate) in contact with brom-benzene saturated water, but forms an insoluble film at a brom-benzene interface.

4. A further series of experiments was carried out to investigate the change of tension with time at the interface between the aqueous egg contents and brom-benzene containing various percentages of egg oil. These results are shown

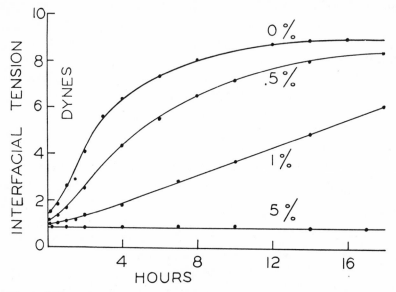

Fig. 2   Effect of egg oil on tension at interface, brom-benzene—egg contents, plotted against time. The figures indicate per cent egg oil in brom-benzene.

on figure 2. Quite small proportions of egg oil are sufficient to markedly decrease the rate of denaturation, and at a concentration of 5 per cent the denaturation is almost entirely stopped. It was also found that small concentrations of lecithin, palmitic acid, and cholesterol effectively reduced the rate of denaturation.

## Nature of the surface-active material

From the experiments described above it is justifiable to conclude that the aqueous part of the contents of the mackerel egg contain a substance which has a very great surface activity and which is responsible for the very low tension at the surface of the egg oil. The changes in interfacial tension with time strongly suggest that this substance is a protein, since we should expect the lowering of surface tension to be permanent with other surface active substances. In addition the surface activity of the egg material could be destroyed by heating. Accordingly, a direct precipitation of the aqueous material with ammonium sulphate was carried out. After the addition of the ammonium sulphate, the mixtures were

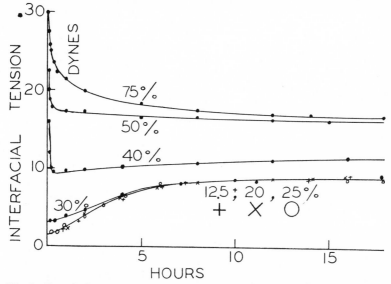

Fig. 3 Interfacial tension of brom-benzene—$(NH_4)_2SO_4$ precipitation filtrates of egg contents plotted against time. The figures give per cent $(NH_4)_2SO_4$ saturation.

allowed to stand for 24 hours, the precipitate removed by centrifuging, and the interfacial tension of the supernatant liquid measured against brom-benzene. The curves obtained in this manner are shown in figure 3. Where the concentration of ammonium sulphate was less than 35 per cent of the saturation values, there was a rapid initial drop in the tension at the surface of the oil, followed by a much slower rise to a limiting value of 8.5 dynes, due to denaturation. Where the concentration was greater than 45 per cent saturation, the behavior was quite different, the interfacial tension fall-

ing to a limiting value of about 16 dynes. The only points on
these curves for which it is possible to make a point for point
comparison with certainty are the limiting values of the interfacial tension after denaturation; these have been plotted in
figure 4; this figure clearly brings out the point that the very
surface active component of the cell contents is removed at a
concentration of ammonium sulphate between 35 and 45 per
cent saturation. This view was confirmed by dissolving the
precipitate in distilled water or sea water in those cases where

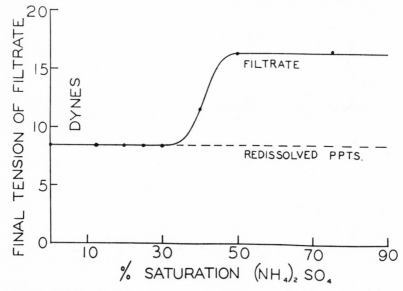

Fig. 4  Final interfacial tension values of figure 3 plotted against per cent
saturation of $(NH_4)_2SO_4$.

the supernatant liquid had lost its surface activity; the re-
dissolved precipitates showed all the surface activity of the
original solutions, and tended to a limiting value of 8.5 dynes,
as indicated by the dotted line in figure 4.

These solubility properties are also consistent with the view
that the substance responsible for the low tensions is a protein,
and the fact that it precipitates in less than half saturation
indicates that it has globulin characteristics. Not too much
importance can be attached to this evidence in view of the
undoubtedly complex nature of the egg extract.

### DISCUSSION

From the results described above it is clear that the low interfacial tension recorded by Harvey and Shapiro in the case of the oil drop inside the mackerel egg is primarily due to a film of protein-like material adsorbed on the surface of the oil from the aqueous part of the egg contents. A diagram of the nature of this interface is shown in figure 5. Passing from the bulk of the oil outward, there is encountered, first, a chaotic mixture of fats, then an approximately unimolecular array of fatty molecules, oriented with their polar (water attractive) groups directed toward the aqueous phase; next an adsorbed layer, also approximately unimolecular, of pro-

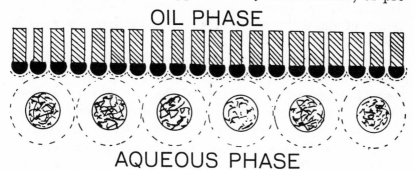

Fig. 5  Schema of molecular conditions at interface, oil—aqueous egg contents. Hydrated protein molecules on bottom, oil molecules on top.

tein molecules, and, lastly, the non-oriented bulk of the aqueous phase. All of the molecules are, of course, in a state of thermal agitation. A preliminary survey has been made of a number of other eggs (Fundulus, Arbacia, Asterias) which has shown that these eggs likewise contain proteins of a surface activity comparable to that of the proteins of the mackerel egg. Work on the albumin and globulins of the white of hen's eggs has shown that these proteins also have the property of producing very low tensions at interfaces between lipoid and aqueous phases.

This surface activity of water-soluble proteins has an important bearing on our conception of the physical structure of the surface of living protoplasm. There is now a very large body of evidence in favor of the view that the position of the surface of the living cell, i.e., the surface giving a living cell its characteristic properties, is defined by a very thin layer of lipoid material.   On the other hand, the work of E. N. Harvey and his collaborators ('31, '32, '33) and of Cole ('32) has shown that the tension at the surface of a number of cells is quite low, well under 2 dynes.   Yet no lipoid[1] is known which has an interfacial tension of less than about 9 dynes at the pH of the cell.   There was thus a sharp contradiction between these two sets of results.   This contradiction can now be resolved, for in this paper it has been shown that the proteins present in some at least of these cells have a very great surface activity, and thus would necessarily become adsorbed on the lipoid layer and lower the tension at the surface of the cells to the order of magnitude observed by Harvey.

Another problem of the behavior of the cell contents also appears to be partly, at least, cleared up by this work, for an explanation can be presented of the fact that intracellular proteins do not suffer denaturation to an appreciable extent on the surface of intracellular oil droplets.   Judging from previous experiments on a few non-living systems proteins denatured rapidly at oil-water interfaces.   In the course of this work it has been shown (fig. 2) that the proteins of the mackerel egg do not denature at an interface unless the interfacial tension is high.   The addition of very small amounts of mackerel oil to an inert solvent-like brom-benzene, of relatively high interfacial tension, results in an immediate marked lowering of the tension due to the heavy adsorption of the surface active oil at the interface.   It is now fairly certain that most proteins exist in solution in approximately spherical units, for Bernal and Crowfoot ('34) have recently produced some x-ray work in support of the evidence of Svedberg on this point. It has been known for some time, from the work of Gorter and Grendal (Adam, '30) that many proteins at an air-water interface will spread out under the influence of the surface forces until each protein unit forms a sheet thousands of

[1] The term lipoid is used here for a substance which is much more soluble in hydrocarbons than in water.

square Angström units in area, and of the order of five Angström units in thickness. Accompanying this change in shape of the protein units is a change in solubility, the film at the interface practically losing its solubility, so that the phenomena is usually referred to as denaturation at the interface. Bearing in mind the facts summarized above, we incline to the view that the major factor determining whether a protein will denature at an oil-water interface is the magnitude of the interfacial tension. If the tension is great enough to pull out the protein units from their spherical structure into their sheet-like structure, then denaturation will take place. This does not imply that the only change taking place in the protein units is their spreading out flat under the action of the surface forces. Many other changes such as intramolecular rearrangements may also be taking place, but will only do so if the interfacial tension is large enough to produce this change in the shape of the protein units.

In the case of the mackerel oil, the interfacial layer formed when the oil is in contact with an aqueous solution is in the first place composed of the hydrated polar heads of the oriented oil molecules (fig. 5). Owing to this hydration, the surface forces are much weaker than would be the case if the oil were a hydrocarbon with no hydrated groups. Consequently, when the proteins, very much more heavily hydrated, become adsorbed the adsorption is onto this already hydrated region of low surface forces, and the contact will not differ very markedly from that experienced when two protein molecules (both heavily hydrated) come into contact in the bulk of the solution; under these circumstances it is quite understandable that no denaturation should take place.

### SUMMARY

An investigation has been made of the tension at the interface between the aqueous part of the contents of mackerel eggs and of the egg oil. The value of the intracellular measurement of this tension made by Harvey and Shapiro has been confirmed. The physical basis for this low interfacial tension has been partly established (probably the adsorption of a globulin-like protein at the oil surface).

The denaturation of the egg proteins at an oil-water interface has been investigated by the method of measurement of interfacial tension, and the mechanism of this denaturation is discussed.

Some conclusions have been drawn concerning the nature of the surface of the living cell and the hypothesis presented that the low tension observed at surfaces of living cells is due to adsorption of protein on a lipoid layer.

Our thanks must be acknowledged for advice and assistance in connection with the handling of mackerel eggs received from Dr. Herbert Shapiro. The U. S. Bureau of Fisheries at Woods Hole very kindly collected the mackerel eggs for us.

## LITERATURE CITED

ADAM, N. K. 1930 The physics and chemisery of surfaces. Clarendon Press, Oxford.

BERNAL, J. D., AND D. CROWFOOT 1934 X-ray pictures of crystalline pepsin. Nature, vol. 133, p. 795.

CHAMBERS, R. 1932 Intracellular hydrogen ion concentrations. V. The pH of the protoplasm of the Fundulus egg. J. Cell. and Comp. Physiol., vol. 1, p. 65.

COLE, K. S. 1932 Surface forces of the Arbacia egg. J. Cell. and Comp. Physiol., vol. 1, p. 1.

COLE, K. S., AND E. V. MICHAELIS 1932 Surface forces of fertilized Arbacia eggs. J. Cell. and Comp. Physiol., vol. 2, p. 121.

DU NOUY, P. LECOMTE 1925 An interfacial tensiometer for universal use. J. Gen. Physiol., vol. 7, p. 625.

HARKINS, W. D. 1926 Surface energy and surface tension. J. Alexander 'Colloid Chemistry,' vol. 1, p. 192. Chemical Catalog Co., New York.

HARVEY, E. N. 1931 The tension at the surface of marine eggs, especially those of the sea urchin, Arbacia. Biol. Bull., vol. 61, p. 273.

———— 1933 The flattening of marine eggs under the influence of gravity. J. Cell. and Comp. Psysiol., vol. 4, p. 35.

HARVEY, E. N., AND D. A. MARSLAND 1932 The tension at the surface of Amoeba dubia, with direct observations on the movement of cytoplasmic particles at high centrifugal speed. J. Cell. and Comp. Physiol., vol. 2, p. 75.

HARVEY, E. N., AND G. FANKHAUSER 1933 The tension at the surface of the eggs of the salamander Trituras (Diemyctylus) viridescens. J. Cell. and Comp. Physiol., vol. 3, p. 463.

HARVEY, E. N., AND H. SHAPIRO 1934 The interfacial tension between oil and protoplasm within the living cell. J. Cell. and Comp. Physiol., vol. 5, p. 255.

PETERS, R. A. 1931 Interfacial tension and hydrogen ion concentration. Proc. Roy. Soc. A, vol. 133, p. 140.

# A CONTRIBUTION TO THE THEORY OF PERMEABILITY OF THIN FILMS [1]

JAMES FREDERIC DANIELLI AND HUGH DAVSON

*Physiological Laboratory, Princeton University, and Department of Biochemistry, University College, London*

TWO FIGURES

## SECTION I

There is now a considerable body of evidence supporting the view that living cells are surrounded by a thin film of lipoidal material. The term lipoid as used here implies only a substance which is very much more soluble in hydrocarbons than in water. The work of Fricke ('25) and McClendon ('26), on the film of the erythrocyte, and of Fricke and Curtis ('34), on yeast cells, supported by that of Danielli ('35), provides a fairly sound argument that in the case of these cells the film which separates the cell contents electrically from the surrounding medium is of between unimolecular and trimolecular thickness. If, as seems reasonable to suppose, the same membrane or film is concerned both with electrical and permeability characteristics, it at once becomes relevant to consider whether the potentialities of a film of such dimensions are sufficient to account for the phenomena observed in biological systems. This paper is a discussion of the permeability properties to be expected from very thin films. It will be shown that the peculiar permeability relations of living cells could be explained if the typical surface (plasma membrane) of the cell were lipoidal and of the dimensions in question. No attempt is made here to show that the surface actually does consist of such a film.

[1] Section III of this paper is the work of both J.F.D. and of H.D., the remainder of J.F.D. alone.

Reprinted by permission of James F. Danielli and The Wistar Institute of Anatomy and Biology from the *Journal of Cellular Physiology*, Vol. 5, No. 4 (February 1935), pp. 495–508.

It is impossible to say what the specific lipoids would be in such a membrane; all that will be assumed about the lipoid layer is 1) that the lipoid molecules will not be radically different in general chemical and physical characteristics from known lipoids; 2) that there will be a proportion both of acidic groups (e.g., carboxyl groups, phosphoric acid residues) and of basic groups (e.g., amino groups) present in the lipoid; 3) that a layer of protein molecules is adsorbed on the lipoid layer from the cell contents. The second assumption is made on the grounds that naturally occurring lipoid mixtures do contain a proportion of acid and basic groups. The third assumption is based on the work of Danielli and Harvey ('35), who have shown that in a number of egg cells proteins are present of a surface activity such that an adsorbed layer is bound to be present on any lipoid in contact with the fluid cell contents, unless the lipoid is of a radically different nature from those hitherto described. In the same paper it was pointed out that the tensions at such surfaces will be of the order of magnitude of those observed by Harvey et al. ('31, '32, '33) and of Cole ('32) at the surface of a number of living cells.

### SECTION II. PORE STRUCTURE AND SOLUBILITY

There has been some questioning as to whether the conceptions of solubility and pore structure are valid in films of the dimensions under consideration. There is a considerable amount of evidence, derived from the study of unimolecular films at air-water interfaces, in support of the validity of these conceptions. We understand the pore theory of Michaelis to be restricted to those cases where penetration occurs through interspaces in a solid structure, where the pores or interspaces have a permanent existence. Penetration must in all cases, whether it occurs through a solid or a liquid film, take place through an interspace; this is a precondition for penetration accepted, at least tacitly, by the advocates of both the pore theory and the solubility theory of permeability. We, therefore, prefer to regard the pore theory as a special

case of the solubility theory.[2]  Michaelis has himself stated
that these two theories should not be regarded as mutually
exclusive.  What we are concerned to show here is 1) that in
such a film as has been described in the previous section it is
possible for a pore structure of molecular dimensions to have
a relatively permanent existence, and that instances of such
films are known, and 2) that the conception of solubility in
so far as it implies, e.g., a differential rate of penetration for
lipoids and non-lipoids, has also a validity based upon experimental observation.

The existence of a rigid pore structure in a unimolecular
(or thicker) lipoid film is only possible when the forces acting between the molecules in the film are great enough to
solidify the film.  At a sufficiently low temperature the forces
will be sufficiently great in the case of any film, and many
substances are known which have solid films at room temperatures (compare Adam, '30, p. 60).  Such substances as
ergosterol and the calcium salts of fatty acids are examples
of naturally occurring lipoids which form solid films at biological temperatures.  Thus it is evident that at least the
possibilities for a pore structure are present in these films
in the lipoid layer.  Furthermore, it was pointed out in the
previous section that such a lipoid film occurring in a cell
would have a layer of protein molecules at least one molecule
thick adsorbed upon it from the interior of the cell.  We may
note in passing that, unless cells are subjected to rigorous
washing, there will also be a similar adsorbed layer of protein
on the outside of the membrane, so that the film as conceived
here will have the appearance indicated in figure 1.  Bernal
and Crowfoot ('34) have recently, as a result of their x-ray
investigation of some crystalline proteins, shown that the
protein units have a dense core surrounded by a less dense
heavily hydrated layer.  Applying this, the adsorbed protein

---

[2] Alternatively stated, the two theories become identical when the detailed
mechanism of penetration is considered.  Penetration must in all cases be determined by a) forces due to ionic charges, b) forces due to electrical dipoles, and
c) relatively short range specific 'molecular' forces.

films will be a molecular mosaic of dense impenetrable areas, interspaced by heavily hydrated areas of molecular dimensions, the whole being a relatively permanent structure. Thus these protein films may in any case be capable of showing selective permeability toward molecules of different size. Toward uncharged non-lipoid substances molecular size will be the chief critical quantity determining rate of penetration. In

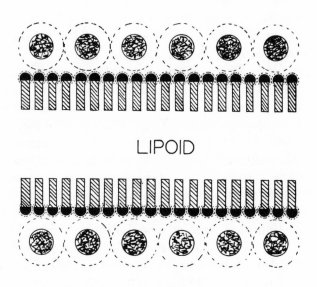

EXTERIOR

LIPOID

INTERIOR

Fig. 1   Schema of molecular conditions at the cell surface.

the case of ions, anions only will pass freely on the acid side of the isoelectric point of the protein film, cations only on the basic side. There may occasionally be breakdowns in this rule due to charges of opposite sign on the protein and lipoid layers, or to an insufficient quantity of ionizable groups in the film to raise the electrical potential high enough to prevent leakage of the wrong type of ion, especially at pH values close to the isoelectric point. Clearly, then, a protein-lipoid film of the type postulated could provide a pore-type structure which would distinguish between molecules of different size (and ions of different charge).

The second point considered in this section was the possibility of such a thin film distinguishing between molecules which are qualitatively different (grossly, lipoidal or non-lipoidal). In the first place, since we are not dealing with quantities of a submolecular scale, there is no a priori reason for supposing that molecular forces would cease to be important in the case of penetration of a unimolecular film. In the second place, the possibility has been realized in practice by Rideal ('25) and Langmuir ('27), who showed that a unimolecular film of lipoidal material markedly decreased the rate of evaporation of water from an air-water interface, but had no such effect on the evaporation of ether, which passed through the film unretarded. These thin films can, therefore, distinguish between molecules which are qualitatively different, i.e., between those molecules which are readily soluble in lipoids and those which are not readily soluble. It is, of course, understood that the question of lipoid solubility is a matter of degree, and that all substances are to some extent soluble both in lipoids and non-lipoids.

### SECTION III. PERMEABILITY AND SALT ANTAGONISM

The antagonistic action of mono- and polyvalent ions on permeability is too well known to require detailed description, and an explanation of this phenomenon is one of the first requirements of a model of the cell surface. In the case of the model suggested here, Clowes' ('18) theory of the reversal of an emulsion is inadequate. There is not sufficient space in the thin lipoid layer postulated in this paper to permit of such changes taking place in a reversible manner. The measurements, e.g., of Jacobs on the erythrocyte and Lucké and McCutcheon on Arbacia eggs, have shown this antagonism to be a very delicate balanced phenomenon, exhibited over a wide range of relative concentrations of the antagonistic ions. It is a continuous rather than a discontinuous process.

For the sake of simplicity and concreteness in the following discussion, sodium will be used as an example of a univalent ion and calcium of a polyvalent ion.

It is well known that the sodium salts of compounds which owe their acidity to carboxyl groups or phosphoric acid residues are relatively soluble in water, while the calcium salts are relatively insoluble. In general, it is equally correct to say that water is relatively soluble in the sodium salts, relatively insoluble in the calcium salts. Now, consider the thin lipoid layer of the film. Carboxyl and phosphoric and other polar groups of the lipoid molecules will be present either at the interface between the lipoid and aqueous phases and thus bathed in the aqueous phase, or else separated by not more than two or three lipoid molecules from the aqueous phase, so that in any case the equilibrium between the ionic contents of the lipoid and aqueous phases will be relatively rapidly established. Thus when bathed in solutions of sodium salts, only sodium salts will be present in the lipoid layer, and water will pass readily through the film because water is relatively soluble in a phase consisting of a sodium salt. There will also be a tendency for the reverse to occur, and the film to be destroyed by dissolving in the aqueous phase. On adding calcium to the aqueous phase the sodium ions in the film will be partly replaced by calcium ions, disproportionately so, owing to the difference between the affinities acting between sodium and carboxyl, and calcium and carboxyl. The lipoid layer will thus be a mixture of sodium and calcium salts (with other substances). In this mixture water will be less soluble than if sodium salt only were present, and more soluble than if calcium salts only were present. Hence the rate of passage of water through the film will be less than in the presence of sodium only, and will decrease more and more as the relative amount of calcium is increased. Since ionic exchange is quite reversible, the changes in permeability to water will be quite reversible unless sufficient calcium is added to break the film down. Accompanying the increase in relative amount of calcium and decrease in permeability will be an increase in the interfacial tension. When the tension reaches a critical value the film will become unstable and break up, with a sudden rapid relatively irreversible increase in permeability. It is this last stage, the break down, which, if any, is to be compared to emulsion reversal; the previous more reversible changes in permeability being due to changes in chemical composition of the film which directly affect the solubility of water in the film.

The same general argument covers the case of any ionic pair, the ion having the more soluble (or, more accurately, water-dissolving) salt will tend to increase permeability to water, and its action will be antagonized by the ion having the less soluble (water-dissolving) salt. There will be large changes in the water-dissolving power of the salts with change in valency of the cation, so that there will be a natural classification of the groups according to valency, and, in general, the higher the valency of the cation the more will it reduce the permeability to water. There will, however, also be minor antagonistic effects between ions of the same valency group.

Changes in permeability to other water-soluble substances due to ionic antagonism are attributable to the same cause. It is correct (at least approximately) to say that water-soluble substances will penetrate the film the more readily the greater the proportion of water in the film itself, i.e., the greater the proportion of sodium compared with calcium. As the lipoid solubility of the penetrating substance increases the importance of the ionic antagonism will decrease. The predominant effect of cations on permeability to water and water-soluble substances will occur only on the alkaline side of the isoelectric point of the surface layer. By the same type of argument used in the case of cations, on the acid side permeability will be decreased by anions which form salts with organic bases which have a small affinity for water. As a first approximation, permeability will be affected only by relative, not by absolute, concentration of the antagonistic ions.

SECTION IV.  THE TEMPERATURUE COEFFICIENT OF PERMEABILITY

In the past the high temperature coefficient of penetration of water-soluble substances into cells has been attributed to a chemical reaction occurring as part of the mechanism of transference. In the case of a film such as that considered here a temperature coefficient of rate of penetration of the same order of magnitude as that of a chemical reaction may be deduced without the necessity of introducing a chemical reaction.

The film may be considered as a potential barrier across which penetrating molecules must pass. The potential at any spot on the film will fluctuate with time as a result of thermal agitation, etc., but the average potential will not change very rapidly with temperature.[3] Assume as a first approximation that all molecules having more than a critical energy of translation will be able to pass through the potential barrier. For a substance which is readily soluble in the film $Q$ will be small, and for substances which are relatively insoluble in the film $Q$ will be large. Now, consider the distribution curves for energy of translation plotted on figure 2 for temperatures $T_1$ and $T_2$. $T_2$ is greater than $T_1$, so that the $T_2$ curve is displaced toward the higher energies relative to the $T_1$ curve, but is otherwise similar. An arbitrary value of $Q$ has been taken in the diagram. The fraction of the area under the curve which is shaded then represents the fraction of the total number of molecules which have an energy greater than $Q$, i.e., the fraction of the molecules which could pass through the potential barrier corresponding to the critical energy $Q$. Inspection of the curves shows that, in the case where $Q$ is large, a relatively small increase in temperature (or total energy) produces a very great increase in the number of molecules which have the energy $Q$. This is due to the peculiar form of the energy distribution. This means that in such a case a small increase in temperature disproportionately increases the number of molecules which can pass through the film, i.e., a high temperature coefficient will be observed for

[3] Unless perhaps a change of state takes place in the lipoid film.

such a system.  Furthermore, the high temperature coefficient of chemical reactions is also due to the shape of the energy distribution curve.  Consequently one can conclude,

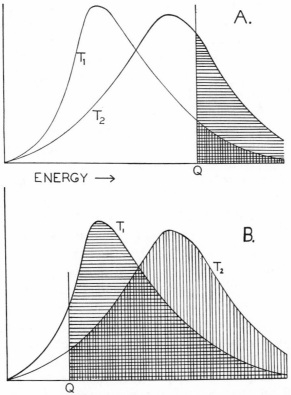

Fig. 2   Diagrams illustrating the distribution of energy of translation among a large number of molecules, energy per molecule plotted horizontally, number of molecules plotted vertically.  The area under a curve represents the total number of molecules.  A) is for the case where Q is large, B) where Q is small.

without postulating a chemical reaction as part of the penetration process, that in such films the temperature coefficient of penetration will be of the same order of magnitude as that of a chemical reaction.[4]

[4] The same general argument applies to the penetration of a cellulose membrane when the pores are of molecular dimensions.

This conclusion will only be valid in the case of penetration of a substance through a film in which it is relatively insoluble. As solubility increases (i.e., Q decreases) the temperature coefficient will more and more approximate to a value characteristic of an ordinary diffusion process due to the fact that all the molecules will have the critical energy necessary to pass the potential barrier, so that only the forces ordinarily involved in diffusion processes will be of importance. The assumption that all molecules with more than an energy Q will pass through the barrier is, of course, correct only for one value of the potential (even this statement is not quite exact, but the error is negligibly small). Correcting for this assumption will not affect the order of magnitude of the derived temperature coefficient.

There are two categories of experimental evidence which support these views. In the first case, that of the penetration of different cells by the same substance, it is found that the cells penetrated most rapidly have the lowest temperature coefficients, e.g., when water is the penetrating substance the temperature coefficient is low in the case of the erythrocyte which is readily permeable, and high in the case of Arbacia eggs which have a relatively small permeability. In the second category, that of the penetration of the same cell by different substances, the substances which penetrate with the greatest difficulty should, according to the theory presented here, have the greatest temperature coefficients. Jacobs has shown that in the case of the erythrocyte this rule holds exactly.

### SECTION V.  FURTHER CONSIDERATIONS

1. The behavior of a mosaic membrane, consisting of a mixture of areas composed of protein and lipoid, has not been considered here, chiefly owing to the difficulty in coming to clear-cut conclusions concerning the stability of such a film. However, the same methods of general analysis presented in the previous sections of this paper would apply to such a film, and the conclusions reached would depend upon the relative

proportions of protein and lipoid. As the relative proportion of lipoid areas became less the question of lipoid solubility would become less important, and since the rate of diffusion of water and small ions in protein gels is relatively unchanged by the gel it would be difficult to account for such high temperature coefficients as are found in the case, e.g., of the Arbacia egg, if any substantial fraction of the surface were covered by a protein film only.

2. Only very general phenomena have been discussed up to the present time. To go into more detail would involve the discussion of the interaction of the fields of particular molecules, and hence is not practicable at the present time. There are also many points which have not been entered into concerning the physical structure and anisotropy of liquid films which will also enter into the more detailed discussion, but cannot profitably be discussed, except in terms of specific molecules. The further development of the views presented here is, therefore, mainly dependent on an advance in our knowledge of the chemical composition of cell surfaces.

3. A great many points of detail could be quoted in which the properties of such a film as has been discussed here are consistent with the surface properties of cells. One example will be given, that of the erythrocyte. It is well known that the erythrocyte loses its haemoglobin sharply at a particular point in swelling; this sudden loss of the cell contents is not readily explained on an assumption of gradually enlarging pores. If, however, the erythrocyte has a surface such as the film described in this paper, there will only be sufficient lipoid in the film to cover a certain area. Consequently, at the moment at which the cell swells so that its surface area is greater than can be covered by the lipoid film, discontinuities will appear in the lipoid layer and haemoglobin will rapidly diffuse out from the cell. Jacobs and Parpart ('32) have shown that urethane increases the amount of swelling which can take place before loss of haemoglobin occurs. According to our theory, this phenomenon would be due to urethane dissolving in the lipoid layer and thereby increasing the amount

of lipoidal material, permitting the cell to swell to an abnormal size before discontinuities appeared. The membrane would not, of course, take up an indefinite amount of urethane, but only just so much as would make the activity of the urethane the same in both in the lipoid film and in the aqueous solution bathing it. This amount naturally increases as the lipoid solubility increases, and it is this increase which accounts for the increasing effectiveness of the higher urethanes in preventing rupture. Whether the permeability of the film would be increased or decreased would depend on the specific character of the urethane and of the lipoids of the film; the problem of deciding what the effect would be in any particular case is that of determining whether the solubility of water in the lipoids of the film would be increased or decreased by the addition of urethane, and adding on to that factor a term for the slight increase in thickness of the lipoid layer which would be caused by the urethane.

This view, that in ordinary osmotic 'reversible' haemolysis the loss of haemoglobin is due to the appearance of discontinuities in the lipoid layer, and not to a minute disintegration of the layer, is supported by the observation of Fricke and Curtis ('33) that such haemolysis does not involve any change in the electrical properties of the surface, which retains a very low permeability to ions. When, however, the erythrocytes were destructively haemolyzed by large amounts of saponin, the electrical properties were changed sharply to those of a homogeneous solution, as is to be expected when the lipoid layer is disintegrated.

## SUMMARY

A model for the cell surface is suggested, consisting of a very thin lipoid film with a protein film adsorbed upon it. It is shown that such a film is capable of distinguishing between molecules of different sizes and solubility characteristics, and ions of different charge.

On the basis of this model, an explanation of salt antagonism is propounded distinct from that of Clowes. A high temperature coefficient for the rate of penetration of slowly penetrating substances is deduced which does not involve a chemical reaction as part of the mechanism of penetration. It is shown that such a theory is in agreement with the experimental evidence, both on the rate of penetration of different cells by the same substance, and on the rate of entry of the same cell by different substances.

As an example of the application of these views, the haemolysis of the erythrocyte is briefly discussed.

We wish to thank the many people who have been kind enough to give us their criticism of these views. We are particularly indebted to Prof. J. C. Drummond, who first introduced us to these problems, to Prof. E. N. Harvey, who has given us very germane advice, and Mr. D. Mazia.

### LITERATURE CITED

ADAM, N. K. 1930 The physics and chemistry of surfaces. Clarendon Press, Oxford.

BERNAL, J. D., AND D. CROWFOOT 1934 X-ray pictures of crystalline pepsin. Nature, vol. 133, p. 795.

CLOWES, G. H. A. 1918 On the action exerted by antagonistic electrolytes on the electrical resistance of emulsion membranes. Proc. Soc. Exptl. Biol. and Med., vol. 15, p. 107.

COLE, K. S. 1932 Surface forces of the Arbacia egg. J. Cell. and Comp. Physiol., vol. 1, p. 1.

DANIELLI, J. F. 1935 The thickness of the cell wall. J. Gen. Physiol. (In press.)

DANIELLI, J. F., AND E. N. HARVEY 1935 The tension at the surface of mackerel egg oil, with remarks on the nature of the cell surface. J. Cell. and Comp. Physiol., vol. 5, p. 483.

FRICKE, H. 1925 The electrical capacity of suspensions of red blood corpuscles. Physical Review, vol. 26, p. 682.

FRICKE, H., AND H. J. CURTIS 1933 Cold Spring Harbor Symposia on Quantitative Biology, vol. 1.

FRICKE, H., AND H. J. CURTIS 1934 Electrical impedance of suspensions of yeast cells. Nature, vol. 134, p. 102.

HARVEY, E. N. 1931 The tension at the surface of marine eggs, especially those of the sea urchin, Arbacia. Biol. Bull., vol. 61, p. 273.

HARVEY, E. N., AND D. A. MARSLAND 1932 The tension at the surface of Amoeba dubia. J. Cell. and Comp. Physiol., vol. 4, p. 35.

HARVEY, E. N., AND G. FANKHAUSER 1933 The tension at the surface of the eggs of the salamander Trituras viridescens. J. Cell. and Comp. Physiol., vol. 3, p. 463.

JACOBS, M. H., AND A. K. PARPART 1932 Is the permeability of the erythrocyte decreased by narcotics? Biol. Bull., vol. 62, p. 313.

LANGMUIR, I. 1927 Effect of monomolecular films on the evaporation of ether solutions. J. Physical Chemistry, vol. 31, p. 1719.

McCLENDON, J. F. 1926 Electrical conductivity and capacity of blood to alternating currents. J. Biol. Chem., vol. 69, p. 733.

RIDEAL, E. K. 1925 On the influence of thin surface films on the rate of evaporation of water. J. Physical Chemistry, vol. 29, p. 1585.

# BIREFRINGENCE AND FINE STRUCTURE
# OF NERVE MYELIN

W. J. Schmidt

(*From the* Zoologischen Institut *Giessen*)

(Received on the 26th of June, 1935)

## INTRODUCTION

It has been known for a long time that the myelin sheath of nerve fibers within the Schmidt-Lantermann (cylindro-conical) incisures contain lipid and nonlipid portions. The latter are evident as the so-called "neurokeratin framework" following treatment with certain reagents as, for example, alcohol. However, since myelin appears perfectly homogeneous in fresh condition, the in vivo existence of the "neurokeratin framework" is justifiably doubted by modern histologists.[1]. . .

I agree with Cristini's[2] explanation of the origin of the neurokeratin framework, that it represents — as I wish to put it — a process of demixing of a system both of whose parts mutually penetrate one another at colloidal dimensions in vivo, but which separate and thus become visible under the microscope following certain operations. I disagree, however, with Cristini's assertion that the material of the myelin sheath is isotropic following extraction of the lipids.

H. Ambronn[3] has already observed that myelinated nerves extracted with ether appear positive with respect to their length. The same is true if myelinated nerves are heated in diluted glycerol to about the boiling point of water. This causes the lipid of the myelin to change from the birefringent condition to the temporary isotropic condition, and a positive birefringence occurs in the nerve. If cooled off, the originally negative birefringence of the

[1] The older literature has been reviewed by W. H. Wynn. Wynn, W. H., 1900. The minute structure of the medullary sheath of nerve fibers. *J. Anat.* 34:381–397.

[2] Cristini, R., 1928. Sulla guaina mielinica e su presente strutture della fibra nervosa midollata, da riferirsi a condizioni chimico-fisiche dell neuroplasma. *Riv. Neurol.* 1, H.4.

[3] Ambronn, H., 1890. Das optische Verhalten markhaltiger und markloser Nervenfasern. *Ber. sächs. Akad. Wiss.*, Leipzig, mathem.-phys. Kl. 42:419–429.

The English translation of Doppelbrechung und Feinbau der markscheide der nervenfasern from *Die Zeitschrift für Zellforschung und mikroskopische Anatomie*, **23**, 657–676 (1936) was prepared expressly for inclusion in this volume by D. Branton, with the approval of W. J. Schmidt.

myelin reappears. Ambronn has inferred from these observations that all nerves have a positive basic substance whose optical effect may be obscured by the myelin. . . .

I have replicated Ambronn's heating experiment and can confirm that the negative birefringence of the myelin sheath disappears at a certain temperature and reappears when cooled off. But I was unable to ascertain whether a positive birefringence appears in the place of the negative birefringence. The great magnification (immersion) needed for deciding this question could not be applied with the heating apparatus available, at the high temperature required (around 100°C).

It appears rather probable that the nonlipid part of the cylindro-conical elements has a birefringence. Göthlin[4] has observed a positive birefringence at the points where the myelin sheath is originally lacking the embedded lipid, namely at the indentations (which, however, are characterized by special structures).

It was my intention to observe directly under the polarization microscope the effect of reagents which dissolve the lipid and cancel the birefringence of isolated myelinated nerves and thus to determine the optical behavior of the nonlipid constituents of the myelin sheath, i.e., the origin of the neurokeratin framework.

In detail, the operation was as follows: The sciatic nerve of a decapitated frog was immediately exposed. In order to examine individual fibers I cut out a piece, 3-4 mm long, and split it — without the addition of liquids — into fine bundles by means of dissecting pins on a slide under the binocular microscope. If one drags such a bundle across the slide by taking hold of one end of it with a dissecting pin, the bundle becomes stretched out in a straight line without strain, and individual fibers or groups of fibers get detached and stick to the slide. Now a cover slip is placed over the fibers and a suitable specimen is found under the polarization microscope.

Next one adds at the edge of the cover slip the liquid whose effect is to be observed. It should be emphasized that the effect varies, depending on whether the liquid immediately surrounds an individual fiber or whether it gradually penetrates into a bundle of fibers. In the latter case, the effect is smaller on the fibers located in the center of a bundle, almost as if the liquid had been diluted. . . .

If examined in physiological saline solution between crossed nicols, an undamaged fiber (Fig. 1), stretched out diagonally, shows the myelin sheath as a brightly shining band with straight edges inside and out, broken up by the Schmidt-Lantermann discontinuities and the nodes of Ranvier. The center of the fiber is either dark or, in a strong light, shows up the weak positive birefringence of the fiber axis (Fig. 1). In the normal position the myelin sheath is extinguished almost completely only where fibers are stretched out in a perfectly straight line, otherwise greater or lesser portions remain more or less bright.

[4] Göthlin, F., 1913. Die doppelbrechenden Eigenschaften des Nervengewebes. *Sv. Akad. Hdl.* 51, Nr 1.

I. THE EFFECT OF ALCOHOL ON THE MYELIN SHEATH (The development of the neurokeratin framework)

It has been known for a long time that alcohol, depending upon its concentration, changes the structure of the nerve myelin in various ways. I refer, for example, to the statements by Lewy.[5]

If one adds anhydrous alcohol to a fresh nerve fiber (I always used isopropyl alcohol) the homogeneous appearance of the medulla suddenly changes. Focused to bring out the surface, the microscope will show the myelin sheath as though it were dotted (Fig. 2) and if focused on the edge, as though it were crosshatched.

At a high focus the "dots" are darker than the embedding network, whereas at a lower focus they are lighter. Hence the dots are characterized as having a lower index of refraction than the embedding network. Their fine detail and

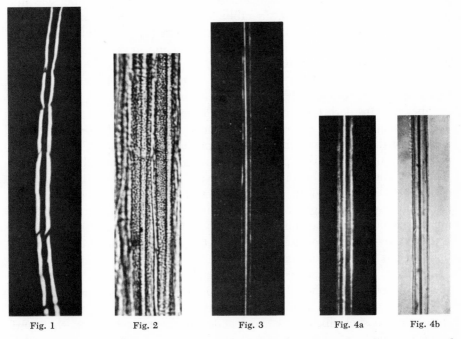

Fig. 1     Fig. 2     Fig. 3     Fig. 4a     Fig. 4b

FIGURE 1. Fiber of a frog sciatic nerve in physiological saline solution, between crossed nicols, 330:1. Myelin sheath, subdivided into the cylindro-conical segments, and axon (in focus) visible.

FIGURE 2. Fiber of a frog sciatic nerve treated with anhydrous alcohol, 450:1. "Dotting."

FIGURE 3. Fiber of a frog sciatic nerve treated with anhydrous alcohol, between crossed nicols, 185:1. In the middle, the shrunken axon; at the edge, the lipid-free myelin sheath and the neurilemma.

FIGURES 4a AND 4b. Fiber of a frog sciatic nerve treated with anhydrous alcohol between crossed nicols under the effect of the rotatable 1/10 λ mica compensator, 330:1; (a) during addition of retardation, (b) during subtraction of retardation. Positive birefringence (with respect to length) of the neurilemma, the lipid-free myelin sheath, and the axon.

[5] Lewy, 1927. Nervengewebe. In *Enzyklopädie der mikroskopischen Technik*, Ed. R. Krause. 3:1636–1676. Berlin and Vienna.

their distance from one another vary from fiber to fiber and even on the same fiber from point to point. The dotting is denser where the alcohol has taken its effect more quickly. For the most part, the dots are irregular in arrangement, although occasionally they appear in diagonal lines. The "hatching" at the edge is the optical cross section of the dot structure so that the lines correspond to the bars of the network. As Nageotte[6] points out, the cross hatching is diagonal to the edge of the fiber.

At the same time, the myelin sheath loses its strong, grease-like shine when affected by the alcohol, and often decreases markedly in thickness. The discontinuities between the cylindro-conical segments are difficult to discern in the optical cross section; however, their outlines on the surface of the fiber often remain distinctly recognizable as straight transverse lines. . . .

Between crossed nicols the following effects of the alcohol take place. As soon as the liquid surrounds an isolated fiber, the birefringence of the myelin sheath is reduced instantly; the edges which had been bright when the fiber was in a diagonal position decrease considerably in brightness and width, while the axis cylinder, now constricted, becomes very bright (Fig. 3). Moreover, at the moment the alcohol appears, numerous tiny spots appear on the surface of the fiber but are immediately extinguished. If these are a little bigger and of longer duration, they can be recognized as tiny spheroids by virtue of their dark cross which corresponds to the optical axes of the nicols. The surface of the fiber remains dark for the most part. Portions that light up are sustained only occasionally. The described phenomena are evidently related to the cleavage of the myelin and the shrinkage of the axis cylinder. The extraction of the lipid, therefore, takes place almost instantly in isolated fibers; in fibers that touch one another this process of course takes much more time.

The optical character of the extracted fiber proves to be positive for all of its parts with respect to length. Since the surface of the fiber appears neutral, the optical axis must be in a radial position as in the original condition — except for the axon — hence the birefringence of the native myelin sheath must be designated as negatively uniaxial.*

In order to find out with certainty how much the lengthwise positive birefringence occurring at the edge of the fiber treated with alcohol stems from the myelin sheath, one has to employ great magnifications and to limit one's observation to such fibers that show a definite contrast between the neurilemma and the hatched myelin sheath as, for example, in Figure 4, particularly at the left edge. The photograph is made at both of the effective positions of the operating $1/10$ λ mica compensator. In Figure 4a (addition of retardation)

    [6] Nageotte, J., 1910. Note sur le mécanisme de la formation des réseaux artificiels dans la gaine de myéline. *C. r. Soc. Biol.*, Paris. 62:228–631.
    * It is not always clear which reference axis Schmidt is using to designate the sign of the birefringence. The myelin sheath is uniaxial with the optical axis being radial. With reference to this radial axis the intrinsic birefringence of the unextracted sheath is positive. With reference to this same axis, the form birefringence seen by Schmidt after lipid extraction is negative. However, using the length of the fiber as the reference axis, the intrinsic birefringence of the unextracted sheath is negative and the form birefringence after lipid extraction is positive.—*Editors' note.*

the neurilemma, the myelin sheath, and the axis cylinder are all correspondingly lighter than the visual field; they are darker (subtraction of retardation) in Figure 4b. The lipid-free myelin sheath has therefore the same sign of birefringence, relative to the length of the fiber, as do the neurilemma and the axon, i.e., it appears positive. It should be remarked that the transverse position of the little rods at the edge of the fiber has no influence on the direction of extinction, which now, as before, occurs parallel to the length of the fiber.

Single fibers hold back tenaciously some residues of the myelin; their myelin sheaths remain weakly negative with respect to length. However, if one places such a slide with the attached isolated fibers in anhydrous alcohol for from one-half to a full day, then the fiber in all of its parts becomes positive with respect to length.

If one transfers the fiber into balsam the birefringence of the neurilemma remains well recognizable; that of the myelin sheath, however, can no longer be recognized with certainty. Evidently its negative uniaxial optical anisotropy is wholly or in part a form birefringence.

The kind of structural change (dotting) which the myelin sheath undergoes under the influence of anhydrous alcohol follows from the behavior of the myelin sheath with more dilute alcohol. Fifty to 70 percent alcohol, too, almost immediately produces a dotting and lowering of the birefringence. However, the dotting is coarser (compare Fig. 5a with Fig. 2; it is to be noted that

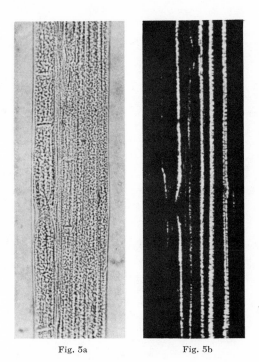

Fig. 5a        Fig. 5b

FIGURES 5a AND 5b. Fiber of a frog sciatic nerve in 50 percent alcohol; (a) in ordinary light, (b) between crossed nicols, 380:1. Note the formation of the neurokeratin framework.

Fig. 2 was taken at higher magnification). The myelin sheath now quite clearly possesses a honeycombed structure whose interstices at a high focus are darker than the bars between them; optically, therefore, the honeycombing behaves like the dotting that occurs as an effect of anhydrous alcohol; it is evidently the same structure on a larger scale. The borders of the cylindro-conical segments once again appear nicely on the fiber as cross stripes (Fig. 5a, left fiber). . . .

With a still lesser concentration of the alcohol, i.e., up to 30 percent, the changes that take place in the myelin sheath may be followed step by step. At first the inside contours of the myelin sheath become irregular so that little curvatures jut out semispherically toward the axis cylinder (Fig. 6a). . . .

Gradually these spheroids become bigger and more numerous; they consume, so to speak, the mass of the myelin sheath (Fig. 7a, middle). Thus the borderlines, which heretofore had been very obvious in polarized light, disappear (Fig. 7b). That part of the myelin sheath which had not given rise to spheroids represents in its entirety a honeycombed, weakly birefringent network, in whose interstices lie the more strongly refractory spheroids (Fig. 7a, middle). Under the continued effect of the alcohol, the spheroids gradually dissolve; they become smaller and smaller — as one can well observe in polarized light (Fig. 7b) — and, finally, in their place remain gaps which correspond to the now empty interstices of the network. At high focus, the bars of the

Fig. 6a    Fig. 6b        Fig. 7a        Fig. 7b

FIGURES 6a AND 6b. Fiber of a frog sciatic nerve at the beginning of the effect of 30 percent alcohol, 330:1; (a) in ordinary light, (b) between crossed nicols. Formation of the spheroids.

FIGURES 7a AND 7b. Fiber of a frog sciatic nerve under the prolonged effect of 30 percent alcohol, 450:1; (a) in ordinary light, (b) between crossed nicols. The fiber at the left edge of Figure 7a shows the neurokeratin framework already formed; the fiber next to it still shows the spheroids in its interstices.

network now appear light, the interstices dark. At the same time, a shrinkage of the bars takes place so that the honeycombing finally takes on the form which is known as the "neurokeratin framework," visible in the left of Figure 7a. Its history of development clearly characterizes it as an artificial product.

Since the spheroids dissolve in alcohol without leaving a residue, while the neurokeratin framework is insoluble in alcohol, one has to suppose that the spheroids consist wholly or in greater part of lipid, as distinct from the substance of the neurokeratin framework, which is essentially nonlipid. Thus, in the course of development of the spheroids and/or the neurokeratin framework the lipid substance separates out of the colloid system of the myelin sheath, becomes subject to the formative forces of surface tension, and, therefore, forms drops, as Nageotte and Cristini maintain. The rest of the myelin sheath becomes devoid of lipid to the extent that the spheroids emerge. Its proteinaceous portion must at first also contain considerable quantities of water as is evident from its continued shrinkage.

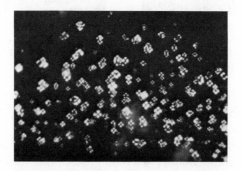

FIGURE 8. Spheroids developed from the myelin of fibers from a frog sciatic nerve in 30 percent alcohol, between crossed nicols, 450:1.

The strong tendency of frog nerve myelin to form spheroids has already been emphasized by Cristini. In the extract, however, fewer spheroids but mostly myelin figures appear. In my preparations I was occasionally able to observe spheroids in alcohol outside the nerve fibers; they had therefore been formed from the extracted lipid (Fig. 8).

## II. THE EFFECT OF OSMIC ACID ON THE MYELIN SHEATH

Osmic acid among other reagents is said to preserve most naturally the structure of the myelin sheath. The lipids extract oxygen from the osmium tetraoxide, they oxidize, and reduce the osmium tetraoxide to osmium dioxide hydrate which gets deposited in the tissue as a black colloidal precipitate. An aqueous 1 percent osmium tetraoxide solution, if added to the nerve fibers on the slide, immediately causes the "dotting" of the myelin sheath (Fig. 9) which is familiar to us from the effect of the alcohol (see above) and which presents itself as "hatching" at the edge of the fiber (Fig. 10). . . .

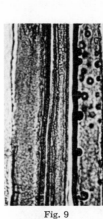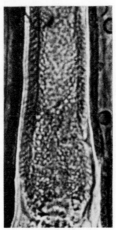

Fig. 9                         Fig. 10

FIGURE 9. Fiber of a frog sciatic nerve in osmic acid, 700:1. Rod structure of the myelin sheath in plane and oblique views; on the right the formation of spheroids.
FIGURE 10. Fiber of a frog sciatic nerve in osmic acid, 1400:1. Rod structure of the myelin sheath.

The analysis of the polarization optics of the myelin sheath's osmified fibers presents many difficulties. Little light passes through the strongly blackened myelin sheath, and, while using a compensator one might mistake the blackening for the compensatory darkening. Also, one must deal with several different effects, namely, the suspended birefringence of the lipid and the oriented deposition of the birefringent osmium dioxide hydrate. As I have recently discovered,[7] one may assert with certainty that the black reaction product of the osmic acid is deposited directionally in the myelin sheath and that it lends to the myelin sheath a weak uniaxial birefringence with the optical axis in a radial position. Thus the osmified myelin sheath shows polarization optics similar to those of in vivo myelin but with strongly reduced birefringence. . . .

The blackening of a tissue due to osmium can, of course, be eliminated with hydrogen peroxide, potassium permanganate, and other oxidizing chemicals. The water insoluble osmium dioxide hydrate becomes reconverted into the water soluble osmium tetraoxide through the acquisition of oxygen.

If one adds at the edge of the cover slip a little drop of hydrogen peroxide to an isolated, strongly osmified nerve lying in water, the blackened myelin sheath pales gradually, becomes golden-yellow, and eventually colorless. At the same time, the previously rigid and brittle fibers take on a soft consistency.

[7] Schmidt, W. J., 1935. Die Doppelbrechung der Markscheide osmierter Nervenfasern. Z. wiss. Mikrosk. 52:158–165.

Furthermore, the rod structure and the subdivision of the myelin sheath into the cylindro-conical segments show beautifully. . . .

The first effect of these processes is the disappearance of the characteristic brown-red polarization color of the myelin sheath due to the embedded osmium dioxide hydrate. Occasionally one observes also a positive birefringence with respect to length of fibers that have attained the golden-yellow hue in ordinary light (see above). As a rule, however, one can find only negative birefringences that become increasingly stronger so that the fiber finally attains the same optical character as before the osmification (of course with a weaker birefringence). With decreasing osmification the original optical character of the myelin sheath evidently reappears and the birefringence of the nonlipid base of the nerve fiber appears to emerge. Perhaps one might imagine that the osmium dioxide hydrate is somehow chemically anchored to the lipid and that this bond is severed again by the reconversion into osmium tetraoxide. That the reappearing negative birefringence with respect to the length of the fiber belongs to the lipid can be determined from the fact that it disappears immediately when alcohol is added.

If one tries to remove the blackening of osmified fibers with potassium permanganate solution, manganous hydroxide is deposited concurrently with the bleaching. The manganous hydroxide colors the fiber brown and lends to it a positive birefringence with respect to length. (Compare with Schmidt, W. J., 1935. Z. *Zellforsch.* 23:261–269.) . . .

## IV. The Fine Structure of the Myelin Sheath

The lipid-containing material of the myelin sheath (i.e., of the cylindro-conical segments) appears perfectly homogeneous in fresh condition. Even the examination of nerve fibers in ultraviolet light has led no further along these lines, as one may infer from the good illustrations by A. Massazza.[8] Furthermore, the myelin sheath appears to be rather uniform between crossed nicols; even at maximum magnification, one is unable to distinguish birefringent particles that might be embedded in a material of a different kind.

The action of the best fixing agents, such as osmic acid, even on isolated fibers, causes the emergence of the rods, often stuck together to form a net and interpreted by Nageotte as mitochondria. Thus the question arises whether the above-mentioned reagents create only the optical conditions for the visibility of the rods or whether these rods arise (as an artifact) through a corresponding fragmentation of a material that is originally homogeneous. That these figures may be represented in the manner of mitochondria is not sufficient proof of their in vivo existence. Their peculiar arrangement, however, may be taken as such evidence because the diagonal position, or crossing, and the structural relations, which appear in the same way after treatment with anhydrous alcohol as with osmic acid, are difficult to comprehend as effects of fixation. One wishes to count either on the in vivo existence of

[8] Massazza, A., 1929. L'istologia del sistema nervoso alla luce ultravioletta. Nota I. La struttura della fibra nervoso a fresco. *Arch. ital. Anat.* 26, H.1.

the rods or on a preformed cleavability of the myelin sheath in certain directions that would easily manifest itself as the rods. These two conceptions are not too different. Like Nageotte I am inclined to believe that the rods are preformed in vivo, but that they are so close to one another in the undamaged myelin sheath that they cannot be resolved by the microscope. Not until the structure is loosened to a certain degree can they be observed. As Nageotte also assumes, the rods are saturated with the birefringent lipid, a fact which may be self-evident, given their interpretation as mitochondria. The lipid separates itself from the proteinaceous base under the influence of certain reagents and gets into the space between the rods; thus the structure of the rods is loosened and they become visible.

Assuming that this conception of the microscopically perceivable structure of the myelin sheath is correct, the following conclusions with regard to the fine structure of the myelin sheath derive from the observed manifestations of the birefringence. The fresh myelin sheath is positively* uniaxial with the optical axis in a radial position as a result of the oriented deposition of the birefringent lipid. For, on the one hand, the negative birefringence* disappears after the extraction of the lipid and, on the other hand, positively birefringent spheroids or myelin figures are separated from the extracted lipid through the evaporation of the solvent. These myelin figures, like liquids, are subject to surface tension. As has been first recognized by Ambronn and later emphasized by many authors, the myelin of the medullary sheath evidently has the property of "fluid crystals," the parallelization of elongated molecules today being considered a characteristic of their fine structure, such that the optical axis falls in the longitudinal direction of the molecules. Therefore the appearance of the fresh myelin sheath forces one to assume that the lipid molecules are located radially with respect to the length of the fiber axis. Furthermore, since it is known that the molecules of fat-like substances are grouped in pairs as, for example, in the oriented layers of fat and wax which one can produce by pressing and heating between metal plates, one should rather expect double molecules in the case of the lipids of the myelin sheath.

After extraction of the myelin from the medullary sheath of the nerve fiber, the myelin sheath shows negative uniaxial birefringence* again with the optical axis in a radial position. This birefringence is wholly or partially form birefringence, for it becomes considerably weaker when nerves extracted in alcohol are transferred into balsam. According to Wiener's theory of composite bodies, the negatively uniaxial form birefringence requires the presence of particles whose greatest diameters are perpendicular to the optical axis (i.e., parallel to the surface of the myelin sheath) and are separated from each other by an interphase of a different refractive index. I am inclined to believe that the presence of such particles is indicated microscopically by the occasionally observable exfoliation of the myelin sheath, that is, by the tendency of the little rods to disintegrate into constituent parts much like tiny plates. It

* See Editors' Note on page 86.

may be left undecided whether these microscopically discerned plates are themselves the elements of the form birefringent system or whether they merely indicate the cleavability of the nonlipid materials parallel to the surface of the myelin sheath, as one might expect from the position of the greatest diameter of the particles. This structuring of the myelin sheath parallel to the surface has been observed by several authors.[9] . . .

One thus arrives at a conception of the fine structure of the myelin sheath as it is represented schematically in Figure 17. The myelin sheath first of all

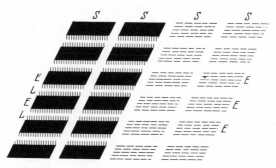

FIGURE 17. Schema of the fine structure of the myelin sheath: S = the rods, E = proteinaceous components, L = lipid components; at the right half of the illustration the myelin sheath is represented in lipid-free condition and, at the same time, the position of the molecules in the nonlipid strata is indicated.

consists of rods (S) in a diagonal position. Although large enough to be discernible microscopically, they are so close to one another in the fresh condition that they cannot be resolved as individual units. Each little rod contains lipid and nonlipid material. With respect to the cleavability (the little plates being piled up parallel to the surface) one should be permitted to assume that lipid and nonlipid layers alternate. According to the optics, the molecules in the lipid layers (L) are in such a position that their long dimension is perpendicular to the surface of the myelin sheath; in the nonlipid layers (E) the molecules are in a position parallel to the surface.

The structure of the myelin sheath is in remarkable agreement with that of the distal segment of visual cells. In both cases the negatively uniaxial form birefringence (caused by a stratified nonlipid material) and the positively uniaxial birefringence (caused by oriented lipid material) have parallel optic axes. Thus, the length of the distal segment corresponds structurally to the radial direction of the myelin sheath. However, it must be noticed that the form birefringence of the myelin sheath is much weaker that than of the distal segment.

[9] Nageotte, J., 1911. Betrachtungen über den tatsächlichen Bau und die kunstlich hervorgerufenen Deformationen der markhaltigen Nervenfaser. *Arch. mikrosk. Anat.* 77:245–279.

## SUMMARY

1. Treatment of fresh isolated frog sciatic nerve fibers with anhydrous alcohol extracts the lipid from the myelin sheath; in doing so the positive uniaxial birefringence, with the optical axis in radial position (due to the oriented deposition of the lipids) is replaced by a weak, negatively uniaxial form birefringence again with the optical axis in a radial position. This form birefringence is due to the nonlipid particles of the myelin sheath. At the same time the birefringence of the heavily shrunken axon is increased considerably.

2. Upon treatment with alcohol (and osmium) the structure of the myelin sheath emerges as diagonal rods (Nageotte's mitochondria), which stick together so that they form a most delicate net. The original cohesion of the myelin sheath becomes loosened up due to the effect of the reagents which cause the lipids to separate from the rods, collect between them, and there form tiny positive spheroids which disappear quickly in the solvent.

3. During the treatment with more dilute alcohol, the spheroids attain considerable size; they shape the lipid-free material compressed between them into the "neurokeratin framework." The spheroids at first lie in the interstices of the framework; they gradually become dissolved in the alcohol.

4. Treatment with osmic acid (by and large) suspends the birefringence of the lipids. The osmium, deposited in an oriented fashion in the myelin sheath, produces a weak positively uniaxial birefringence with the optical axis in a radial position.

5. Hydrogen peroxide extracts the deposited osmium dioxide hydrate from the osmified nerve fibers; at the same time the myelin sheath takes on again the original positive birefringence with the optical axis in a radial position. Apparently the lipid is returned to its original condition.

6. During treatment of osmified nerve fibers with potassium permanganate, the osmium dioxide hydrate is exchanged for manganous dioxide deposited in an oriented fashion so that the myelin sheath has a negatively uniaxial birefringence with an optical axis in a radial position. . . .

8. According to optical polarization analysis, the molecules of the lipid are in a normal position relative to the surface of the myelin sheath. In the nonlipid material, by contrast, the greatest diameter of the particles lies parallel to the surface. The result shows a remarkable analogy between the fine structure of the myelin sheath and the fine structure of the distal segments of the visual cells.

# X-RAY DIFFRACTION STUDIES ON NERVE

By Francis O. Schmitt, Ph.D., Richard S. Bear, Ph.D. (St Louis), and
George L. Clark, Ph.D. (Urbana, Illinois)

From the Departments of Zoology, Washington University, and of Chemistry,
University of Illinois[1]

From analysis by means of polarized light it has long been known that
nerves possess a high degree of molecular organization. The axis cylinder is
positively birefringent due to the presence of anisotropic material, the optic
axis of which lies parallel to the long axis of the fiber. The myelin sheath is
constructed of lipoid fluid crystals with optic axes perpendicular to the direction of the fiber and radially oriented (Schmidt, 18). The positive birefringence of the axis cylinder is due presumably to the protein neurofibrils which,
though visible in fixed and stained preparations, have never been demonstrated in living medullated axons under physiological conditions (Peterfi, 16).
In view of the success with which the x-ray diffraction method for fine-struc-
ture analysis has been applied to certain other fibrous animal tissues such as
hair, chitin, connective tissue, etc., it is desirable that full use be made of this
tool in the case of nerve, particularly since modern research on nerve energetics reveals that impulse propagation takes place with but extremely small
initial energy liberation. Hill (11) has shown, for example, that the heat
production immediately accompanying the propagated disturbance in frog
nerve at room temperature is so low as to be near the limit of measurement.
It seems obvious that any mechanism capable of propagating an electric potential wave at a velocity of 30 meters per second so efficiently must owe its
properties in no small measure to the molecular organization which acts as the
physical substratum for the impulse propagation.

Considerable advance has already been made in this direction (Herzog and
Janke, 10, Handovsky and Thiessen, 8, Handovsky, 9, and Boehm, 5). Boehm,
whose work is the most extensive thus far, obtained the following results: The
pattern for fresh nerve consists of a ring with meridianal sickles at 4.8 Å. and
equatorial points at 17 Å. The latter points decrease with drying to 11 Å. By a
comparative study of nerves with varying proportions and degrees of develop-

---

[1] We are greatly indebted for excellent assistance in producing the x-ray patterns
with greatly improved technic to Dr. J. N. Mrgudich, N. C. Schieltz, and E. A.
Parker, of the X-ray Laboratories, Department of Chemistry, University of Illinois,
and for aid in the making of electrical tests to Mr. Otto Schmitt, of the Physics Department, Washington University.

Reprinted by permission of Francis O. Schmitt and The
Radiological Society from Radiology, 25, 131–151 (1935).

ment of the myelin sheath, axis cylinder, and connective tissue, he concluded that the 4.8 Å. ring is produced by the radial fluid crystals of the myelin sheath, while the 17 Å. equatorial points are produced by connective tissue. Neurofibrils, according to him, either do not exist or have a side spacing greater than 25 Å. (limit of his apparatus); the axis cylinder is a tube filled with a structureless, rather viscous gel.

Schmitt and Wade (19, 21, 22) found that nerve shows striking thermal shortening and reacts to solvating and desolvating agents in a manner similar to that of other fibrous tissues such as tendon. These effects were thought to be due, at least partially, to the axis cylinder. In view of the recent work on the significance of thermal shortening and swelling of fibrous tissues (see particularly Meyer, 15, and Kuentzel and Prakke, 13), this indicated a certain degree of orientation in the fresh axis cylinder. We entered upon the present work not only with the hope of obtaining further information regarding the structure of the axis cylinder but also because of the feeling that by improved technic more details of the fine structure of nerve might be acquired by the diffraction method, the number of spacings reported by Boehm and others being disappointingly few.

## METHODS AND APPARATUS

Since the spacings in nerve are large it is desirable to use large wave lengths. In this work the $K_{\alpha}$ radiation of copper was used as obtained from a Philips Metalix tube operated at 35–40 K.V. and 20–25 milliamperes. The film was held in a flat holder, the distance from specimen to film varying with the experiment; in most cases the distance was 3 centimeters. The diameter of the pinholes depended also upon the type of experiment being performed. At distances of 3 cm. both front and back pinholes were 0.6 mm. in diameter. For work on large spacings (specimen-to-film distances up to 20 cm.) the pinholes were reduced to a diameter of 0.2 millimeter. The lead beads were always as small as possible and were very carefully centered before each exposure. These precautions with bead and pinhole size are of great importance. Boehm, using 2 mm. pinholes, failed to observe the large equatorial points at 40–45 Å. and thus was led to an incorrect interpretation of certain features of the remainder of the pattern.

Dried preparations were simply laid over the pinhole and held attached by means of plasticene. For short exposures the patterns of fresh nerves were obtained in a similar manner except that the nerve was kept moist by frequent spraying with Ringer solution from an atomizer. At large specimen-to-film distances when the time of exposure was prolonged the nerve was suspended on a thin glass stirrup and kept in a moist chamber of very small volume to prevent drying. The stirrup was connected to a mechanism by means of which the nerve could be moved in front of the pinhole so as to change the radiated point frequently. The moist chamber was provided with glass windows approximately $5\mu$ in thickness.

Boehm, as a result of his work on muscle (4), which indicated that the radiation has a decidedly toxic effect, took the precaution of changing the radiated region of the nerve during the exposure. This is obviously an important point, and we determined its significance at the outset of our work. If the radiation produces artificial changes, the patterns resulting may likewise be patterns of the artifacts. To test this point under the worst possible conditions we simply laid a fresh nerve, still connected to its muscle, over the pinhole, keeping the muscle and unexposed portions of the nerve moist with cotton soaked in Ringer solution and moistening the exposed portion of the nerve with an atomizer frequently. Using the threshold method it was found that radiating sufficiently long to obtain a good pattern (10 min.), without

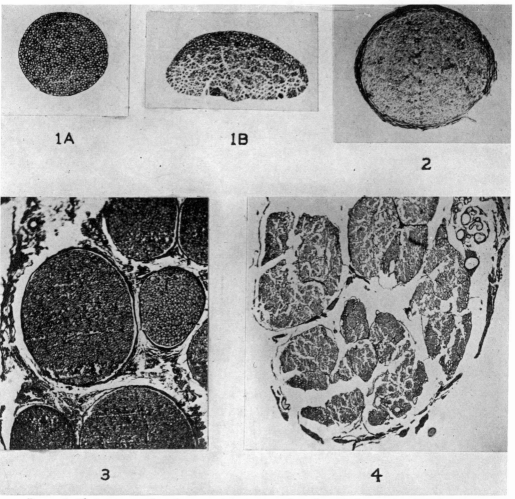

PLATE 1. Photomicrographs of nerve tissue prepared as described in text. Magnification: Figs. 1 to 3, 48×; Fig. 4, 62×. Fig. 1-A. Bull frog motor root. Fig. 1-B. Cat motor root. Fig. 2. Branch of bull frog sciatic. Fig. 3. Cat sciatic. Fig. 4. Lobster leg nerve.

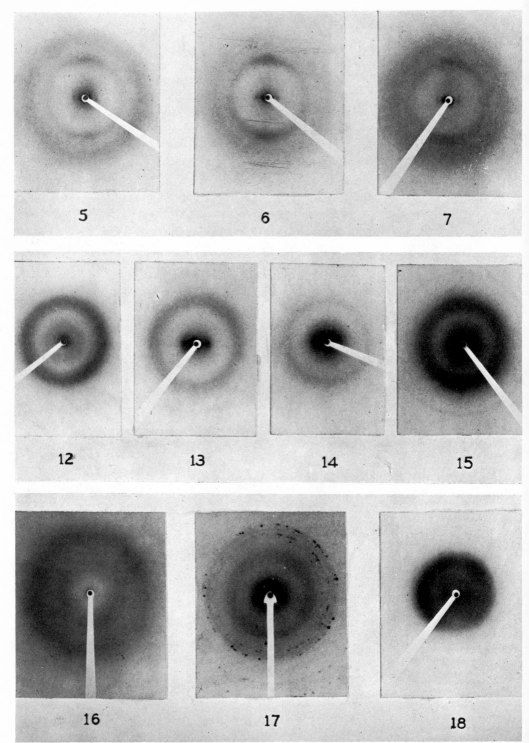

Plate 2

changing the radiated spot, had no effect whatever on the irritability of the nerve as measured by the threshold method. This method, however, tests the condition of the most irritable fibers only. To obtain information on the condition of the nerve as a whole, action potentials were measured with the cathode-ray oscillograph before and after radiation. The results show that as long as the nerve was not allowed to dry, the radiation produced no decrease in the action potential, even when the usual exposure time was trebled; indeed, in several instances the action potential was slightly increased by the radiation. Nerves tested in this manner were the sciatic of the frog and motor and sensory roots of the bull frog and cat.

*Selection of Material.* — Boehm's choice of material with which to make a comparative study of the rôle of axis cylinder, myelin sheath, and connective tissue was incomplete. The structures to which physiological interest attaches are the myelin sheath and axis cylinder, and nerve types should have been selected so that at least one representative type contained these two structures well developed, but no connective tissue. To provide such types we chose the following tissues: corpus callosum, motor roots, sensory roots, sciatic nerve. The corpus callosum may be regarded as the simplest type of medullated material, containing not only no connective tissue, with the exception of glia cells, the chemical nature of which is uncertain, but also no sheaths of Henle or Schwann; moreover, the axis cylinder is not interrupted by nodes of Ranvier. The motor roots of the cat are practically entirely free of connective tissue. In the frog there is a thin outer membrane enveloping the roots, and interfibrillary connective tissue is very scanty. The Schwann sheath is present and the axis cylinder is interrupted by nodes of Ranvier. The sensory roots resemble the motor roots except that there is slightly more interfibrillary connective tissue, the amount being small as compared with peripheral nerve. In the sciatic, the connective tissue is said to constitute over half the bulk of the nerve. To check the statements found in the literature regarding the structure of these nerves we made a histological examination of the various types under discussion with methods designed to differentiate connective tissue.[2] Immediately after obtaining a diffraction pattern each nerve was plunged into formol-Zenker solution and after embedding in paraffin, sectioned and stained. Figures 1 to 3 show the great difference in amount of the connective tissue in spinal roots and sciatics. The present series provides an excellent opportunity to study the possible orientation, not only in myelin sheath, axis cylinder, and interfibrillary connective tissue, but also in the Schwann sheath. . . .

[2] We are much indebted to Dr. James O'Leary for advice and assistance with the neurohistological technic.

---

PLATE 2. Diffraction patterns of nerves under various conditions. Distance from specimen to film (D) = 3.0 cm. All patterns are reproduced without alteration in size. Fiber axis is vertical in each case. Fig. 5. Fresh frog sciatic. Fig. 6. Fresh cat motor root. Fig. 7. Fresh cat corpus callosum. Fig. 12. Cat corpus callosum dried in desiccator. Fig. 13. Cat sciatic dehydrated in alcohol under tension. Fig. 14. Bull frog motor root dehydrated in alcohol under tension. Fig. 15. Frog sciatic dehydrated by the Scott freezing drying technic. Fig. 16. Lobster claw nerve fresh. Fig. 17. Lobster claw nerve dried in desiccator. Fig. 18. Lobster claw nerve dehydrated in alcohol under tension.

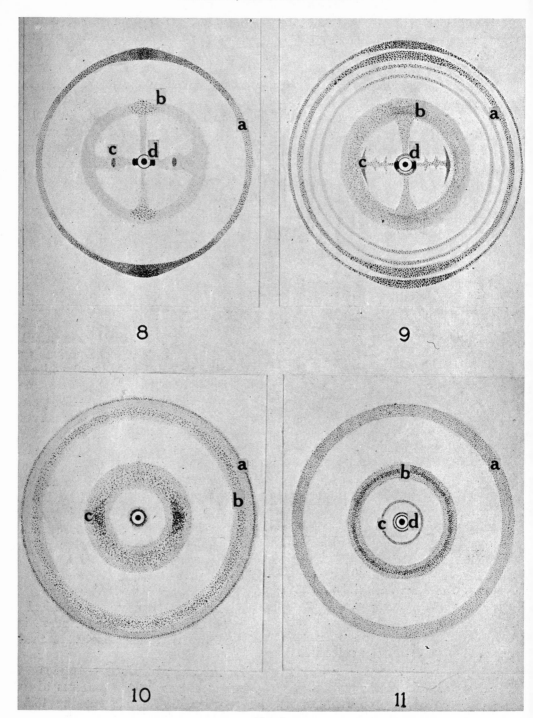

Plate 3

*Interpretation of Nerve Patterns.* — These patterns of fresh and dried medullated and non-medullated nerves were previously interpreted as follows (20). In the first place it was pointed out that the 15.5 Å. equatorial points of fresh medullated nerves are not due exclusively to connective tissue, as claimed by Boehm. If this were true, then, in our series, fresh sciatics should show the spacing best and spinal roots and corpus callosum not at all. Just the opposite is the case. The clearest and best oriented examples of this spacing were obtained with fresh corpus callosum and spinal roots. The remote possibility that the thin epineural sheath of spinal roots, which does show positive birefringence, or the Schwann sheath may be responsible for the spacing is ruled out by the clearness of the points in corpus callosum, which is devoid of such sheaths.

It is impossible to say that connective tissue in such nerves as the sciatic does not contribute to the spacing at 15–17 Å. typical of medullated nerve. That this contribution must be small, however, is indicated by the fact that even fresh muscle, which is rich in connective tissue, yields no such characteristic spacing (Boehm, 4).

The analogy with collagen fibrils, pointed out by Boehm, is striking. In nerves, just as in collagen, drying causes the disappearance of the 15–17 Å. spacing and the appearance of a more or less oriented equatorial spacing at 11–13 Å. On the assumption that protein fibrils are the cause of both spacings, the decrease with drying would indicate intramicellar swelling. Since connective tissue was ruled out as the source of the 15.5 Å. points, the tentative view was taken that this spacing is produced by axis cylinder proteins. This view was strengthened by the fact that while, to be sure, no points at 15.5 Å. were obtained in fresh lobster nerve, very clear equatorial points and sickles at 11–13 Å. were gotten from lobster and crab nerve slowly dehydrated under tension in alcohol. Crab claw nerve is said by Boehm to be practically 100 percent axis cylinder material. That the 4.7 Å. ring with meridianal sickles may be another protein spacing, presumably representing periodicities along the lengths of much folded chains, was suggested largely because this spacing was found also in dried lobster and crab nerve; the latter, according to Boehm, contains only negligible amounts of lipoid. . . .

*Diffraction Patterns from Extracted Nerve Lipoids.* — To obtain more decisive evidence of the origin of the various parts of the nerve pattern, the lipoid and protein components were separated by a process of fractionation and the patterns of each constituent studied separately. Lipoid fractions were

---

PLATE 3. Fig. 8. Fresh medullated nerve. *a*, 4.7 Å. meridianally sickled rings; *b*, 9.4 Å. meridianal spot; *c*, 15.5 Å. equatorial point; *d*, large-spacing equatorial points. Fig. 9. Stretched and dried medullated nerve. *a*, meridianally accentuated rings at 4.20, 4.67, 5.20, and 5.8 Å.; *b*, 10 Å. meridianally accentuated ring; *c*, 11.5 Å. equatorial point; *d*, large-spacing equatorially accentuated rings. Fig. 10. Lobster or crab claw or leg nerves dehydrated in alcohol under tension. *a*, 4.2 Å. ring; *b*, 4.8 Å. ring; *c*, 11.5 Å. equatorial sickle. Fig. 11. Artificial fiber made by spinning nucleoprotein solutions (neutral-soluble extract or neurostromin from dried lobster nerves or cow spinal cord) into alcoholic acetic acid. *a*, 4.8 Å. ring; *b*, 9.1–11.5 Å. ring; *c*, 23 Å. ring; *d*, 48 Å. ring.

**101**

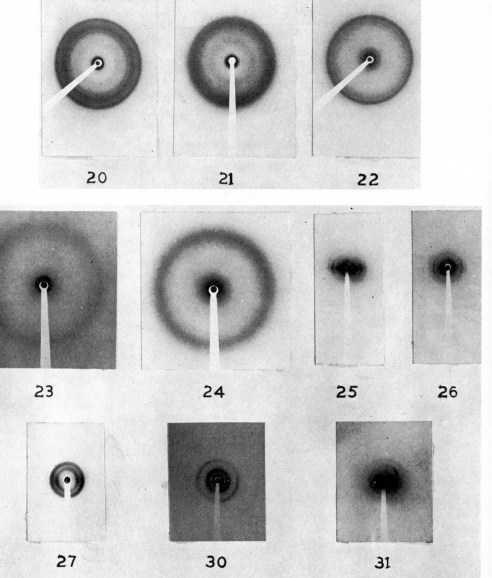

Plate 4

obtained by extraction of dried cow spinal cord with a mixture of 95 percent benzol and 5 percent alcohol. Such extracts were evaporated and the dried solid placed in loops before the pinhole (Fig. 20). The protein extraction will be described later.

These photographs (Figs. 20 to 22) revealed at once that the 4.7 Å. ring is due to the lipoids of the myelin sheath. Indeed, as will be shown, with the exception of the orientation effect,[3] the lipoids gave patterns which almost completely reproduced those of fresh medullated nerve including the 40–45 Å. spacing.

Since dried extracted lipoids gave patterns similar to those of dried medullated nerve, we next attempted to identify individual components responsible for the patterns of each. For this purpose it would have been desirable to obtain patterns from lecithin, cholesterol, cephalin, sphingomyelin, kerasin, phrenosin, nervon, and hydroxynervon, as the principal components of the myelin sheath. Of these we have so far tried only lecithin, as an example of the phosphatids, and cholesterol, to which the strong birefringence of the myelin is in great part due (see Göthlin, 7). Boehm believed the 4.8 Å. ring in fresh nerve due particularly to mixtures of cephalin and cerebrosides. These and other members of the above-named group will be investigated in the near future.

Powder crystal photographs of cholesterol revealed the spacings shown in Table I. Lecithin was obtained according to the method of Levene and Rolf (14). Although the sample used was somewhat darker in appearance than when freshly prepared, the degree of saturation was doubtless low. The material was rubbed into a loop and placed before the pinhole for radiation. The chief spacings found for lecithin are also given in Table I, the pattern and reproduction in Figure 21. It will be seen that the rings, observed in dried and stretched medullated nerves, at 4.20, 4.67, 5.20 and 5.7–5.9 Å. appear also in

---

[3] In several of these smear preparations the patterns showed decided orientation, due presumably to the momentary stroking necessary in rubbing the material into the loop or stirrup. In such cases the same mutual directions of accentuation of the rings were observed with the lipoids as in nerve patterns.

---

PLATE 4. . . . (20) Lipoids from benzene extract of dried cow spinal cord. D = 3.0 cm. (21) Lecithin. D = 3.0 cm. (22) Artificial fiber made by spinning a benzene extract of dried cow spinal cord into acetone. D = 3.0 cm. (23) Benzene extract of dried cow spinal cord rubbed up with water and mounted on loop before pinhole. D = 4.4 cm. (24) Same as Figure 23 except that lipoids had been allowed to dry for three hours. D = 4.44 cm. (25) Fresh bull frog motor root mounted on stirrup in moist chamber. D = 10.95 cm. (26) Fresh frog sciatic mounted on stirrup in moist chamber. D = 11.11 cm. (27) Lipoids from benzene extract of dried cow spinal cord. D = 12.80 cm. (29) Bull frog motor root dried in desiccator. D = 20.80 cm. (30) Mixture of cholesterol and lecithin rubbed up with water and smeared on stirrup in moist chamber; further details in text. D = 11.10 cm. (31) Same as Figure 30 except that stirrup had been removed from moist chamber and lipoids dried for seven hours. D = 12.30 cm. (32) Lecithin rubbed up with water, mounted on stirrup and placed in moist chamber. D = 11.10 cm. (33) Same as Figure 32 except that stirrup had been removed from moist chamber and lecithin allowed to dry for seven hours. D = 11.19 cm.

these lipoids, the 4.20 and 4.67 Å.[4] spacings apparently belonging to phosphatid and the 5.20 and 5.8 Å. spacings to cholesterol. Furthermore, extraction of the lipoids with acetone results in material for which the 5.2 and 5.8 rings are considerably weaker (Fig. 22). It is not implied that other nerve lipoids may not contribute to the pattern beside lecithin and cholesterol; it is very probable that they might, since the region from 4 to 6 Å. might well correspond to a dimension of the unit cell of any of them.

Since individual components of the myelin sheath (phosphatid and cholesterol) can be identified from the series of rings into which the 4.7 Å. ring of fresh nerve breaks up upon drying, we next attempted to reproduce the 4.7 Å. ring itself from wet lipoids. For this purpose the dried solid obtained by evaporation of the benzene extract of cow spinal cord was rubbed up with water and placed on the stirrup in the moist chamber before the pinhole. The patterns contained rings at 4.6 and 15.7 Å., both being spacings observed in fresh medullated nerve. The wet lipoids were then removed from the moist chamber and allowed to dry for three or four hours and another photograph made for the purpose of comparing the wet and dry pictures from one and the same preparation. The results are shown in Table I and Figures 23 and 24. Of significance in these patterns is the fact that not only do the extracted lipoids reproduce the behavior of drying medullated nerve with respect to the 4.6–4.8 Å. ring but also with respect to the 15.5 Å. ring. The latter spacing, which is prominent in the pattern of wet lipoids, greatly fades and almost disappears upon drying. Similar results were obtained also with lecithin and with a cholesterol-lecithin mixture.

This discovery of the presence of a spacing at approximately 15.5 Å. in lipoids and of the fact that this spacing tends to fade with drying necessitated a radical change in our views of the rôle of axis cylinder proteins in nerve patterns. Up to this time we had assumed, in analogy with the case of collagen, that the 11.5 Å. equatorial points of dried nerve corresponded to the 15.5 Å. points of fresh nerve, the decrease in spacing being caused by intramicellar desolvation. The possibility now presented itself that there may be no connection between the 15.5 Å. and 11.5 Å. spacings, since the behavior, in nerve, of the former with drying can be reproduced with lipoids free of protein. Such an eventuality would remove our diffraction evidence for the existence of oriented protein chains in the axis cylinder of fresh nerve, hence the interpretation of this spacing became one of our chief concerns.

If this spacing is due to lipoid, it almost certainly must represent a spacing in the $c$ direction because of its orientation and because the lipoids in the myelin sheath are known to be incorporated in fluid crystals whose optic axes lie radially. However, Thiessen and Spychalski (27) had shown that lipoids such as the oleates associate end-to-end in pairs giving $c$ spacings of the order

[4] The 4.67 Å. spacing is undoubtedly complex, as pictures taken at large specimen-to-film distances with nerve lipoids have indicated. However, the greater proportion of phospholipids present in nerve would make it seem likely that scattering in this position is in greater part related to the 4.65 lecithin (or phospholipid) spacing.

of 42–45 Å. We had in fact come to regard our 40–45 Å. equatorial points as representing such a spacing in the fluid crystals of the myelin sheath, since similar spacings were observed in extracted lipoids and in lecithin smears. The clue which led to the solution of the problem was the fact that several of our 3-cm. photographs of fresh motor roots in which the bead happened to be slightly off-center showed the 40–45 Å. spacing undoubtedly complex, with an outer difficultly measurable point lying roughly at 35 Å. This suggested the possibility that both the 15.5 and the 35 Å. points might be higher orders of a larger fundamental spacing which was indicated in our pictures but which was too close to the primary beam for measurement.

*Large Spacing Photographs.* — To obtain greater detail with respect to the large spacings, photographs were made with very small pinholes (0.2, 0.2, 0.2 mm.), well centered small beads, and with distances of 10–20 cm. from specimen to film. The exposure time was considerably greater for these photographs, although very good patterns were obtained from lipoids, for example, in one-hour periods. The results were surprising and highly significant. Fresh bull frog motor root or green frog sciatic showed rings with very clear equatorial accentuation at 85.5, 56.8, 42.7, 34.2, and 15.5 Å. (Figs. 25 and 26). The first four clearly represent the second, third, fourth, and fifth orders of a unit spacing of 171 Å. On this basis, the 15.5 Å. represents the eleventh order. Why the eleventh order should show up when all the intervening orders are either absent or too faint to be measured is not clear, although the intensities are such that the 15.5 spacing might very easily represent such a high order.

The discovery of such large spacings previously unsuspected for nerve or other animal tissues caused us to reinvestigate all of our material with the object of revealing large spacings. The results are included in Table I, which is a composite table without reference to the specimen-to-film distance at which each spacing was obtained.

Considering first the light which these long-distance photographs throw on the structure of medullated nerve, one can say with considerable certainty that the 15.5–16 Å. equatorial points and sickles of fresh nerve are produced by the lipoid fluid crystals of the myelin sheath. The entire picture, therefore, of fresh medullated nerve, would be due to the myelin sheath. This interpretation requires the assumption that the *c* axes of the myelin sheath fluid crystals are surprisingly well oriented. Is this assumption justified? To answer this question a calculation was made[5] of the intensity to be expected at any point

[5] The theoretical curve of Figure 28 was calculated from the relation:

$$I = \sqrt{\frac{1 - \cos^2 \beta \cos^2 \frac{a}{2} (2 - \cos^2 \beta)}{1 - \cos^2 \frac{a}{2} \cos^2 \beta}}$$

in which *a* is the angle of scattering and $\beta$ is the angle which expresses the departure of the scattering from the meridian. *I* is an intensity relative to the intensity for $\beta = 90°$. The Bragg requirement $n\lambda = 2d \sin a/2$ determines *a* for any given *d*. The calculated curve of Figure 23 is actually for $a = 10°$, and is therefore sufficiently close to that for $d = 4.7$ Å. to which the experimental curve refers.

TABLE 1. COMPOSITE TABLE OF SPACINGS FOUND IN NERVES AND IN LIPOID AND PROTEIN EXTRACTS OF NERVES

| Fresh Medullated Nerve | Alcohol-dried Medullated Nerve | Alcohol-dried Non-medullated Nerve | Stretched Dried Medullated Nerve | Dried Nerve Lipoids | Wet Nerve Lipoids | Wet Lecithin | Dry Lecithin | Cholesterol Powder Diagram (Principal Rings) | Wet Lecithin-cholesterol Mixture | Dry Lecithin-cholesterol Mixture | Nerve Lipoids Spun into Acetone | Nerve Protein Fibers |
|---|---|---|---|---|---|---|---|---|---|---|---|---|
| 2.73 A. fMS | 2.73 A. fMS | 2.81 A. | 2.77 A. fMS | 3.36 fR | | | | 3.55 mfR | 3.80 A. fR | 3.80 A. fR | 3.34 fR | |
| 4.6– | 4.2 mmMR | 4.2 mR | 4.20 sMR | 4.17 sR | | | 4.22 A. sR | | 3.90 ffR | 3.88 ffR | 4.18 sR | |
| 4.8# sMSR | 4.8* mMR | 4.8* | 4.67* mMR | 4.66* mR | 4.6 A. sR | 4.6 A. sR | 4.65 sR | 4.97 A. sR | 4.77 mfR | 4.75 mfR | 4.62 mR | 4.8 mR |
| | | | 5.20 mMR | 5.20 sR | | | | 5.28 sR | 5.02 mfR | 4.98 mfR | 5.18 fR | |
| | | | | | | | | | 5.25 fR | 5.13 fR | | |
| | | | | | | | | | 5.47 mfR | 5.37 mfR | | |
| | | | 5.8 fMR | 5.8 mR | | | | 5.95 sR | 5.62 mfR | 5.55 mfR | | |
| | | | | 6.4 fR | | | | | 6.00 sR | 5.91 sR | | |
| | | | | | | | | | 6.55 mR | 6.48 mR | | |
| 9.4 ffMS | 10 ffMR | | 10 fMR | 7.3–10.4' fR | | | 7.2–10.1' fR | 8.2–11.0' fR | | | 7.2–10.3' fR | 9.1–11.5' ssR |
| | 11.5 mES | (11–13)# mES | 11.5 mES | | | | | | | | | |
| 15.5 mfES | | | | 16 ffR | 15.7 mR | 18.3 ffR | | 17.5 mR | 17.1 fR | 17 ffR | 15–16# fR | 23 mR |
| | | | | 23 ffR | | | | | | | | |
| 34.2 mES | See Stretched-dried Nerve | | 43 sER | 33.3 fR | Too Dense for Measurement | 31.7 mR | | 34.8 sR | 34.6 sR | 34.5 mR | Not Photographed | 48 sR |
| 42.7 ssES | | | | 44.5 ssR | | | 44–50# ssR | | | 50 sR | | |
| 56.8 mES | | | 71 sES | 67.5 ssR | | 63.3 ssR | | | 68.7 ssR | | | |
| 85.5 ssES | | | 140 ffES | | | 126 mR | | | | | | |

Explanation: ff, f, mf, m, s, ss indicate degrees of increasing intensity from very faint to very strong.
M and E indicate meridianal (along fiber) and equatorial (transverse) intensifications, respectively.
S is employed to indicate strong intensification in a specified direction; R represents a ring.
' Figures given are limits of diffuse rings.
# Figures given show variation in center of intensity.
* The spacing is probably multiple.

Intensities are indicated very roughly and should be compared with caution between different columns and between widely separated portions of the same column.

along the 4.6–4.8 Å. ring of fresh nerve on the assumption that the $c$ direction (planes parallel to which are considered to be forming the ring) of the myelin sheath crystals is always directed radially and perpendicular to the direction of the fiber, while the $a$ and $b$ axes are in completely random orientation. Figure 28 shows the calculated curve and an experimental curve obtained by measuring the relative intensities of a typical photograph with a densitometer. It will be seen that the maxima and the minima of the curves coincide and that the shapes of the two curves show sufficient agreement to substantiate the fundamental assumption. The departure of the experimental from the calculated curve is simply a measure of the departure from perfect orientation, to be expected in such biological material.

With drying the large-spacing pattern of medullated nerve changes in an interesting manner. Equatorial points are to be distinguished at 140 and 71 Å. and a ring with equatorial accentuation appears at 43 Å. (Fig. 29). This behavior indicates that drying causes a separation of lipoidal components. In the fresh condition the lipoids appear to be associated in a single type of fluid crystal, presumably of the smectogenic type. With drying this organization is disrupted and individual components behave differently, some remaining well oriented (140 Å. — cholesterol-rich fraction?), others being disoriented (43 Å. — phosphatids?). This separation of lipoidal components is indicated also by the change from an indistinct ring with meridianal sickles at 4.6–4.8 Å. to a series of rings each with meridianal sickling, to which reference has already

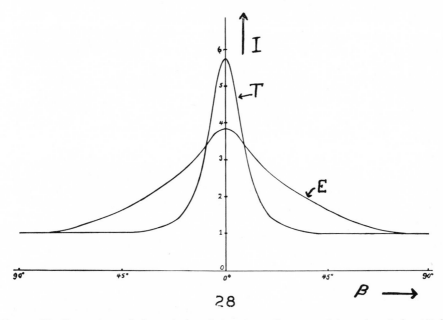

28

FIGURE 28. Comparison of theoretical and experimental curves of intensity of the 4.7 Å. ring. $I$ represents intensities relative to that on the equator; $\beta$ represents the angle of departure from the meridian; $T$ is the theoretical curve; $E$ is the curve obtained from densitometer readings of a typical pattern of fresh medullated nerve. For further details see text.

been made. This behavior may be observed also in mixtures of single components. Table I shows the effect in the case of a lecithin-cholesterol mixture. Lecithin and cholesterol were dissolved separately in hot chloroform, mixed, and evaporated to dryness. The dry lipoids were then rubbed up with water and the resulting paste smeared onto the glass stirrup of the moist chamber and placed before the pinhole for radiation. After obtaining a photograph at large specimen-to-film distance the stirrup was removed from the moist chamber and, without disturbing the material, placed in a desiccator. After drying, a large-distance photograph was again made. A similar set of photographs was obtained from lecithin alone. The results are shown in Table I, while Figures 30 to 33 are the patterns obtained.[6]

From these results with wet and dry nerves, extracted nerve lipoids, pure lipoids, and with mixtures of pure lipoids it is obvious that the patterns will depend greatly upon the state of hydration and on the percentage composition of the mixture being radiated. This makes it extremely difficult to reproduce nerve patterns exactly by means of artificial mixtures, particularly as regards the large spacings. It is also difficult to attempt to identify any single lipoid in nerve by means of a characteristic spacing, since association with other lipoids changes the behavior of the individual components. While these difficulties are realized, certain points appear reasonable, and these will now be discussed, although owing to the limited knowledge of the chemistry of the lipoids the conclusions are to be regarded as tentative.

As has been stated, the lipoids of the myelin sheath appear to be organized as a mixed fluid crystal, presumably smectogenic in type. The dimensions of the unit aggregate may be placed tentatively at from $4.7 \times 9.4 \times 171$ Å. The $a$ and $b$ dimensions are reasonable values for the thickness of aggregates containing, in cross-section, four phosphatid molecules arranged in two "puckered" planes. The 171 Å. spacing in the $c$ axis of the aggregate is presumably caused by an end-to-end association of eight lipoid molecules which are astonishingly well oriented radially, as brought out in Figure 28 and the discussion above.[7] It is highly desirable to know whether all the various lipoids

[6] The spacings from 3.8 to 6.5 Å. for the lecithin-cholesterol mixture (Columns 11 and 12, Table I) are apparently not entirely comparable to those of the nerve lipoid pictures, probably in large part because of the fact that the mixture employed was rather rich in cholesterol. Thus these spacings are comparable in both dry and wet condition, presumably being ascribable to cholesterol-rich liquid crystal structures of the two substances. Only at large spacings does the separation of lecithin from the cholesterol become apparent, with orders of a 68.7 (or multiple thereof) $c$ spacing becoming, upon drying, rings typical of dry lecithin and cholesterol as observed from each in the pure condition.

[7] The 4.7 Å. spacing represents the dimension perpendicular to the planes of the "flat" sides of the single molecules, while the 9.4 Å. spacing is that of the width of the pairs of "leaflet" molecules. Thus, with eight molecular lengths forming the $c$ dimension, the unit aggregate contains 32 molecules in all. It might be argued that the meridianal accentuations at 4.7 and 9.4 Å. are orders of the same spacing, hence the view presented above must assume a coincidence by which the strong 4.7 Å. ring is composed of second order reflections from a 9.4 Å. spacing and first order ones from the 4.7 Å. dimension. Such a coincidence seems reasonable from the consideration of

of the myelin sheath associate to form this characteristic fluid crystal type or whether only a few of the lipoids are so associated, the remainder being distributed at random or forming a multiplicity of fluid crystal types, none of which is sufficiently often reproduced to give rise to diffraction patterns. If the myelin sheath is made up of concentric layers of these leaflet fluid crystals, each having a thickness of eight molecules, or 171 Å., there would be something less than two hundred such layers even in the thickest myelin sheath and perhaps only of the order of several dozen in thin sheaths. It is, of course, not impossible that the actual aggregate has a $c$ dimension some multiple of 171 Å. Our present information merely tells us that 171 Å. is the smallest value, but it is entirely possible that subsequent work either with longer wave lengths, longer distances, or both may reveal this higher organization. We have indeed observed diffraction phenomena with the Spierer lens which indicate a higher organization of the myelin sheath, but the difficulties of interpretation of the results with this method appear insurmountable at present.

That this high degree of organization of the myelin sheath must be of physiological significance is patent. Omitting for the present any discussion of the bearing which this structure may have on the electric resistance, permeability, and polarizability of the myelin sheath, we should like to make only one point of application. It has been found (25) that nerve may be dried to a certain point (loss of over 60 percent of its water) without irreversible loss of irritability. Further drying makes it impossible to restore irritability by subsequent soaking in Ringer solution. From the above considerations it is not impossible that the limits of reversibility are set by the ability of the crystals, which have segregated upon drying, to reorganize into the original mixed crystal type. This and other physiological consequences of this organization are being investigated.

Non-medullated nerve, fresh or dried, produced no pattern in the large spacing range. Since we have come to regard the lipoids as responsible for the easily obtainable large spacings, this means that the lipoids of lobster and crab nerve are not sufficiently oriented to produce diffraction. Analysis of lobster nerve (3), however, shows that sufficient lipoid is present to produce a pattern if it were oriented. From this it would appear that the chief difference between the lipoids in the axis cylinder and those in the myelin sheath concerns the degree of orientation and organization. . . .

---

the unit given above, and particularly in view of the observation that lecithin upon drying shows a separation of this ring into two components. Just why this recurrence of structure in the $c$ direction is observed every eight molecules is not clear, but one might suppose a repetition, with this frequency, of a definite order of various types of molecules (including also cholesterol, sphingomyelin, or cerebrosides); or it is possible that unit aggregates or groups of them may be arranged at random in planes much as single molecules are considered to be arranged in smectic fluid crystals. The distance between such plane boundaries would then be 171 Å. Assuming random orientation of such aggregates about their $c$ axes, which are usually radially oriented, the theoretical curve of Figure 28 shows that any dimension perpendicular to the $c$ axis (*i.e.*, both $a$ and $b$ spacings) will be represented by meridianal accentuation, as is observed.

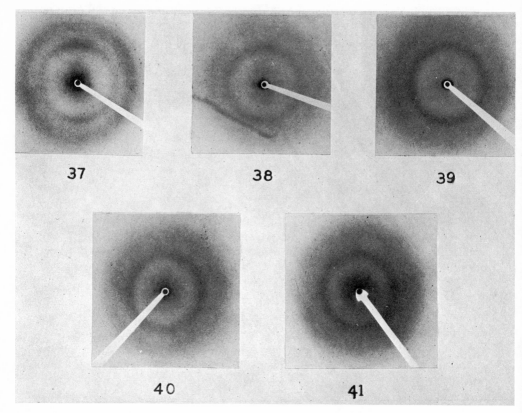

PLATE 5. . . . Fig. 37. Fresh frog sciatic heated to 42°C. for 15 min. Action potential was unaffected by the heating. D = 3.0 cm. Fig. 38. Fresh frog sciatic heated to 44°C. for 15 min. Action potential was reduced 78 percent by the heating. D = 3.0 cm. Fig. 39. Fresh frog sciatic heated to 46°C. for 15 min. Action potential extinguished by the heating. D = 3.0 cm. Fig. 40. Fresh frog sciatic heated to 70°C. for 1 min. Shortening = 48 percent. D = 3.0 cm. Fig. 41. Fresh frog sciatic soaked for one hour in 2M NaCNS at 31°C. Shortening = 60 percent. D = 3.0 cm.

*Proteins of Nerve.* — As pointed out above, while the pattern of fresh nerve appears to be explicable on the basis of lipoids exclusively, that of dried nerve contains spacings not so far found in lipoids. To identify this portion of the pattern was the next problem.

The protein chemistry of medullated nerve is at best only poorly understood and that of non-medullated nerve practically uninvestigated. It, therefore, became necessary to do preliminary work upon this phase of the problem, particularly because of the lack of information concerning nonmedullated nerve, which is representative of axis cylinder material generally. It was found (23, 3) that the soluble proteins of cow spinal cord are similar to those of lobster claw nerve and consist essentially of two nucleoproteins, one soluble in neutral and slightly alkaline solutions and the other (neurostromin) soluble at a $pH$ of about 13; globulins appear to be absent. The possibility of another protein soluble at $pH$ 14 or greater, perhaps collagenous in nature, and present in relatively small amounts has not been ruled out. Spun into an alcoholic solution of acetic acid ($pH$ = ca. 5.0) from a capillary pipette, both neucleoproteins form threads which show weak positive birefringence. Upon drying, these artificial fibers become strongly positively birefringent and to some extent resemble dried lobster nerves, except for the fact that it has so far been impossible to cause them to swell in water or to show strong thermal shortening. . . .

*Thermal Shortening.* — Patterns were obtained from maximally shortened frog sciatics, motor and sensory roots, cat sensory roots, and lobster claw nerve. All pictures were made at a distance of 3 centimeters. For shortening of 50 percent the usual effect is simply a decrease in the orientation of the entire patterns. The 15.5 Å. points become elongated into sickles or into a ring and the meridianal accentuation of the 4.7 Å. ring is decreased. This effect is due in part to the irregular folding of the myelin sheath shown to result from thermal shortening by Schmitt and Wade (21). When shortened nerves are examined with polarized light, the contorted myelin sheath shows regions of negative birefringence alternating with regions of positivity depending on the orientation of each portion of the sheath.

There is some indication that thermal disorientation of the lipoids may precede the major shortening process. This was brought out in an experiment planned to determine whether thermal inactivation of the irritable mechanism involves disorientation of the myelin sheath fluid crystals. Frog sciatics were placed in Ringer solution at 42, 44, and 46° C. for fifteen minutes. At the end of this period they were returned to Ringer solution at room temperature and their action potentials determined with the cathode-ray oscillograph. The action potential of the nerve subjected to 42° was the same as that before heating, that at 44° was reduced 78 percent, and that at 46° was completely extinguished. Although the lengths were not measured accurately, no visible shortening was observed in any of the nerves. The diffraction pattern of the nerve at 42° was typical of sciatics at room temperature (Fig. 37). The 15.5 Å. equatorial spacing was represented by slightly elongated points and the 4.7 Å. ring showed marked meridianal accentuation. The large spacing close to the bead also showed strong orientation. The pattern of the nerve kept at 44° showed a decided decrease in orientation (Fig. 38). The 15.5 Å. points were elongated into definite sickles and the 4.7 Å. ring showed only slight meridianal accentuation. The nerve kept at 46° gave a pattern practically identical with that of nerves which had undergone maximal shortening by heating to 70°. The 15.5 Å. spacing is represented by a ring or by thin elongated segments of a ring and the large spacing appears to be equally disoriented; no meridianal accentuation is visible in the 4.7 Å. ring (Figs. 39 and 40).

Aside from concluding from this evidence that lower temperatures are required to disorient the fluid crystals of the myelin sheath than to cause shortening of the protein structures, it is tempting to infer that the cause of thermal loss of irritability is the disorientation of the lipoids. It has been found that the action potential of frog sciatics declines abruptly at 43–44° C.

and becomes zero at 45–46° C. (24). That the orientation of the lipoids is not the sole cause of this failure, however, is shown by the fact that there is a similar abrupt decline in respiration and in dehydrogenase activity at approximately similar temperatures (19, 24).

*The Effect of Reagents and Conditions on Nerve Patterns.* — Sodium thiocyanate and dilute acid cause great swelling — shortening of medullated and non-medullated nerves (12). As is to be expected, this type of shortening, as well as thermal shortening, causes great buckling of the myelin sheath and a consequent disorientation of the diffraction patterns. Figure 41 shows a pattern of a frog sciatic which had shortened 60 percent in 2M NaCNS. Similar patterns were obtained from motor and sensory roots both in thiocyanate and in M/100 HCl. There is a tendency for the spacing in these patterns to be somewhat larger than in those of fresh nerves, averaging 16.5 Å. instead of 15.5 Å. The reason for this is not clear.

Calcium excess is said to favor the precipitation out of neurofibrils in the axis cylinder of teased medullated nerves (6). To test this effect we soaked a nerve in isotonic calcium chloride solution. The pattern obtained from this nerve after one hour of soaking departed little from the normal. After twelve hours of soaking the pattern showed disorientation which might have been expected from such abnormal treatment.

In an attempt to bring out the protein structure of the axis cylinder we prepared frog sciatics in cytological fixatives known to preserve neurofibrils. Formol-Zenker solution and isotonic potassium dichromate were tried. Some of these nerves were dehydrated by running through the alcohols and others were radiated without dehydration. The patterns revealed no new structures but on the contrary were indistinct and considerably disoriented. This disorientation has been observed in every case in which formalin was used as a preservative.

It is known that impregnation of lipoids with osmic acid abolishes their birefringence (18). We, therefore, treated nerves with osmic acid until quite black and studied the diffraction pattern with the remote hope that if the pattern of the lipoids is destroyed a typical protein pattern might become more apparent. The resulting pattern showed little of the 4.7 Å. ring and nothing of the 15.5 Å. spacing, but there was considerable general scattering about the primary beam indicating the presence of large lipoidal aggregates probably in random orientation.

Because of the marked effect of polarizing currents, both upon the irritability of nerve and upon structure, we arranged to pass current through a frog sciatic during the radiation. At 22.5 volts a current of 2.5 milliamperes was passed continuously during the radiation period which lasted fifteen minutes. The pattern so obtained was one of the clearest and best oriented ever gotten from fresh sciatics. The equatorial points had a spacing of 17.5 Å. instead of the usual 15.5 Å. and the meridianal intensification at 9.5–10 Å. was more apparent than in the average pattern of frog sciatics. The significance of these effects is not clear at present.

*The Effect of Asphyxial Block on Nerve Patterns.* — Frog sciatics still attached to the gastrocnemius muscles were placed in M/500 NaCN in buffered Ringer solution until the nerve became non-irritable. Patterns obtained from nerves radiated in this condition appeared to be similar to the normal pattern, indicating that the primary course of asphyxial block is not a disorientation of the lipoids of the myelin sheath. The work of Boehm (5) and of Handovsky (9) indicates that lipoid soluble narcotics can disorient the lipoids reversibly. It appears from the work of the latter that chloroform narcosis causes the 4.7 Å. spacing to break up into several rings. It is conceivable that these rings are comparable to the rings described above, which appear as a result of stretching and drying and which are caused by a separation out of components of the fluid crystals of the myelin sheath. Since Handovsky does not state the spacings of these rings, it is impossible to determine this point. Further investigation along this line is highly desirable.

## SUMMARY

1. The diffraction patterns of fresh and dried medullated and non-medullated nerves are described. Medullated nerves are represented by the sciatic, motor, and sensory roots of the frog and cat and by the corpus callosum of the cat; non-medullated nerves by the claw and leg nerves of the lobster and crab.

2. The pattern of fresh medullated nerve is probably due entirely to oriented fluid crystals of the myelin sheath, for it can be reproduced fairly completely in preparations made by rubbing up a benzene extract of spinal cord with water. The fundamental aggregate of these fluid crystals appears to have dimensions of $4.7 \times 9.4 \times 171$ Å., the various lipoids being associated in a mixed crystal fashion. The $c$ spacing lies radial and perpendicular to the long direction of the axon. This means that in thinly myelinated fibers the myelin sheath is composed of but relatively few layers of these oriented lipoids associated end to end.

3. With the exception of the equatorial sickles at 11.5 Å., the patterns of dried medullated nerve can be reproduced by dried extracted lipoids. Rings with spacings characteristic of phosphatids and of cholesterol can be identified in the pattern of dried nerve. Drying disorients certain of the components of the myelin, leaving others fairly well oriented.

4. Heating frog sciatics causes a disorientation of the lipoids which appears to occur at or about the same temperature at which the action potential is extinguished. Higher temperatures, which cause maximal shortening, have little further effect on the x-ray patterns.

5. Patterns of frog sciatics treated with cyanide until the action potential was blocked departed little from the normal. . . .

## REFERENCES

(1) ASTBURY, W. T.: Fundamentals of Fiber Structure. Oxford Univ. Press, 1933.
(2) Idem: Nature, 135, 95.
(3) BEAR, R. S., and SCHMITT, F. O.: Unpublished.
(4) BOEHM, G.: Ztschr. f. Biol., 1931, 91, 203.
(5) Idem: Koll. Ztschr., 1933, 62, 22.
(6) ETTISCH, G., and JOCHIMS, J.: Pflüger's Arch., 1926, 215, 519.
(7) GÖTHLIN, G. F.: Kungliga Svensk. Vetenskapakad. Handl., 1913, 51, 1.
(8) HANDOVSKY, H., and THIESSEN, P. W.: Nachr. d. Ges. der Wiss. Göttingen, 1930, p. 147.
(9) HANDOVSKY, H.: Koll. Ztschr., 1933, 62, 21.
(10) HERZOG, R. O., and JANKE, W.: Festschr. d. Kaiser Wilhelm. Ges., 1921, p. 118.
(11) HILL, A. V.: Proc. Roy. Soc., 1932, 111, 106.
(12) KATZ, J. R., and DE ROOY, A.: Rec. Trav. Chem., 1933, 52, 742.
(13) KUENTZEL, A., and PRAKKE, F.: Biochem. Ztschr., 1933, 267, 243.
(14) LEVENE, P. A., and ROLF, I. P.: Jour. Biol. Chem., 1927, 72, 587.
(15) MEYER, K. H.: Biochem. Ztschr., 1929, 208, 1; 214, 253.
(16) PETERFI, T.: Handb. d. norm. u. path. Physiol., 1929, 9, 81.
(17) DE RENYI, G. S.: Jour. Comp. Neurol., 1929, 48, 441.
(18) SCHMIDT, W. J.: Die Bausteine des Tierkörpers in Polarisiertem Lichte. Friederich Cohen, 1924, Bonn.
(19) SCHMITT, F. O., and WADE, L. J.: Am. Jour. Physiol., 1934, 109, 93.
(20) SCHMITT, F. O., CLARK, G. L., and MRGUDICH, J. N.: Science, 1934, 80, 567.
(21) SCHMITT, F. O., and WADE, L. J.: Am. Jour. Physiol., 1935, 111, 159.
(22) Idem: Am. Jour. Physiol., 1935, 111, 169.
(23) SCHMITT, F. O., and BEAR, R. S.: Proc. Soc. Exp. Biol. and Med., 1935, 32, 943.
(24) SCHMITT, F. O., and WADE, L. J.: In press.
(25) SCHMITT, F. O.: Unpublished.
(26) THIBAUD, J., and TRILLAT, J. J.: Compt. Rend., 1929, 189, 751, 907.
(27) THIESSEN, P. A., and SPYCHALSKI, R.: Ztschr. phys. Chem., 1931, 156, 435.

# ELECTRON MICROSCOPE AND LOW-ANGLE X-RAY DIFFRACTION STUDIES OF THE NERVE MYELIN SHEATH

By H. FERNÁNDEZ-MORÁN, Ph.D., and J. B. FINEAN, Ph.D.*

*(From the Nerve Ultrastructure Department, Venezuelan Institute for Neurology and Brain Research (IVNIC), Caracas, Venezuela)*

Plates 229 to 240

(Received for publication, April 23, 1957)

The myelin sheath of nerve fibers represents one of the most highly organized components of biological systems, which, despite its marked lability, has proved to be uniquely suitable for a systematic analysis by combined application of physical and chemical techniques. Extensive polarized light studies (4, 34, 48–51) of the strong birefringence of the sheath suggested it to be built up of concentrically disposed protein lamellae alternating with submicroscopic layers of lipide molecules oriented with their long axes in the radial direction. Low-angle x-ray diffraction studies (1, 5–7, 21–32, 51–55) supported this concept and furnished quantitative data on the highly ordered arrangement of the lipide, protein, and water components in the normal myelin structure. The fundamental x-ray diffraction spacings of 170 A found in amphibian and of 180 to 185 A in mammalian nerves were assumed to correspond to the thickness of the concentric lipide-protein layers deduced from polarized light investigations.

The postulated layers and their exceptionally regular concentric arrangement in the myelin sheath were subsequently observed directly in the electron microscope (8–20, 35). However, this remarkable demonstration of structural regularity at the macromolecular level achieved by direct and indirect methods is still inadequate if it cannot be referred to the specific localization of chemical components in the sheath. Thus, the concentric laminated structure observed in electron micrographs of thin nerve sections is simply a pattern of the selective deposition of osmium at certain sites, and cannot as yet be interpreted in terms of specific regions containing lipides, lipoproteins, or protein constitutents. Likewise, the low angle x-ray diffraction patterns recorded from normal nerve can only furnish general information on the dimensions and approximate distribution of scattering groups in the radial direction of the sheath. Further attempts to correlate these structural parameters with the chemical composition of the sheath are thwarted by our lack of knowledge of the chemical nature and

* Permanent address: Department of Medical Biochemistry, Medical School, Birmingham, England.

Reprinted by permission of H. Fernández-Morán and The Rockefeller University Press from the *Journal of Cellular Biology*, 3, 725–748 (1957). The photographs here reproduced from printed halftone copy inevitably show a loss of detail, and the quality of the results is not representative of the originals.

localization of the sheath proteins, the lipides, and the various other components of myelin.

Earlier investigations of controlled physical (temperature (6) and water content variations (5, 28)) and chemical modifications (treatment with lipide solvents (7, 10–13) and enzymatic digestion (10–13)) of normal nerve, which were carried out independently with x-ray diffraction techniques and electron microscopy (10–13, 15, 20), have already given valuable clues regarding the thickness of the lipide and protein layers and the general arrangement of molecules within these layers. It seemed, therefore, worthwhile to attempt a systematic study of the normal and modified myelin sheath through the combined application of low-angle x-ray diffraction techniques and high resolution electron microscopy which supplement each other in many ways. The x-ray diffraction method offers the significant advantage of being applicable to the intact nerve trunk under physiological conditions (52, 5) without having to sever its connections with living tissues or to isolate single fibers. Moreover, since the radiation exposure required for recording the patterns appears to have negligible effects upon the action potentials and irritability of nerve, the parameters derived from the x-ray diffraction pattern of normal active nerve can be considered a reliable basis for all structural analyses of the myelin sheath. In connection with the extraction experiments carried out on fresh myelin, x-ray diffraction is also a valuable tool for identifying the extracted and dried lipides which give characteristic x-ray diffraction patterns (44, 53).

An additional advantage of x-ray diffraction studies in connection with electron microscopy derives from the averaging character of the recording process, since a single pattern represents an average of the main structural parameters of all the nerve fibers in the exposed nerve trunk which contribute to the diffraction. This considerably reduces the time and effort required for a satisfactory ultrastructural survey.

Electron microscopy has, however, the decisive advantage of directly visualizing the structural details of macromolecular dimensions and depicting the complex patterns of organization in the submicroscopic domain which no other method can reveal. The results of controlled modifications of the myelin sheath can also often be observed at various stages in a restricted area. The obvious disadvantage of having to work with material subjected to extensive preparative procedures which may produce artifacts, can be partly offset by controlling the results with x-ray diffraction techniques.

In order to achieve a satisfactory correlation of electron microscopy with x-ray diffraction techniques, it was found necessary to examine a large number of serial ultrathin sections prepared from the same specimen utilized for the low-angle diffraction studies. The use of a diamond knife (14, 17, 18) was an important contributing factor, since it facilitated the preparation of several thousand undistorted ultrathin serial sections of nerve with an appreciable saving of time and effort. In addition to the established methacrylate-embedding techniques, a new embedding procedure has been successfully tried out, utilizing a water-soluble medium (gelatin) which gives excellent preservation of the myelin sheath structure. This gelatin-embedding technique was used in combination with potassium permanganate fixation (40) as an alternative to osmium tetroxide. The attainment of a consistently high resolution of the order of 10 to 20 A in a large number of plates was also necessary for adequate evaluation of the data reported here.

Although the observations described in this paper deal exclusively with the fine structure of the myelin sheath, many of the results may be relevant to the submicroscopic organization of other biological systems. Thus, the work of Geren *et al.* (35–38), which indicates that the myelin sheath derives from a rolled-up Schwann cell surface, implies that there is a close structural relationship between the layers of the myelin sheath and the cell surface membranes. If we tentatively adopt this analogy, then the myelin sheath can be regarded as a model system formed by multiple unit membranes closely packed in highly regular array and ideally suited for x-ray diffraction studies, which could never be applied directly to the study of a single cell membrane. Furthermore, although the electron microscope is capable of visualizing a single cell membrane, the repetitive structure provides a far more reliable basis for the consideration of the structural significance of controlled modifications of the system. It, therefore, represents an exceptionally favourable cell membrane model for detailed analysis by x-ray diffraction and electron microscopy of the structural changes induced by controlled physical and chemical modifications.

It is hoped that the present investigation may serve to illustrate how electron microscopy and x-ray diffraction techniques can be applied together and their results correlated to gain further insight into the ultrastructure of living tissues.

## Materials and Methods

*Materials.*—The peripheral and central nerves used in this study were obtained from living, anesthetized, mature rats of an adapted Sprague Dawley strain, from mice of the C 57 L strain, from *Rana pipiens*, and from Venezuelan giant toads (*Bufo marinus*). The peripheral nerves (sciatics and brachial plexus) and central nerves (optics and small blocks of white matter from the brain and spinal cord) were exposed by careful dissection and immediately prepared for electron microscopy and/or x-ray diffraction.

*Fixation.*—In many cases the specimens were fixed *in situ* by dripping cold fixative directly onto the exposed and still intact nerve trunks. The following fixation agents were used:

(*a*) Fresh solutions of 1 or 2 per cent osmium tetroxide in isotonic veronal-acetate buffer (pH 7.2) applied at a temperature of 1–4°C. for a period of 1 to 4 hours;

(*b*) Potassium permanganate applied according to the procedure described by Luft (40) at a concentration of 0.6 per cent in veronal-acetate buffer (pH 7.5) for 1 to 4 hours at 0°C;

(*c*) Phosphomolybdic and phosphotungstic acids in 1 to 2 per cent solutions applied for 15 minutes to 2 hours at 0°C.

(*d*) Fresh solutions of 1 or 2 per cent uranyl acetate in Ringer or 4 per cent formalin applied for 15 minutes to 2 hours at 0°C.

(e) Fresh solutions of 1 or 2 per cent lanthanum nitrate in Ringer or 4 per cent formalin applied at a temperature of 4°C. for 1 to 6 hours.

*Embedding.*—After fixation the following embedding procedures were used alternatively:

(a) *Embedding in n-butyl methacrylate* after dehydration by passage through a graded series of ethanol (70 per cent to absolute ethanol by increments of 10 per cent) following the procedure described by Palade (43) using 2 per cent luperco CDB as catalyst. Prepolymerization of the methacrylate was frequently used.

(b) *Gelatin embedding:* After adequate fixation the small specimen blocks (1 to 3 cubic mm.) were rinsed briefly with isotonic veronal-acetate buffer, and then immersed in a fresh 10 per cent solution of bacteriological gelatin (Merck) at 40°C. for 15 to 30 minutes. This was followed by transfer to a 20 per cent gelatin solution for 15 minutes, and then to 30 per cent gelatin prepared in a 2 per cent glycerin solution for a further 15 to 30 minutes. This gelatin solution containing the specimens was solidified by pouring it into a Petri dish in the icebox at 4°C. Upon reaching a suitable consistency, small gelatin cubes of 4 to 5 millimeters, each with the specimen in the center, were cut out and placed in a desiccator connected to a mechanical forepump reaching a vacuum of $10^{-3}$ mm. Hg. After 5 to 6 hours the gelatin blocks had dried and were hard enough for ultrathin sectioning. The blocks containing the specimens were trimmed down and affixed to wooden pegs in the desired orientation using commercial glue. These pegs were then mounted on the specimen holder of the ultramicrotome. The gelatin matrix is usually so hard that it has to be cut with a diamond knife, but the sections obtained are just as thin as those of methacrylate-embedded material. This embedding technique obviates the use of ethanol and other chemical dehydrating (and extracting) agents, and yields excellent preservation of the fine structure of the myelin sheath, particularly in connection with osmium and permanganate fixation.

*Microtomy.*—The ultrathin serial sections of 100 to 300 A used in this investigation were prepared with a Morán ultramicrotome (16, 18) equipped with a diamond knife (14, 17). The exceptional durability and high quality of the diamond cutting edge (the same knife can be used continuously for a period of 6 to 12 months without resharpening), which is permanently attached to the microtome and rarely needs readjustment, were important technical factors in obtaining the large number of satisfactory ultrathin serial sections required. The sharpness of the diamond cutting edge and the high degree of stability of the Morán ultramicrotome ensured regular production of the very thin serial sections (50 to 100 A thick) required for high resolution studies. A notable feature of the sections cut with the diamond knife is the lack of compression and distortion of the myelin sheath, which is important in a quantitative evaluation of its periodic fine structure. The freezing-ultrathin sectioning technique described earlier (9–12) which can be applied directly to fresh or fixed, unembedded nerve was also used for control purposes. Most of the sections for high resolution work were deposited on special formvar films with uniformly distributed holes of 500 to 5,000 A diameter. These films were prepared by coating clean glass slides with a 0.1 or 0.2 per cent solution of formvar in 1,2-dichloroethane in an atmosphere of precisely controlled relative humidity (80 to 90 per cent). The films were then stabilized by vacuum evaporation of a thin carbon film, or by cathode sputtering in a naphthalene atmosphere. By using these fenestrated films certain areas of the sections which were stretched across the holes could be examined free from any background structure, while the edges of the minute holes provided an adequate reference for focusing rapidly, thus avoiding contamination of the specimen.

*Experimental Modifications of the Myelin Sheath.*—In order to study the effects of controlled physical and chemical modifications the following experiments were performed on fresh peripheral and central nerves:

(a) *Freezing and thawing:* Immediately after removal from the living animal, the nerve trunks were plunged into liquid nitrogen or liquid helium (at −269°C.) contained in a Dewar flask and left there for 3 to 5 minutes before being taken out and thawed at room temperature (22°C.). The thawed nerves were subsequently fixed in 1 or 2 per cent buffered osmium tetroxide solutions and embedded in n-butyl methacrylate or in gelatin. Parallel freezing experiments were also conducted at −30°C., the preparation remaining frozen for 1 hour and then returning to room temperature for 1 hour before further treatment.

(b) *Ultracentrifugation of fresh whole nerve:* Fresh nerve trunks were carefully inserted into closely fitting glass capillaries which were then sealed and introduced in the transverse or longitudinally oriented holes of the special plexiglas chambers (Fig. 2) described earlier (19). These plexiglas chambers were subjected to ultracentrifugation (140,000 to 200,000 g) in the Spinco preparative or analytical ultracentrifuges at temperatures of 4–12°C. during periods ranging from 2 to 24 hours.

With the described arrangement the nerves could be extracted intact after the ultracentrifugation run by cracking the glass capillaries in a small vise. The nerves were immediately fixed in 1 or 2 per cent buffered osmium tetroxide solutions and embedded in methacrylate or gelatin.

(c) *Trypsin digestion:* Fresh whole nerve trunks were placed in a solution of 1 per cent crystalline trypsin (from Worthington Chemical Co.) in veronal-acetate buffer at 37°C. during periods ranging from 8 to 12 hours. The slightly swollen and mushy looking nerves were quickly rinsed in veronal-acetate buffer of the same pH and fixed in 1 per cent buffered osmium tetroxide solutions before embedding in methacrylate or in gelatin.

(d) *Extraction with lipide solvents:* Several series of experiments were carried out in which fresh whole nerve trunks were extracted with 30 ml. of pure acetone (Merck pro analysis), or pure ethanol, ethanol-ether, or chloroform-methanol (3:1) for 12 hours at 0°C. The extracted nerves were transferred to 2 per cent osmium tetroxide solutions after a brief rinsing in veronal-acetate buffer or in Tyrode solution, and then embedded in n-butyl methacrylate or in gelatin. The extraction fluid was evaporated down in a partial vacuum, and the resulting dried lipide extract prepared for examination by x-ray diffraction, or for electron microscopy and electron diffraction after treatment with 1 to 2 per cent buffered osmium tetroxide solution.

*Electron Microscopy.*—Many of the sections were examined with an RCA EMU 3B electron microscope connected to the specially regulated electrical power supply of this laboratory (with less than 0.2 per cent voltage variations), using the high gain specimen holder designed by Reisner and objective apertures of 15 to 20 microns diameter. The high voltage stability of this instrument working at 50 and 100 kv. made it possible to use special Kodak high resolution plates (KP 41394) with exposure times of 10 to 15 seconds when taking micrographs at electron optical magnifications of 12,000 to 51,000. Because of the extremely fine grain of the emulsion, these plates can be enlarged 50 to 100 times, thus giving final magnifications of 1 to 2 million diameters, which permit the evaluation of details of the order of 10 to 20 A. In the latter part of this investigation a Siemens Elmiskop 1 a was also used, working mostly at 80 kv., and provided with objective apertures of 30 and 50 microns diameter. With this instrument the micrographs were taken at electron optical magnifications of 30,000 to 98,000 and subsequently enlarged 10 to 30 times, using accurately measured specimen grids for precise calibration of the enlargements. The average spacing of the concentric laminated structure of the sheath could be determined with considerable accuracy by measuring directly large areas of the plates with a Cambridge universal measuring machine. The observations described here are based on the evaluation of 3,000 electron micrographs, in which an average resolution of 10 to 30 A was consistently achieved.

*X-Ray Diffraction.*—Most of the x-ray diffraction patterns considered in this paper were recorded photographically using a low-angle vacuum camera of a design described in detail in previous publications (22, 27). This camera was used in conjunction with CuKα radiation from the 0.1 mm. line focus of a North American Philips x-ray diffraction unit. The whole width of the focus was utilized by horizontal defining and guard apertures close to the entrance to the camera, and all low-angle reflections from myelin (up to 250 A) could be recorded at a speci-men-to-film distance of 140 mm. in a 2 hour exposure. Moist specimens to be examined in the vacuum camera were sealed in thin walled pyrex glass capillary tubes containing the appropriate immersion medium. Embedded preparations, which had been used for thin sectioning for electron microscopy, were subsequently trimmed down to remove as much as possible of the surrounding embedding medium and then mounted directly on the specimen holder in the vacuum camera.

When a more rapid recording of the principal low-angle reflections was required, as for instance whilst the nerve specimen was kept in the frozen state, a Geiger counter recording was used. The counting equipment available was a North American Philips wide range goniometer. By inserting a very fine (0.1 mm.) defining slit (divergence slit) in the "divergence slit assembly," and placing the appropriate size of guard aperture at the axis of rotation of the counter arm, it was possible to record reflections at diffracting angles below 5° from a single nerve trunk placed very close to the guard aperture. This simple adaptation did not interfere with the normal use of the goniometer, and the low-angle performance was adequate for the requirements of these experiments. A photograph of the x-ray equipment is shown in Fig. 1.

## RESULTS

The standard of reference for the study of myelin structure is provided by the x-ray diffraction pattern of fresh intact nerve, which features a diffuse wide-angle reflection at about 4.7 A and a number of very well defined reflections at low angles. When the nerve trunk is examined at right angles to the fiber direction, with a pinhole collimating system for the x-ray beam, the wide-angle diffraction shows meridional intensifications and the low-angle reflections exhibit a precise equatorial orientation. These characteristic low-angle reflections can be accounted for as the first five orders of a fundamental spacing varying from 170 A in amphibians to 184 A in mammalian peripheral nerve (52, 53). The actual values determined in these studies were 171 A for *Rana pipiens*, 174 for Venezuelan *Bufo marinus* (Fig. 3 a), and 178 for the rat strains available here (Fig. 1 b). These low-angle reflections show a characteristic alternation of intensities in the even and odd orders. When a slit collimating system is applied in order to obtain shorter exposure times the orientation effects are masked, and patterns such as those reproduced in this paper recorded.

Since fresh nerve cannot be examined directly in the electron microscope, and dried, unfixed nerve shows no well defined structure, an initial common basis for comparison has been sought in osmium-fixed preparations. The osmium tetroxide treatment introduces marked changes in the low-angle x-ray diffraction patterns, as illustrated in Fig. 3. There is a shrinkage of the radial repeating unit by about 20 A in all types of specimens examined. In addition, there is a drastic modification of the distribution of x-ray scattering power within the unit, as indicated in particular by the increase in intensity of the first order reflection. A detailed comparison of the relative intensities of reflections in the diffraction patterns of osmium-fixed frog and rat sciatic nerves reveals considerable differences. Whereas the intensities show an approximately regular decrease with increasing diffraction order in the case of the amphibian nerve (Fig. 3 b), in the pattern of the mammalian preparation (Fig. 3 c) the third order is unusually intense, and longer exposures bring up the fifth order reflection without the fourth order being detected. A further difference can be detected between the rat sciatic (Fig. 3 c) and the rat optic (Fig. 3 d) preparations, the fourth order being clearly observed in the $OsO_4$-fixed rat optic, while its third order reflection is much less marked than that of the sciatic nerve.

Three techniques have so far been successfully applied in obtaining thin sections of the osmium-fixed nerve suitable for examination in the electron microscope. The first demonstration of the concentric laminated structure of the myelin sheath was obtained through freeze-sectioning (9–12). Subsequently sections from embeddings in methacrylate (13, 35, 47) and in gelatin revealed this periodic structure with greater clarity.

*Freezing-Sectioning.*—When frozen sections of unembedded, osmium-fixed peripheral nerve were first examined by electron microscopy (9–12), a concentric laminated structure was observed in the myelin sheath. It consisted of a series of dense lines alternating with light spaces giving an average period of 58 A in frog sciatic and 71 A in rat sciatic nerves. Repetition of these experiments with improved techniques has revealed the same type of periodicity formed by lines of approximately equal density (Fig. 5) with an average separation of 60 A in frog nerve. However, in many areas a larger period of about 120 A is apparent with a faint intermediate line at the half period (Fig. 5 b). The prominence of each type of structure would appear to depend to some extent on the preparative procedure.

A change in the x-ray diffraction pattern occurs when $OsO_4$-fixed peripheral nerve is frozen, the repeating unit shrinking by about 20 A and the second order reflection strengthening markedly in relation to the first order. There is, however, a complete reversal of the change when the specimen is thawed, so that no permanent modification results from the freezing procedure. Based on these observations, it would, therefore, be anticipated that the changes produced by freeze-sectioning followed by electron microscope examination are largely due to the drying of the $OsO_4$-fixed specimen. Actually, the diffraction pattern of an osmium-fixed preparation which has been frozen and thawed before drying (Fig. 5 c) does not differ significantly from the dried $OsO_4$-fixed preparation. As compared with the moist $OsO_4$-fixed frog nerve (Fig. 3 b), the corresponding dried preparation (Fig. 5 c) shows a considerable shrinkage of the structural unit and a marked intensification of the second order diffraction.

*Gelatin Embedding.*—

A diffraction pattern very similar to that of the osmium tetroxide–fixed and air-dried preparation is obtained when the $OsO_4$-fixed nerve is embedded and dehydrated in gelatin (Fig. 6 *b*). Addition of 2 per cent glycerin to facilitate thin sectioning appears to effect a small increase in layer spacing to 130 A as compared with 124 A in the pure gelatin preparation. In the corresponding electron micrograph (Fig. 6) of a cross-sectioned frog sciatic nerve fiber embedded in gelatin with admixture of 2 per cent glycerin, the concentric laminated structure of the myelin sheath appears very well preserved. The average period of 120 A is in good agreement with the x-ray spacing, and consists of a uniformly dense line (*d*) 20 to 30 A thick with occasional discontinuities, alternating with a light region containing an intermediate line (*i*) of about 15 A. The intermediate lines show varying degrees of intensity, generally appearing enhanced often to the point of resembling the dense lines. The greater stability of the gelatin-embedded sections under an intense electron beam makes it possible to discern within the light regions uniformly distributed dense particles of 10 to 20 A (20), which may represent elementary osmium deposits.

*Methacrylate Embedding.*—

In the low-angle diffraction pattern obtained from sciatic nerve embedded in *n*-butyl methacrylate (Fig. 4 *b*) the second order reflection is relatively weak, and the layer spacing is of the same order as that recorded from the moist OsO$_4$-fixed specimen (Fig. 3 *b*). A closer x-ray diffraction study of the intermediate stages of the preparative procedure yielded the series of diffraction patterns shown in Figs. 7 *b* to *f*. The most striking point about this series of patterns is that the layer spacing shrinks markedly during the dehydration in the graded alcohol series (32) and then expands again in the methacrylate. The shrinkage, which is of the same order as that produced by air drying, does not result in an intensification of the second order reflection. There is, however, some indication of an apparently independent reflection appearing close to the third order diffraction at some stages of the process. The second and third order reflections are markedly reduced in intensity during this treatment. When the dehydrated specimen is immersed in the methacrylate monomer there is a rapid reexpansion of structure and a strengthening of second and third order reflections, the set of diffractions finally reverting to a pattern which closely resembles that of the original moist OsO$_4$-fixed preparation. Prolonged immersion in methacrylate before polymerization does not seem to produce excessive expansion, but rather to restore the spacing to its original dimension in the moist state. Beyond this, it eventually produces a broadening of the reflections indicating distortion of the structure. When the methacrylate is polymerized, a further expansion of the structure by a few angstroms per unit is frequently observed, and usually there is a marked deterioration in the definition of the diffraction bands.

The corresponding electron micrographs of the myelin sheath in cross-sectioned rat sciatic nerve fibers are shown in Figs. 4 and 7. The spacings of the layers vary widely, and the average period of 130 to 140 A (Fig. 4 *c*) is invariably some 10 to 20 A lower than the x-ray fundamental spacing recorded from the same methacrylate-embedded specimen which is used for electron microscopy. The variation in the dimensions of the radial repeating period depends on the preparation techniques, the mounting of the specimen film, and frequently also on the thickness of the myelin sheath under examination. The most striking feature observed in the methacrylate-embedded specimens is the common occurrence of splitting of the 40 A thick dense lines into two finer lines ($d'$) each of 20 A or the dissociation into granular formations of about 60 A. The intermediate line ($i$) of approximately 15 A located in the central part of the light region usually has a faint appearance and a tendency to granulation. At the highest magnifications (Fig. 7) the concentric lamination can be resolved into extremely fine particles (10 to 15 A) arranged in various states of aggregation, which may represent primary osmium deposits.

*Potassium Permanganate Fixation.—*

The normal low-angle diffraction pattern of fresh toad sciatic nerve shown in Fig. 8 $c$ can be compared with the patterns recorded from the same nerve after fixation with 0.6 per cent $KMnO_4$ following the procedure recommended by Luft (40). The layer spacing is changed very little, but the third, fourth, and fifth order reflections are no longer detected so that the emphasis is now on the second order reflection (Fig. 8 $d$).

When the $KMnO_4$-fixed specimens were embedded in methacrylate by normal procedures, the diffraction patterns subsequently recorded indicated that there had been an extensive breakdown of structure as judged from the diffuse low-angle scatter which almost completely obscured the diffraction bands. Gelatin embedding, on the other hand, seemed to give a very good preservation of structure (Fig. 8 $e$). The diffraction pattern of the toad sciatic nerve embedded in gelatin with 5 per cent glycerin reveals a layer spacing of about 150 A and a continued accentuation of the second order reflection (Fig. 8 $e$). The layer spacing found in the air-dried preparation was some 20 A lower than this.

Electron micrographs of ultrathin nerve sections fixed with $KMnO_4$ and embedded in methacrylate showed a poor preservation of the layered structure of the sheath. In restricted areas where the layering could be observed the period was of the order of 120 A, and consisted of the usual dense line with an enhanced intermediate line, closely resembling the fine structure described by Luft (40) in the mouse sciatic nerve.

In accordance with the x-ray diffraction data, electron micrographs of $KMnO_4$-fixed nerve embedded in gelatin showed an excellent preservation of the concentric laminated structure of the sheath (Fig. 8). The myelin sheath appeared compact and devoid of the usual crevices. In both transverse and longitudinal sections a regular layering with a fundamental period of approximately 125 to 130 A is seen running uninterrupted throughout the sheath (Fig.

8). This period consists of uniform dense lines about 20 to 30 A thick alternating with light spaces occupied by intermediate lines ($i$) which are fully comparable in thickness and density with the main dense lines ($d$). As a result, the layer spacing in these preparations often appears to be one-half of that indicated by the diffraction data. This is in keeping with the marked enhancement of the second order diffraction observed in the corresponding x-ray diffraction pattern (Fig. 8 $e$). In many areas of these preparations the individual layers often show a tendency to dissociate into granular formations (Fig. 8 $b$). Occasionally, the regular alignment of these formations is such as to produce a periodic cross-banding effect which is particularly noticeable in the axonal part of the myelin sheath. Similar cross-grating structures are frequently encountered in specimens which generally show a poor state of preservation of the sheath, and they may be related to artificial myelin forms (34). Preliminary experiments with peripheral nerves fixed with either phosphomolybdic acid, phosphotungstic acid, uranyl acetate, or lanthanum nitrate, and subsequently embedded in methacrylate or gelatin, indicate similar features in the fine structure of the myelin sheath. In these preparations the intermediate lines are usually enhanced, and the cross-banding effect is particularly noticeable in poorly preserved areas of the myelin sheath.

*The Myelin Sheath of Central Nerve Fibers.—*

There is a wide variation in the thickness and number of concentric layers forming the myelin sheaths of central nerve fibers, particularly in the white matter of the brain and spinal cord (20, 41). The absence of a connective tissue sheath around individual fibers leads to a widespread confluence of the myelin sheaths which merge into each other without distinct boundaries. The concentric laminated structure of the myelin of central origin is very similar to that of peripheral nerve, since it shows a similar radial repeating period of 120 to 130 A and essentially the same type of fine structure.

The present studies of central nerve myelin by electron microscopy and x-ray diffraction have been confined to preparations fixed with buffered osmium tetroxide and embedded in methacrylate or in gelatin.

Whereas the low-angle diffraction pattern of the normal rat optic nerve (Fig. 9 $c$) differs appreciably from that of the rat sciatic (Fig. 1 $b$), the treatment with osmium tetroxide tends to mask the differences. After embedding in methacrylate or in gelatin the differences are further reduced, so that the diffraction patterns of $OsO_4$-fixed optic and sciatic nerves are then practically indistinguishable. Thus, the electron micrographs and the x-ray diffraction patterns of central nerve fibers are in general agreement.

Two characteristic features observed in the myelin sheaths of central nerve fibers by electron microscopy seem, however, to distinguish them from peripheral nerve myelin (19). The first is the frequent occurrence of two (Fig. 9) or three closely spaced concentric dense lines which form a delimiting band between the internal part of the myelin sheath and its outer portion. Three lines are most commonly observed, and this could be accounted for by assuming an intensification of the normally faint intermediate line in this area. The second distinguishing feature observed (19) is even more consistent with this assumption, since it appears as a compact series of concentric layers measuring only one-half the thickness (approximately 60 A) of the fundamental radial period, forming a clearly delimited zone around the axon (Fig. 9 b). This halving of the fundamental layer spacing, apparently brought about by intensification of the intermediate line, might be related to the marked tendency towards halving evident in the x-ray diffraction pattern of normal central nerve fibers (Fig. 9 c). In Fig. 10 the spiral course of the few layers forming the myelin sheath of the smallest central nerve fibers can be clearly discerned, indicating that we are dealing with a continuous membrane closely wrapped several times about the axon (19). The axon is bounded by a broad membrane (a') which appears to be continuous with the typical dense line of the laminated structure. After completing its spiral course the dense line again merges with the diffuse membrane (m) of an adjacent cell. Pictures of this type, commonly encountered in nerve fibers of central origin, closely resemble the formations described by Geren et al. (35–38) during myelogenesis in chick embryos.

*Experimental Modifications of Myelin before Fixation.—*

*Freezing and Thawing.*—In previous x-ray diffraction studies (6) considerable significance has been attached to the structural modifications resulting from freezing and thawing of fresh nerve. In peripheral nerve, such treatment results in a complete halving of the radial repeat; the two layers which are suggested as constituting this repeat become identical in x-ray–scattering power (Fig. 11 e). Subsequent fixation with osmium tetroxide gives an osmium distribution which differs from that of the normal $OsO_4$-fixed myelin. This difference is indicated in the low-angle x-ray diffraction pattern (Fig. 11 f) by the marked increase in low-angle diffuse scatter and the intensification of the second order reflection. These effects persist after methacrylate embedding (Fig. 11 g).

The corresponding electron micrographs show a series of characteristic changes depending upon the conditions of freezing and thawing. In frozen and thawed nerve specimens which have been osmium-fixed and embedded in methacrylate, diffuse patches of varying size (100 to 2000 A) are seen distributed irregularly throughout the myelin sheath. These localized areas of structural distortion probably result from ice crystal formation and other effects of freezing. In addition, the majority of the preparations examined showed an increased general structural breakdown, and a marked intensification and broadening (Fig. 11) of the intermediate line (i), as compared with the normal methacrylate-embedded preparation. The appearance of very dense placodes is also observed at the sites normally occupied by the intermediate line. These structures, which stain intensely with osmium tetroxide, may represent localized aggregates produced by the increased internal salt concentration resulting from freezing. Extreme cases of the structural modifications induced by freezing and thawing are shown in Figs. 11 *b* and *c*. Here the ice crystal formation has largely obliterated the regular laminations of the sheath, producing a splitting of the dense lines into two to four finer layers, and the dissociation of the intermediate bands into two to three fine lines.

*Ultracentrifugation of Fresh Nerve.—*

In connection with earlier electron microscope studies (12, 15) ultracentrifugation of fresh whole nerve trunks was successfully applied to produce a displacement of certain components within the fibers, and as a reproducible form of oriented microdissection at the submicroscopic level (19). The marked shortening produced by ultracentrifugation of a fresh nerve trunk in the longitudinal direction is shown in Fig. 2 *b*. Ultracentrifugation at right angles to the fiber direction produces a distinct flattening of the whole nerve trunk (Fig. 2 *c*). Examination of nerve subjected to ultracentrifugation in the longitudinal direction revealed that the axonal material had been largely concentrated at the distal end of the fibers, while the myelin sheath was markedly compressed and crumpled (12).

When ultracentrifugation (140,000 *g*) was carried out on fresh whole nerve at right angles to the fiber direction during relatively short periods (2 to 3 hours), the myelin sheath appeared partially detached from the external fibrous sheath, forming characteristic multiple folds which did not, however, coalesce into droplets. In confirmation of previous observations (12, 19, 20), the concentric laminated structure of the myelin sheath was found to be well preserved and only slightly modified in these ultracentrifuged specimens. The radial period of the layers was slightly contracted or expanded in certain areas of folding, and some dissociation of the dense and intermediate lines into regular granular formations could be detected. These changes were even more pronounced when higher centrifugal forces (150,000 to 200,000 *g*) had been applied for long periods (8 to 24 hours). In these specimens all transitions were observed between a slight warping of the sheath lamination and a gradual compression of the individual layers leading to a collapse of the fundamental radial repeating unit (19, 20), visible over large areas of the sheath. As shown in Figs. 12 and 12 *b* the two dense lines of each period have apparently been squeezed together, resulting in a system of double dense lines separated by a considerably reduced light space to give an average period of only 80 to 90 A. The dimensions of these paired dense lines representing the contracted period remain fairly constant, while the intercalated irregular light spaces vary widely (30 to 120 A) in different areas of the modified myelin sheath. The described modifications are reproducible, and the possibility of a preparation artifact could be excluded by performing parallel control experiments. The low-angle x-ray diffraction pattern of the fresh nerve obtained immediately after an ultracentrifugation run of 8 hours at 150,000 $g$ (Figs. 12 $c$ and $d$) showed the normal reflections together with several additional reflections which could not be accounted for in relation to the normal radial unit. Of these reflections, one at 65 A was fairly intense, but the others were weak, and it is difficult to relate them to any one fundamental period. When the preparation was fixed with osmium tetroxide the low-angle diffractions again corresponded to a single structure. These preliminary experiments indicate that the changes induced by ultracentrifugation of fresh whole nerve are evident both in the electron micrographs and in the x-ray diffraction patterns.

*Trypsin Digestion of Fresh Nerve.*—

Fresh nerve trunks from the rat or frog sciatic which had been incubated in crystalline trypsin acquired a peculiar swollen and softened appearance. In ultrathin sections of these specimens (osmium-fixed and embedded in methacrylate or in gelatin) the myelin sheath showed characteristic structural modifications. The period of the concentric lamination was usually slightly expanded (140 to 145 A), and there was a marked accentuation of the granularity of the dense lines. In certain areas (Figs. 13 and 13 $b$) the dense layers appeared dissociated into well defined granules 30 to 50 A wide and often elongated (40 to 60 A long) in the radial direction to the extent of bridging the light bands. These granules were separated from each other by regular light spaces of approximately 50 to 60 A, and frequently appeared well aligned in consecutive layers. In preparations with this prevalent granularity the faint intermediate line was usually not discernible. This appearance of the layers in thin sections is in striking agreement with earlier observations (10, 12–15) made on the isolated lamellae of the myelin sheath which, after trypsin digestion, disintegrate into rod-like granules (approximately 50 × 100 A) staining intensely with osmium.

*Extraction of Fresh Nerve with Acetone.*—

Earlier experiments (7) showed that the lipide extracted from fresh peripheral nerve fibers immersed in acetone at 0°C. for 12 hours was almost entirely cholesterol. Chemical analysis revealed that about 30 per cent of the total cholesterol had been removed from the nerve, but that other lipide components remained intact.

The present experiments were repeated under exactly the same conditions, and the low-angle x-ray diffraction pattern of the lipide extract (Fig. 14 $c$) showed a very strong 34.2 A band characteristic of cholesterol, with no indications of higher reflections which might represent phospholipide or cerebroside components. The residual nerve tissue gave a low-angle diffraction pattern

(Fig. 14 *d*) very similar to that of the normal dried nerve, though the residual lipoprotein spacing was somewhat higher (170 A as compared with 145 A). The specimen which had been fixed with buffered osmium tetroxide immediately after extraction, and subsequently embedded in methacrylate (Fig. 14 *e*), showed first and second order reflections of a 170 A layer spacing, and a further broad band in the region of 50 A which would appear to correspond to one or more additional components.

High resolution electron microscopy revealed a series of striking modifications in the myelin sheath of nerves extracted with acetone at 0°C. In contrast to the action of other lipide solvents at higher temperatures, which produce a drastic alteration of the myelin sheath organization, the effects of acetone extraction at low temperature are relatively so mild that, after osmium fixation and methacrylate or gelatin embedding, large areas of the myelin sheath are still well preserved, and exhibit in addition the following interesting structural features:

(*a*) In transverse and logitudinal thin sections the myelin sheath shows varying degrees of extraction resulting in an irregular fibrous network, but major portions of the concentric laminated sheath structure are still very well preserved. In such areas (Figs. 14, 15, 16) 10 to 20 or more perfectly regular concentric layers with an average period of 160 A (as compared with 130 to 140 A in the normal) can be counted. Upon closer examination this period is seen to differ from the normal, not only in its larger dimensions, but also as regards the fine structural pattern of its dense and light bands. On either side of each dense line (Fig. 16) (20 to 30 A) there is a well defined light band ($d_o$, 20 A), and each layer also includes two distinct intermediate lines ($i_o$, 15 A). Thus, a full period comprises one dense line, two light bands, and two intermediate lines (Fig. 16: $d$, $d_o$, $i_o$, $i_o$, $d_o$).

(*b*) There are distinct transitions (Figs. 14 and 14 *b*) between this differentiated period of 160 A and a simpler system of closely spaced dense lines (20 A thick) with an average period of 45 to 50 A. In these transitional areas the direct continuity of the dense lines and the intermediate lines of the larger period with the osmiophilic layers of the condensed period can be clearly established. The two intermediate lines seem to coalesce so as to form a single compact layer of the condensed system (Fig. 14).

(*c*) In addition to these condensed systems of 45 to 50 A connected directly with the larger period, there are also isolated regions featuring a series of dense layers of widely varying periods (30 to 75 A) (Figs. 15 *c*, 16 *b* and *c*).

(*d*) Throughout the well preserved regions of the sheath typical dense fusiform swellings (*e*) are seen associated at irregular intervals with the dense lines of the modified concentric laminated structure (Figs. 15 and 15 *b*; 16 *c*). These fusiform swellings of widely varying dimensions (about 100 to 1,000 A long) are osmiophilic, and frequently show internal formation of dense layers. There are also transitions between these fusiform swellings and the described zones of condensed layers ($p$) (Fig. 16 $c$).

*Extraction of Fresh Nerve with Alcohol.—*

Much more lipide was extracted from fresh nerve by treatment with alcohol at 0°C. for 12 hours than with acetone. The low-angle x-ray diffraction pattern of the lipide extract (Fig. 17 $e$) showed it to contain a phospholipide (and/or cerebroside) component which gives a strong reflection at 57 A. The diffraction diagram of the residual nerve (Fig. 17 $f$) indicated a much more extensive breakdown of the lipoprotein structure, and the $OsO_4$-fixed and gelatin-embedded preparation (Fig. 17 $g$) showed only faint and diffuse diffraction bands at 82 A and 43 A.

The myelin sheath of nerves extracted with alcohol, $OsO_4$-fixed, and embedded in methacrylate presents the well known picture of a distorted fibrous network with complete obliteration of the concentric laminated structure. Only occasionally could remnants of an organized layered structure be detected and these showed patches of dense layers with a period of 40 to 50 A (Fig. 17). Larger patches of organized structure were encountered in gelatin-embedded preparations, where two main types of layered system could be observed. Both systems feature a regular arrangement of dense lines (20 to 30 A thick) alternating with light spaces, but the period is in one case of the order of 70 A (Figs. 17 $b$ and $c$), and in the other 30 to 40 A (Fig. 17 $d$). Direct transitions between the two systems were observed (Fig. 17 $b$).

## DISCUSSION

A satisfactory correlation has been achieved between electron microscope and x-ray diffraction observations performed on the same nerve preparations. In nearly all cases it has been possible to identify the repetitive features observed in the high resolution electron micrographs with corresponding reflections in the low-angle x-ray diffraction diagrams.

Moreover, based on the information provided by x-ray diffraction studies of nerve under physiological conditions, and of the modifications introduced by the preparative procedures used in electron microscopy, an attempt can be made to relate the structure of myelin as seen in the electron microscope to the normal organization of the myelin sheath.

The structural significance of electron microscope and x-ray diffraction observations on myelin can be considered in relation to two directions in the sheath, the radial direction, and a direction within the layers and perpendicular to the fiber axis. Most of the available data relates to the radial direction, and the main features of the low-angle x-ray diffraction patterns of the myelin preparations can now be equated with the layer separations observed in the electron micrographs.

In normal $OsO_4$-fixed and methacrylate-embedded preparations the periodic arrangement of the dense layers of osmium deposition visualized in the electron microscope corresponds to the fundamental radial repeat indicated by the low-angle x-ray diffraction patterns. There is a consistent discrepancy of 10 to 20 A between the x-ray fundamental spacing and the layer thickness measured in the high resolution electron micrographs. It is suggested that this difference is due to a further minor shrinkage of the whole structure in the course of preparation of thin sections and their examination in the electron microscope.

In addition to the dense band of osmium, all types of preparation show an intermediate line, commonly of lower density, but susceptible of considerable variation both in width and in density according to the preparative procedures employed. In almost all of the preparations so far studied, the x-ray diffraction pattern has shown a first order reflection in the range of 120 to 170 A, though the second order reflection exhibits a marked variation in intensity relative to the first order, apparently correlative with the variation in density of the intermediate line. Thus, the relationship between the densities of the two bands of osmium deposition seen in the electron micrographs is reflected in the relative intensities of the two low-angle reflections in the x-ray diffraction patterns. There is also a close correlation between the amount of distortion seen in the preparation and the definition of the x-ray reflections, and also between the extent of structural breakdown and the intensity of diffuse scatter of x-rays at low angles.

*Analysis of the Modifications Introduced by the Preparative Procedures.—*

The available x-ray diffraction data from normal and modified nerve myelin has been related to a radial repeat consisting of two lipoprotein layers distinguished by a difference factor, which has an appreciable effect on the distribution of x-ray scattering power in the case of peripheral nerve, but none in the case of fresh myelin of central origin. This difference factor furnishes an important criterion for characterizing the normal myelin structure.

The studies of $OsO_4$ fixation in relation to electron microscopy have revealed a very marked difference between the two layers as regards their reaction with osmium tetroxide, and this applies to both peripheral and central nerve myelin. This difference factor manifests itself in the low-angle pattern as an increase in the intensity of the first order reflection and in the electron micrographs as a variation in the densities of the two principal bands of osmium deposition. The question of whether these difference factors, which show up under two diverse conditions, are actually identical, cannot as yet be answered with certainty. However, some of the modification experiments provide data suggesting that there is some relationship between the two factors. A further modification introduced by osmium tetroxide treatment is a shrinkage of the layer spacing by about 20 A and a stabilization of the system which is largely responsible for the preservation of organized structure during the subsequent preparative procedures for electron microscopy.

Potassium permanganate now provides an alternative method of fixation for electron microscopy of the myelin sheath, which presents certain interesting supplementary features. In contrast to the osmium tetroxide fixation, the shrinkage produced in myelin by $KMnO_4$ treatment is relatively small, and the second order reflection of the low-angle diffraction pattern remains dominant, indicating almost complete halving of the structure. The dominance of the second order reflection persists through the dehydration and embedding procedures, and there is thus a strong possibility that the density variations seen in the electron micrographs of $KMnO_4$-fixed preparations embedded in gelatin are not far removed from those of the normal structure. The manganese atom is a relatively light one (atomic weight of 55) as compared with osmium (atomic weight of 190), and its effect on the distribution of scattering power within the structure may not be sufficient to mask the contributions of phosphorus, sulfur, calcium, and potassium which are the heaviest atoms present in the normal structure. The action of $KMnO_4$ may thus be principally one of stabilization of structure without a dominant staining effect such as is introduced by osmium. It is interesting to note that, from the point of view of both x-ray diffraction and electron microscopy, gelatin embedding gives a better preservation of the $KMnO_4$-fixed myelin structure than does methacrylate embedding.

The x-ray diffraction data also presents useful information bearing on the relative merits of methacrylate and gelatin embedding of osmium tetroxide-fixed myelin. It has been observed previously that the layer spacing in the methacrylate-embedded specimen is very similar to that of the freshly fixed material, as though perhaps methacrylate substitutes for water in the structure and prevents shrinkage. The observations reported here now make it clear that the layer spacing does shrink markedly during the alcohol dehydration and expands again when immersed in methacrylate. It is by no means certain that if methacrylate were to reexpand this structure it would do so at ionic interfaces. Hence, if it is simply a matter of removal of water layers, the methacrylate might in fact falsify the structural picture still further when it reexpands it. On the other hand, the final 30 A shrinkage of the osmium tetroxide–fixed preparation may result from a reorganization of lipide or protein components. The methacrylate treatment might then simply be restoring the original organization and therefore present a more closely equivalent picture of the osmium distribution in myelin. However, the methacrylate polymerization does cause some structural distortions which are not evident in the gelatin-embedded material, and therefore, in general, both methods of embedding should be applied to provide complementary data.

The freeze-sectioning method dispenses altogether with embedding procedures, but the subsequent dehydration of the unsupported structures increases the tendency towards halving of the fundamental radial unit. This probably accounts for the reduced spacings reported in the earlier electron microscope studies of the myelin sheath.

*Analysis of the Experimental Modifications of Myelin Structure.—*

*Physical Methods.*—The intensification of the intermediate line by freezing and thawing the peripheral nerve preparation prior to $OsO_4$ fixation and methacrylate embedding indicates that the difference factor for osmium tetroxide may be related to that prominent in the normal peripheral nerve myelin, which is also markedly affected by this treatment. This enhancement further suggests that the intermediate line may be associated with a protein or lipoprotein region, which would be expected to be more readily affected by freezing and thawing than would a region featuring lipide hydrocarbon chains.

The collapsing of the radial repeating unit observed in the myelin sheath after intense and prolonged ultracentrifugation might be interpreted as an indication of the greater stability of the dense lines, as compared with the compressed light areas. This would be in keeping with the tentative location of long-chain lipides arranged radially in the light areas. These lipide molecules would be more exposed to the effects of transverse ultracentrifugation and might therefore tilt more readily, thereby reducing the layer spacing. The stability of the dense lines is compatible with their identification as concentrically arranged protein layers which should be more resistant to transverse centrifugal forces.

*Lipide Extraction Experiments.*—By analogy with earlier studies using x-ray diffraction and chemical analysis techniques, it can be assumed that extraction of fresh nerve with acetone at $0°C$. in the present experiments has removed about 30 per cent of the cholesterol without extracting any appreciable amount of other lipides. However, in now introducing electron microscope observations on the acetone-extracted preparations, it must be emphasized that this does not permit a quantitative assessment of the amount of lipide that has been removed from any particular area viewed in the electron microscope. It is, nevertheless, interesting that acetone extraction carried out at low temperatures produces differentiated reproducible modifications of the concentric laminated structure of the myelin sheath. This suggests the feasibility of correlating, at least qualitatively, the preferential extraction of an important component like cholesterol with certain structural modifications in the still highly organized residual myelin as revealed by electron microscopy and x-ray diffraction. The electron microscope reveals at least two main modifications of the layered structure, and a further disorganized phase which must also be represented in the chemical composition. One of these structures has a layer dimension which is about 10 per cent greater than that of the normal preparation, and the appearance of the layers is changed considerably. The expansion of the layers is also apparent in the diffraction pattern of the acetone-extracted and dried tissue in which the residual lipoprotein spacing is considerably higher than in the normal preparation. It is thus seen to be a true expansion of the lipoprotein structure. Such an expansion has previously been explained in terms of an uncurling of phospholipide or cerebroside molecules which are assumed to be accommodated in a shortened form in the normal structure. This type of structural rearrangement might result from the removal of a portion of the cholesterol from the system. One of the most striking features of the modified structure is the appearance of an almost unstained region adjacent to the densely stained band. Again, the change should be related to removal of cholesterol from the system, but it is unlikely that this light area can be accounted for simply as the site from which the cholesterol component has been removed. It is notable, however, that the fusiform swellings, which are probably linked with the extraction process, appear invariably associated with the dense lines. It is, therefore, possible that the material accumulating in these swellings is drawn from the dense lines and the regions immediately adjacent to them. On the other hand, the removal of cholesterol from the system would undoubtedly lead to an extensive structural rearrangement within the layers, which in itself might account for some of the changes in the banded structure. A further interesting feature is the layer separation appearing as a kind of ribbon formation, each ribbon apparently representing a complete period bounded by two narrow dense lines.

The system of closely spaced bands seen in other parts of the myelin sheath may represent more than one type of structural arrangement. One type of arrangement is certainly derived directly from the more complex layered structure previously considered. In certain electron micrographs it is clearly demonstrated that the thicker layer collapses, so that the intermediate line becomes much more intense, and is comparable with the normally very dense line. The simplest way of accounting for this change in layered structure is in terms of different degrees of extraction, the collapsed structure probably having suffered the greater loss of lipide material.

It is probably significant that the dense lines seem to be relatively unaffected by the lipide extraction. This observation lends support to the suggestion that the heaviest osmium deposition is in the region of a protein layer. The fact that the intermediate line also persists in the collapsed layered structure may mean that this also features a protein component. In order to account for the various types of condensed layer systems found separately in the sheath, the possibility must be considered of recrystallization of free lipides in the disorganized parts of the sheath.

Similar considerations apply also to the alcohol extraction experiments. Alcohol is a well known agent for the breakdown of lipoprotein associations, and the fact that only very fine layered structures are observed in the alcohol-extracted myelin may mean that only the protein skeleton of the original lipoprotein layers remains, and possibly also some recrystallized lipide. Although there are no quantitative chemical data available, it is evident that the structural breakdown and lipide extraction are carried further in the alcohol experiments than in the acetone extraction. These experiments stress two very important points in relation to myelin structure. The first is the importance of cholesterol, and the second is the probability that the heaviest osmium deposition is connected with the protein layers rather than with unsaturated hydrocarbon chains of lipide molecules.

*Significance of the Findings in Relation to the Molecular Organization of Myelin.—*

The nature of the sites of the osmium deposition is a basic question from the point of view of electron microscopy. The dense layer is 30 to 40 A thick, and in many preparations can be seen to split into two narrow lines. This observation can be related directly to the demonstrated formation of the myelin sheath from the Schwann cell membrane in peripheral nerve. Electron micrographs of developing nerve fibers show the process to consist of a rolling of the Schwann cell membrane around the axon in a double layer, and the formation of the dense band is clearly shown to result from an apposition of the fine osmium lines at the inner surface of the Schwann cell membrane. In the preparations in which the intermediate line is intensified, this is also seen to split into finer lines. Again, a division into two lines can be readily accounted for in terms of the band resulting from the close apposition of the two outer surfaces of the Schwann cell membrane.

It is tempting to think of these densely staining surface layers as protein layers, and although the evidence is not conclusive, there are already significant points in favor of a concentration of osmium at the protein layer or at the lipoprotein interfaces rather than among the hydrocarbon chains of the lipide molecules. It is, at the moment, impossible to decide the point from the available chemical knowledge because of the uncertainty of the exact chemical composition of the sheath, and the ability of osmium tetroxide to react with a wide variety of chemical groups which might occur in either lipide or protein.

The additional evidence now supplied by the freezing and thawing and by the extraction experiments gives considerable support to the assumption that the primary site of osmium deposition is at the lipoprotein interfaces.

In many electron micrographs of several different types of preparation, a strong tendency for the myelin layers to break up into granular formations has been observed. These granules appear to be of fairly uniform dimensions, and frequently give rise to a periodicity of 60 to 80 A along the layers. Although this granulation is often present in the normal osmium-fixed and methacrylate-embedded preparations, it is still more marked when the specimen has been frozen and thawed before fixation, and particularly when fresh nerve has been digested with trypsin before fixation. $KMnO_4$-fixed preparations also reveal this type of organization within the plane of the layers, and in many areas the structure appears as a regular two-dimensional array of 50 to 60 A wide particles. The x-ray reflections corresponding to such an organization would be expected to coincide with the second order reflection of the radial repeating unit, and might, therefore, not be distinguished in these preparations. However, it has been remarked previously that many features of the x-ray diffraction data require a strong 60 to 70 A vector to account for the relative intensities of the equatorial low-angle reflections. Such a vector is not provided by the present concept of the organization in the radial direction, and it has been noted that the vector could equally well be accounted for in the direction of the layers but perpendicular to the fiber direction. In view of the electron microscope observations indicating a strong tendency for the structure to break up into particles of these dimensions, a greater emphasis is now placed on the possibility of a considerable degree of organization within the plane of the lipoprotein layers.

Further data on the specific chemical composition of the myelin sheath, and on the localization of its protein and lipide components, is needed in order to achieve a detailed interpretation of the structural parameters derived from the electron microscope and x-ray diffraction studies. It is also essential to obtain quantitative information on the water content of the myelin sheath and its localization within the layered structure. A promising approach to this problem is offered by the new techniques of high resolution nuclear magnetic resonance spectrometry (19), which can be applied to determine accurately the water content of fresh whole nerve, and the hydration state of its components, in a rapid and non-destructive way.

The interesting results already obtained by controlled extraction of fresh whole nerve with acetone at low temperatures indicate the potential value of extending and refining these experiments. Similarly, it will be of interest to apply more specific enzymes such as the phosphatases to effect a chemical dissection of the myelin structure at the submicroscopic level, which can be followed by combined application of high resolution electron microscopy and x-ray diffraction methods. The introduction of water-soluble embedding media such as gelatin may facilitate the application of micro-incineration techniques, and of selective extraction and digestion procedures carried out directly on suitably mounted ultrathin sections.

In view of the remarkable similarities of the myelin organization and the regular laminated structure of specialized energy converting systems like chloroplasts (39) and retinal rods (56, 15), the type of combined studies reported here might be usefully extended to these highly ordered components.

### SUMMARY

1. A close correlation has been obtained between high resolution electron microscopy and low-angle x-ray diffraction studies of the myelin sheath of frog and rat peripheral and central nerves. Extensive studies were performed by application of both techniques to the same specimens, prepared for examination

by $OsO_4$ or $KMnO_4$ fixation, and embedding either in methacrylate or in gelatin employing a new procedure. Controlled physical and chemical modifications of the myelin sheath prior to fixation were also investigated.

2. A correspondence was established between the layer spacings observed in electron micrographs and the fundamental radial repeating unit indicated by the low-angle x-ray diffraction patterns. The variations in relative intensities of the low-angle x-ray reflections could be related to the radial density distributions seen in the electron micrographs.

3. An analysis of the preparation procedures revealed that $OsO_4$ fixation introduces a greater shrinkage of the layer spacings and more pronounced changes in the density distribution within the layers than $KMnO_4$ fixation. The effects of methacrylate and gelatin embedding are described, and their relative merits considered in relation to the preservation of myelin structure by $OsO_4$ fixation.

4. The experimental modifications introduced by freezing and thawing of fresh whole nerve are described, particularly the enhancement of the intermediate lines and the dissociation of the layer components in the myelin sheath. A characteristic collapsing of the radial period of the sheath is observed after subjecting fresh nerve trunks to prolonged and intense ultracentrifugation.

5. Controlled extraction of fresh nerve with acetone at 0°C., which preferentially removes cholesterol, produces characteristic, differentiated modifications of the myelin sheath structure. Electron microscopy reveals several types of modifications within a single preparation, including both expanded and collapsed layer systems, and internal rearrangements of the layer components. Alcohol extraction leads to a more extensive structural breakdown, but in certain areas collapsed layer systems can still be observed. The components of the lipide extracts could be identified by means of x-ray diffraction. These modifications emphasize the importance of cholesterol in the myelin structure, and disclose a resistance of the dense osmiophilic lines to lipide solvents.

6. The significance of these structures is discussed in relation to present concepts of the molecular organization of myelin. The available evidence is consistent with the suggestion that the primary site of osmium deposition is at the lipoprotein interfaces and that the light bands probably represent regions occupied by lipide chains. The electron microscope and x-ray diffraction data also indicate the possibility of a regular organization within the plane of the layers, probably involving units of 60 to 80 A. The myelin sheath is regarded as a favourable cell membrane model for detailed analysis by combined application of x-ray diffraction and electron microscopy.

The authors wish to express their sincere thanks to Engs. J. Suter, W. Rawyler, O. Zehnder, R. Hauser, H. Kabe, A. Trommer, and S. Liendo for the essential technical collaboration in the various aspects of this work. The valuable assistance of Dr. G. Ochsner in the preparation of the manuscript is gratefully acknowledged.

## BIBLIOGRAPHY

1. Bear, R. S., Palmer, K. J., and Schmitt, F. O., *J. Cell. and Comp. Physiol.*, 1941, **17**, 355.
2. Boettiger, E. G., *J. Cell. and Comp. Physiol.*, 1946, **28**, 139.
3. Collin, R., and Chavarot, M., *Compt. rend. Soc. biol.*, 1934, **115**, 561.
4. Ehrenberg, Ch. G., *Monatsber. preuss. Akad. Wissensch.*, 1849, **64**, 73.
5. Elkes, J., and Finean, J. B., Lipoproteins, *Discussions Faraday Soc.*, 1949, **6**, 134.
6. Elkes, J., and Finean, J. B., *Exp. Cell Research*, 1953, **4**, 69.
7. Elkes, J., and Finean, J. B., *Exp. Cell Research*, 1953, **4**, 82.
8. Fernández-Morán, H., *J. Scient. Instr.*, 1949, **26**, 164.
9. Fernández-Morán, H., *Exp. Cell Research*, 1950, **1**, 141.
10. Fernández-Morán, H., *Exp. Cell Research*, 1950, **1**, 309.
11. Fernández-Morán, H., *Exp. Cell Research*, 1951, **2**, 673.
12. Fernández-Morán, H., *Exp. Cell Research*, 1952, **3**, 282.
13. Fernández-Morán, H., *Bol. Acad. Cien. fís. mat. Caracas*, 1953, **51**, 1.
14. Fernández-Morán, H., *Exp. Cell Research*, 1953, **5**, 255.
15. Fernández-Morán, H., *Progr. Biophysics*, 1954, **4**, 112.
16. Fernández-Morán, H., VI Congreso Latinoamericano Neurocirugía, Montevideo, 1955, 599.
17. Fernández-Morán, H., *J. Biophysic. and Biochem. Cytol.*, 1956, **2**, No 4, suppl., 29.
18. Fernández-Morán, H., *Ind. Diamond Rev.*, 1956, **16**, 128.
19. Fernández-Morán, H., 2nd International Neurochemical Symposium, Aarhus, 1956, London, Pergamon Press, in press.
20. Fernández-Morán, H., Symposium on the Submicroscopic Organization and Function of Nerve Cells, Caracas, 1957, in press (to be published in supplement to *Experimental Cell Research*).
21. Finean, J. B., *Exp. Cell Research*, 1953, **5**, 202.
22. Finean, J. B., *J. Scient. Instr.*, 1953, **30**, 60.
23. Finean, J. B., *Exp. Cell Research*, 1954, **6**, 283.
24. Finean, J. B., *Nature*, 1954, **173**, 549.
25. Finean, J. B., International Conference on Biochemical Problems of Lipids, Brussels, 1953, 82.
26. Finean, J. B., Conference on Biochemical Problems of Lipids, Ghent, 1955, London, Butterworth, 127.
27. Finean, J. B., *J. Scient. Instr.*, 1956, **33**, 161.
28. Finean, J. B., and Millington, P. F., *J. Biophysic. and Biochem. Cytol.*, 1957, **3**, 89.
29. Finean, J. B., *J. Biophysic. and Biochem. Cytol.*, 1957, **3**, 95.
30. Finean, J. B., Hawthorne, J. N., and Patterson, J. D. E., *J. Neurochem.*, in press.
31. Finean, J. B., 2nd International Neurochemical Symposium, Aarhus, 1956, London, Pergamon Press, in press.
32. Finean, J. B., Symposium on the Submicroscopic Organization and Function of Nerve Cells, Caracas, 1957, in press.
33. Folch-Pi, J., and Sperry, W. M., *Ann. Rev. Biochem.*, 1948, **17**, 147.
34. Frey-Wyssling, A., Submicroscopic Morphology of Protoplasm, 2nd edition, 1953, Houston, Elsevier Press.

35. Geren, B. B., and Raskind, J., *Proc. Nat. Acad. Sc.*, 1953, **39**, 880.
36. Geren, B. B., *Exp. Cell Research*, 1954, **7**, 558.
37. Geren, B. B., and Schmitt, F. O., *Proc. Nat. Acad. Sc.*, 1954, **40**, 863.
38. Geren, B. B., Fourteenth Growth Symposium, Princeton University Press, 1956.
39. Hodge, A. J., McLean, J. D., and Mercer, F. V., *J. Biophysic. and Biochem. Cytol.*, 1955, **1**, 605.
40. Luft, J. H., *J. Biophysic. and Biochem. Cytol.*, 1956, **2**, 799.
41. Luse, S. A., *J. Biophysic. and Biochem. Cytol.*, 1956, **2**, 777.
42. Palade, G. E., *J. Exp. Med.*, 1952, **95**, 285.
43. Palade, G. E., *J. Histochem. and Cytochem.*, 1953, **1**, 188.
44. Palmer, K. J., and Schmitt, F. O., *J. Cell. and Comp. Physiol.*, 1941, **17**, 385.
45. Porter, K. R., and Blum, J., *Anat. Rec.*, 1953, **117**, 685.
46. Ramon y Cajal, S., Degeneration and Regeneration of the Nervous System, Oxford University Press, 1928.
47. Robertson, J. D., *J. Biophysic. and Biochem. Cytol.*, 1955, **1**, 371.
48. Schmidt, W. J., Die Bausteine des Tierkörpers in polarisiertem Licht, Bonn, 1924, a.
49. Schmidt, W. J., Die Doppelbrechung von Karyoplasma, Zytoplasma und Metaplasma, Berlin, 1937.
50. Schmidt, W. J., *Z. wissensch. mikr.*, 1937, **54**, 159.
51. Schmitt, F. O., *Cold Spring Harbor Symp. Quant. Biol.*, 1936, **4**, 7.
52. Schmitt, F. O., Bear, R. S., and Clark, G. L., *Radiology*, 1935, **25**, 131.
53. Schmitt, F. O., Bear, R. S., and Palmer, K. J., *J. Cell. and Comp. Physiol.*, 1941, **18**, 31.
54. Schmitt, F. O., and Bear, R. S., *J. Cell. and Comp. Physiol.*, 1937, **9**, 261.
55. Schmitt, F. O., *Research Pub., Assn. Research Nerv. and Ment. Dis.*, 1950, **28**, 247.
56. Sjöstrand, F. S., *J. Cell and Comp. Physiol.*, 1949, **33**, 383.

## EXPLANATION OF PLATES

### PLATE 229

FIG. 1. x-ray diffraction equipment.
Left: Low-angle vacuum camera.
Right: Geiger counter goniometer adapted for low-angle recording.

FIG. 1 b. Low-angle x-ray diffraction pattern of a fresh rat sciatic nerve recorded in the low-angle vacuum camera.

FIG. 2. Special plexiglas chamber used for transverse ultracentrifugation of fresh nerve trunks. These chambers fit into the plastic tubes of the Spinco preparative ultracentrifuge.

FIG. 2 b. Fresh rat nerve contained in a glass capillary before (right) and after (left) prolonged ultracentrifugation (150,000 $g$ for 8 hours in the longitudinal direction) which produces marked shortening of the nerve.

FIG. 2 c. Fresh rat nerve contained in a glass capillary before (left) and after (right) prolonged transverse ultracentrifugation (150,000 $g$ for 12 hours) which produces pronounced flattening of the nerve.

PLATE 229
VOL. 3

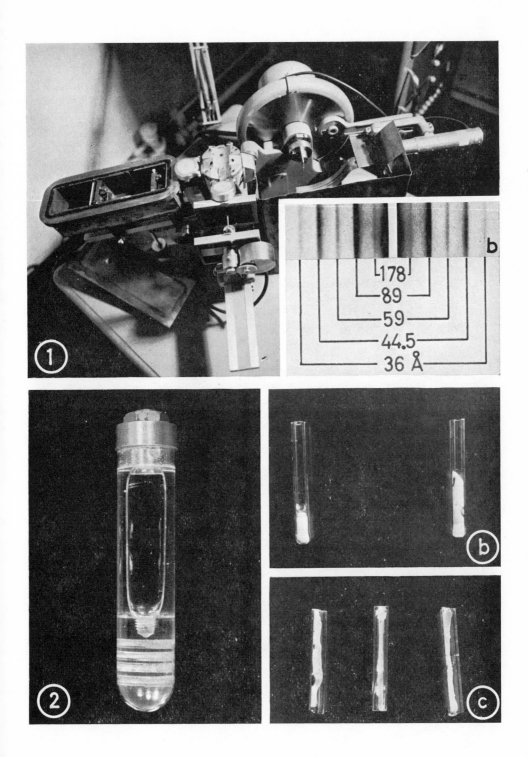

PLATE 230

FIG. 3. Low-angle x-ray diffraction patterns showing the effects of osmium tetroxide fixation on the structure of the myelin sheath.

FIG. 3 *a*. Fresh giant toad sciatic nerve.

FIG. 3 *b*. Giant toad sciatic nerve treated with buffered 1 per cent osmium tetroxide solution for 4 hours.

FIG. 3 *c*. Rat sciatic nerve treated with buffered 1 per cent isotonic osmium tetroxide solution for 4 hours.

FIG. 3 *d*. Rat optic nerve treated with buffered 1 per cent isotonic osmium tetroxide solution for 4 hours.

FIG. 4. Transverse ultrathin section of rat sciatic nerve fiber, fixed in buffered 1 per cent osmium tetroxide solution, and embedded in methacrylate, showing the regular arrangement of the myelin sheath layers. The dense lines (*d*) and the faint intermediate lines (*i*) of varying density stand out clearly. $\times$ 575,000.

FIG. 4 *b*. Low-angle x-ray diffraction pattern of the embedded preparation from which the thin section seen in Fig. 4 was obtained.

FIG. 4 *c*. Diagrammatic representation of the various features observed in high resolution electron micrographs of osmium tetroxide–fixed and methacrylate-embedded nerve myelin preparations. Notice tendency of the dense osmium line to split along its length and also to dissociate into granular units.

PLATE 230
VOL. 3

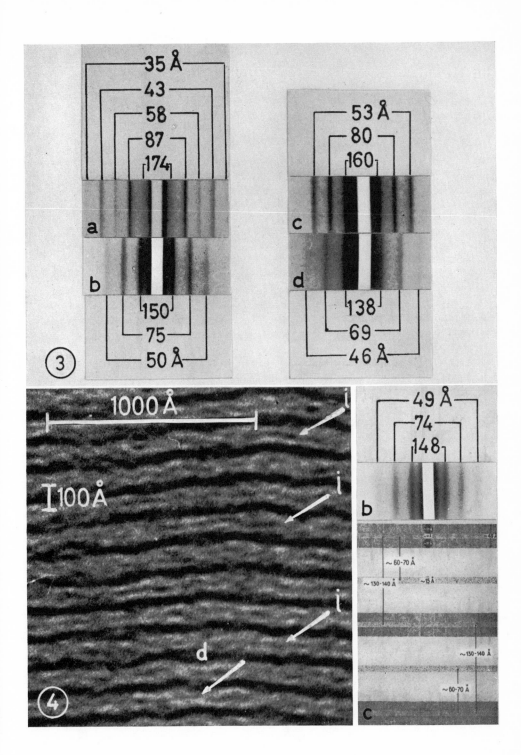

PLATE 231

FIG. 5. Ultrathin frozen section of osmium–fixed, unembedded frog sciatic nerve showing the concentric laminated structure of the sheath. Enhancement of the normally faint intermediate line ($i$) gives rise to a radial period (65 A) which is only half of the fundamental repeating unit. × 520,000.

FIG. 5 $b$. Ultrathin frozen section of osmium–fixed, unembedded frog sciatic nerve, showing the concentric laminated structure of the sheath featuring a fundamental period of 120 A with a faint intermediate line ($i$), which is the most commonly encountered type of structure. × 250,000.

FIG. 5 $c$. Low-angle x-ray diffraction pattern of osmium tetroxide–fixed giant toad sciatic nerve which had been frozen and thawed before drying.

FIG. 6. Myelin sheath segment from a transverse section of an osmium–fixed rat sciatic nerve embedded in gelatin. The average layer spacing is 110 A. Note compact and well preserved dense lines, and moderate enhancement of the intermediate lines ($i$). × 820,000.

FIG. 6 $b$. Low-angle x-ray diffraction pattern of osmium tetroxide–fixed rat sciatic nerve embedded in gelatin.

PLATE 231
VOL. 3

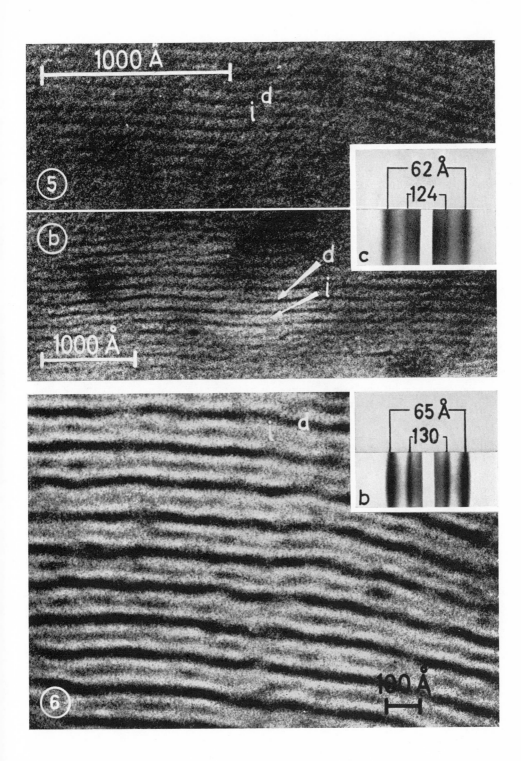

PLATE 232

FIG. 7. High resolution electron micrograph of myelin sheath segment from a transverse section of osmium tetroxide–fixed rat sciatic nerve embedded in methacrylate showing fine structure of the concentric layers. Note the splitting of the dense lines ($d'$) and the variation in intensity of the intermediate line ($i$). Minute dense particles of 10 to 15 A, which probably represent primary osmium deposits, are seen distributed at random throughout the preparation. × 1,200,000.

FIGS. 7 $b$ to $f$. Series of low-angle x-ray diffraction patterns recorded after different stages in the preparation of a rat sciatic nerve for examination in the electron microscope.

FIG. 7 $b$. Rat sciatic nerve after treatment with buffered 1 per cent isotonic osmium tetroxide solution for 4 hours.

FIG. 7 $c$. Same preparation as in ($b$) after immersion in 70 per cent ethanol overnight.

FIG. 7 $d$. Same preparation as in ($c$) after immersion in 90 per cent ethanol for 2 hours.

FIG. 7 $e$. Same preparation as in ($d$) after immersion in 100 per cent ethanol for 3 hours followed by 2 hours in $n$-butyl methacrylate.

FIG. 7 $f$. Same preparation as in ($e$) after polymerization of $n$-butyl methacrylate at 55°C.

PLATE 232
VOL. 3

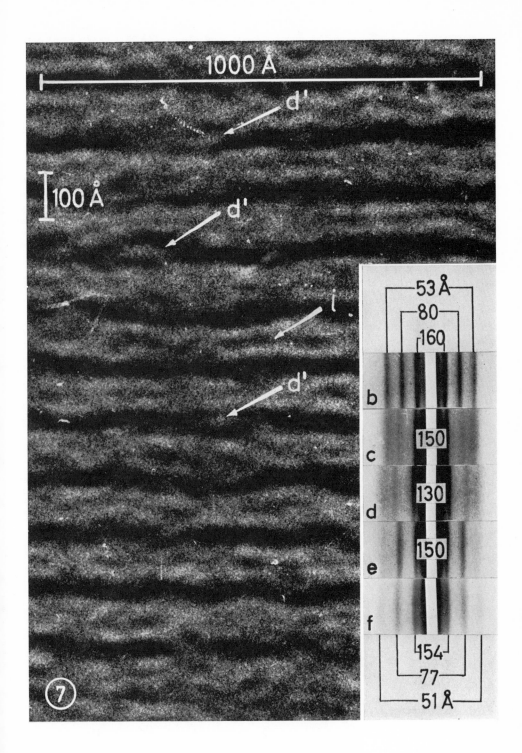

PLATE 233

FIG. 8. Myelin sheath segment from a transverse section of giant toad sciatic nerve fixed in buffered 0.6 per cent $KMnO_4$ solution and embedded in gelatin. Note the excellent preservation of the laminated structure with an average period of 130 A, and the marked enhancement of the intermediate lines ($i$) which closely resemble the dense lines ($d$). × 1,100,000.

FIG. 8 $b$. Myelin sheath segment from a transverse section of giant toad sciatic nerve fixed in buffered 0.6 per cent $KMnO_4$ solution and embedded in gelatin. Note the irregular configuration of the dense ($d$) and intermediate lines ($i$) which appear to be segmented. × 900,000.

FIGS. 8 $c$ to $e$. Low-angle x-ray diffraction patterns showing the effects of $KMnO_4$ fixation and gelatin embedding.

FIG. 8 $c$. Fresh giant toad sciatic nerve.

FIG. 8 $d$. Fresh giant toad sciatic nerve after fixation in buffered 0.6 per cent $KMnO_4$ solution.

FIG. 8 $e$. Same preparation as in ($d$) after embedding in gelatin.

PLATE 233
VOL. 3

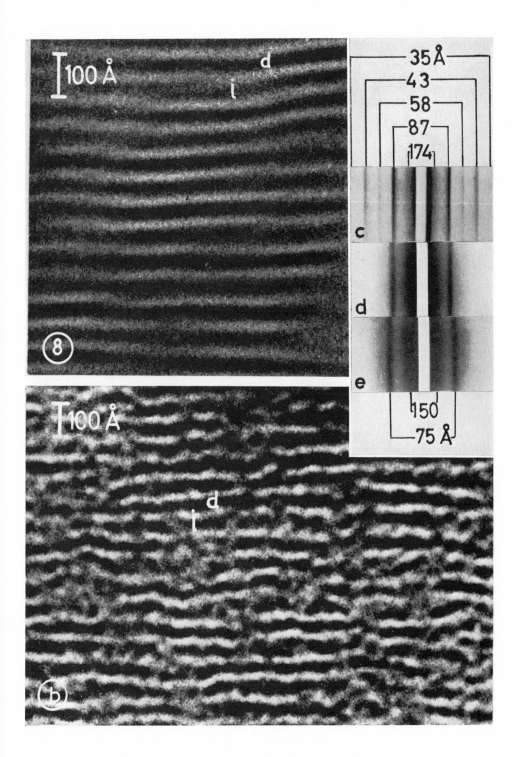

PLATE 234

FIG. 9. Myelin sheath segment from a transverse section through a central nerve fiber from the mouse thalamus after osmium tetroxide fixation and embedding in methacrylate. Notice the double dense line (arrows) which demarcates the axonal portion of the myelin sheath from the outer part. × 380,000.

FIG. 9 b. Myelin sheath segment from a transverse section through a central nerve fiber from the mouse thalamus after osmium tetroxide fixation and embedding in methacrylate. Notice the series of closely spaced dense lines (arrows) with an average period of 60 A surrounding the axon. × 290,000.

FIG. 9 c. Low-angle x-ray diffraction pattern of fresh rat optic nerve.

FIG. 10. Ultrathin transverse section through a small central nerve fiber from the mouse thalamus (osmium–fixed and methacrylate–embedded) showing the spiral course of the myelin layer, which connects with the axon membrane at $a'$ and merges with the membrane ($m$) of an adjacent cell. × 220,000.

PLATE 234
VOL. 3

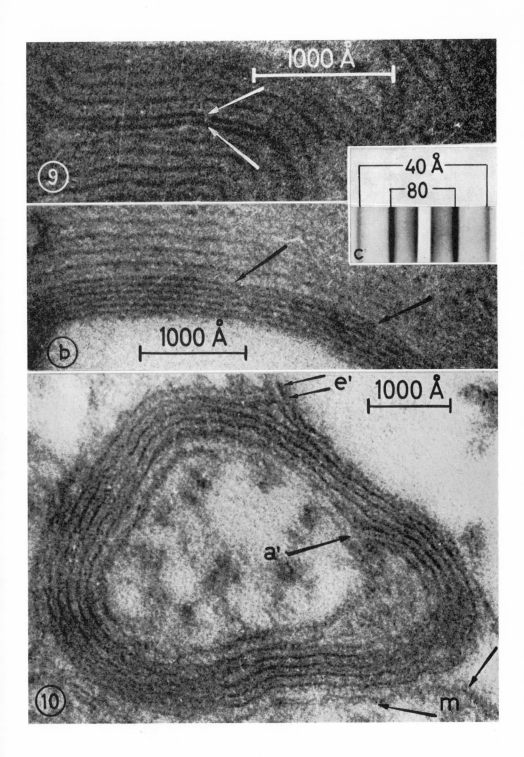

PLATE 235

FIG. 11. Myelin sheath segment from a frog sciatic nerve frozen ($-30°$C.) and thawed prior to fixation with buffered 1 per cent isotonic osmium tetroxide solution and embedded in $n$-butyl methacrylate. Notice the enhancement of the intermediate line ($l$) and the general granulation of the layer components. $\times$ 730,000.

FIG. 11 $b$. Myelin sheath segment from a rat sciatic nerve frozen with liquid helium ($-269°$C.) and thawed rapidly to 22°C. prior to fixation with buffered 1 per cent isotonic osmium tetroxide solution and embedding in $n$-butyl methacrylate. Notice the general disruption and marked splitting (arrows) of the dense and intermediate lines. The irregular light patches probably result from submicroscopic ice crystal formation. $\times$ 580,000.

FIG. 11 $c$. High resolution electron micrograph of a myelin sheath segment from a rat sciatic nerve frozen with liquid helium ($-269°$C.) and thawed rapidly to 22°C. prior to fixation with buffered 1 per cent isotonic osmium tetroxide solution and embedding in $n$-butyl methacrylate. The multiple splitting of the dense and intermediate lines (arrows) and the general disruption of the layer fine structure can be seen. $\times$ 1,160,000.

FIGS. 11 $d$ to $g$. Low-angle x-ray diffraction patterns showing the effects of freezing and thawing on the myelin sheath.

FIG. 11 $d$. Fresh giant toad sciatic nerve.

FIG. 11 $e$. Same specimen as in ($d$) after freezing at $-20°$C. for 1 hour and thawing for one hour.

FIG. 11 $f$. Same specimen as in ($e$) after treatment with buffered 1 per cent isotonic osmium tetroxide solution for 4 hours.

FIG. 11 $g$. Same specimen as in ($f$) after embedding in $n$-butyl methacrylate.

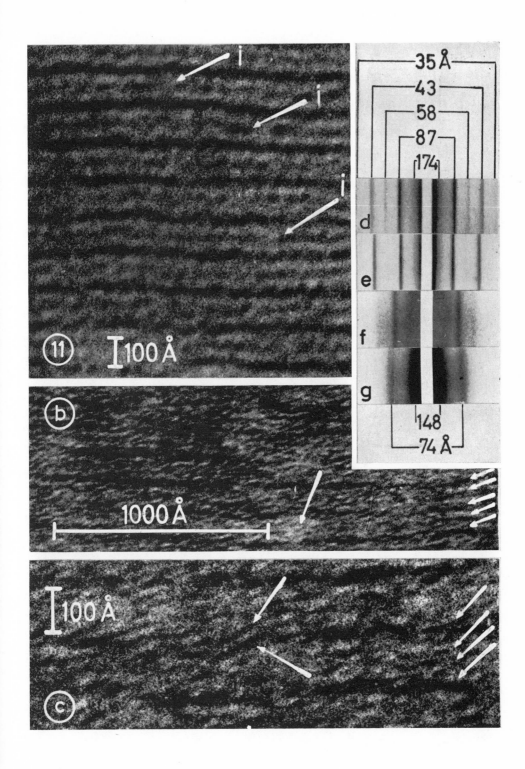

PLATE 235
VOL. 3

PLATE 236

FIG. 12. High resolution electron micrograph of myelin sheath segment from fresh giant toad sciatic nerves subjected to intense and prolonged ultracentrifugation (150,000 $g$ for 12 hours) at right angles to the fiber direction, and then fixed in 1 per cent osmium tetroxide followed by embedding in $n$-butyl methacrylate. Notice the collapsing of the myelin layers into dense double line systems (arrows-$d$-) with an average period of 60 to 70 A. $\times$ 800,000.

FIG. 12 $b$. Myelin sheath segment from the same specimen shown in Fig. 12 demonstrating the collapsed myelin layers produced by ultracentrifugation. $\times$ 400,000.

FIG. 12 $c$. Low-angle x-ray diffraction pattern of giant toad sciatic nerve subjected to intense ultracentrifugation (150,000 $g$ for 8 hours) at right angles to the fiber direction.

FIG. 12 $d$. Same specimen as in 12 $c$ after fixation in buffered 1 per cent osmium tetroxide solution.

FIG. 13. Myelin sheath segment from a rat sciatic nerve which was incubated with 1 per cent crystalline trypsin for 12 hours prior to fixation in buffered 1 per cent isotonic osmium tetroxide solution and embedding in $n$-butyl methacrylate. Notice the marked dissociation of the dense lines (arrows) into granules elongated in the radial direction. $\times$ 380,000.

FIG. 13 $b$. Same preparation as in Fig. 13 at higher magnification, showing the granular dissociation of the dense lines (arrows) and the absence of an intermediate line. $\times$ 480,000.

PLATE 236
VOL. 3

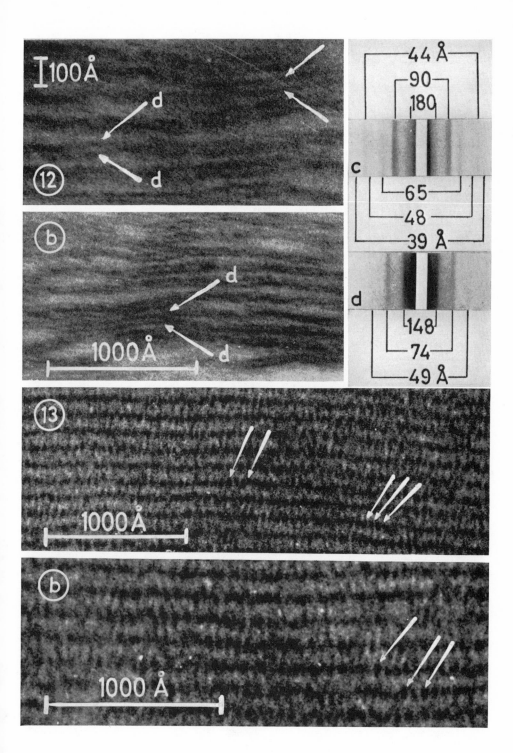

PLATE 237

FIG. 14. Myelin sheath segment from transverse section of fresh rat sciatic nerve extracted with acetone at 0°C. for 12 hours prior to fixation with 2 per cent osmium tetroxide and embedding in *n*-butyl methacrylate. Notice the expanded periods (160 A) of the modified layers to the right and the transitions (arrows) to the collapsed period (43 A) at the left. × 420,000.

FIG. 14 *b*. Myelin sheath segment from longitudinal section of fresh rat sciatic nerve extracted with acetone at 0°C. for 12 hours prior to fixation with 2 per cent osmium tetroxide and embedding in *n*-butyl methacrylate. Notice the transitions (arrows) from the expanded layer system to the collapsed layer system. × 390,000.

FIG. 14 *c*. Low-angle x-ray diffraction pattern of the lipide material extracted from fresh rat sciatic nerve by immersion in acetone at 0°C. for 12 hours (shows the characteristic cholesterol spacing at 34.2 A).

FIG. 14 *d*. Low-angle x-ray diffraction pattern of residual dried rat sciatic nerve after extraction with acetone at 0°C. for 12 hours.

FIG. 14 *e*. Low-angle x-ray diffraction pattern of acetone–extracted nerve fixed with buffered 2 per cent osmium tetroxide and embedded in methacrylate.

PLATE 237
VOL. 3

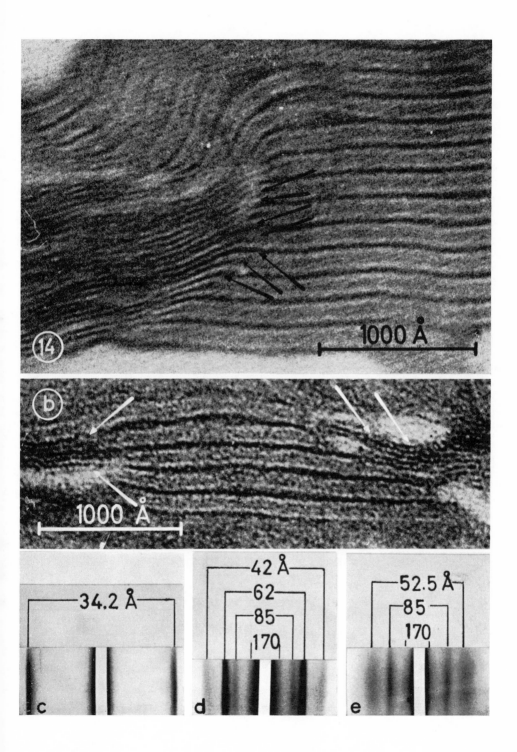

155

PLATE 238

FIG. 15. Myelin sheath segment from transverse section of fresh rat sciatic nerve extracted with acetone at 0°C. for 12 hours prior to fixation with buffered 2 per cent osmium tetroxide solution and embedding in $n$-butyl methacrylate. Notice the regularity of the expanded period, each of which contains two intermediate lines ($i_o$) and two light bands adjacent to the dense lines. Fusiform swellings ($e$) connected with the extraction process are regularly associated with the dense lines. × 400,000.

FIG. 15 $b$. High resolution electron micrograph of same specimen as in Fig. 15, showing the typical fusiform swellings ($e$) associated with the dense lines, and the double intermediate lines ($i_o$) in each expanded period. × 400,000.

FIG. 15 $c$. High resolution electron micrograph of same specimen as in Fig. 15, showing the condensed layer system with an average period of 33 A formed by dense osmiophilic lines with indications of granular fine structure. × 680,000.

PLATE 238
VOL. 3

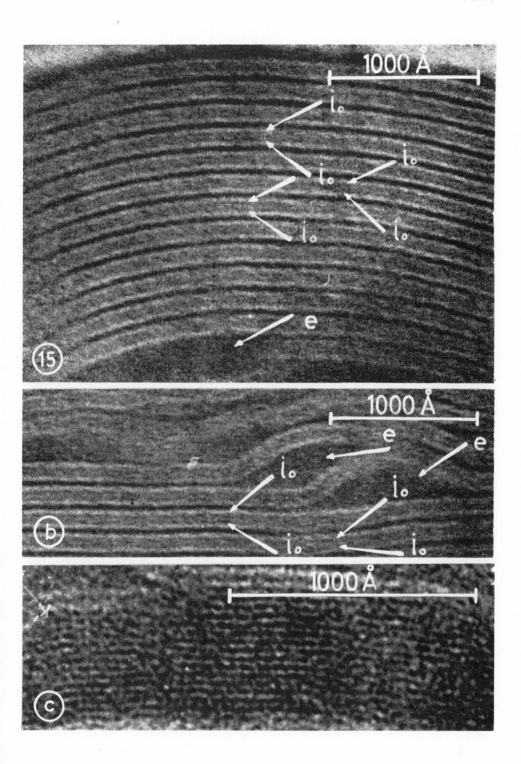

PLATE 239

FIG. 16. Myelin sheath segment from transverse section of fresh rat sciatic nerve extracted with acetone at 0°C. for 12 hours prior to fixation with buffered 2 per cent osmium tetroxide solution and embedding in $n$-butyl methacrylate. Notice the characteristic fine structure of the expanded layers, each period of 160 A containing two light bands ($d_o$) adjacent to the dense lines, and two intermediate lines ($i_o$). × 700,000.

FIG. 16 $b$. Myelin sheath segment from transverse section of fresh rat sciatic nerve extracted with acetone at 0°C. for 12 hours prior to fixation with buffered 2 per cent osmium tetroxide solution and embedding in $n$-butyl methacrylate. Notice the condensed layer system with an average period of 70 to 80 A. × 300,000.

FIG. 16 $c$. Myelin sheath segment from the same preparation as in Fig. 16 showing the characteristic fusiform swellings ($e$) associated with the formation of ribbon-like structures ($b$) during the process of extraction. Notice the separation taking place along the dense lines, and the relationship of the condensed layer system ($p$) with the fusiform swellings. × 160,000.

PLATE 239
VOL. 3

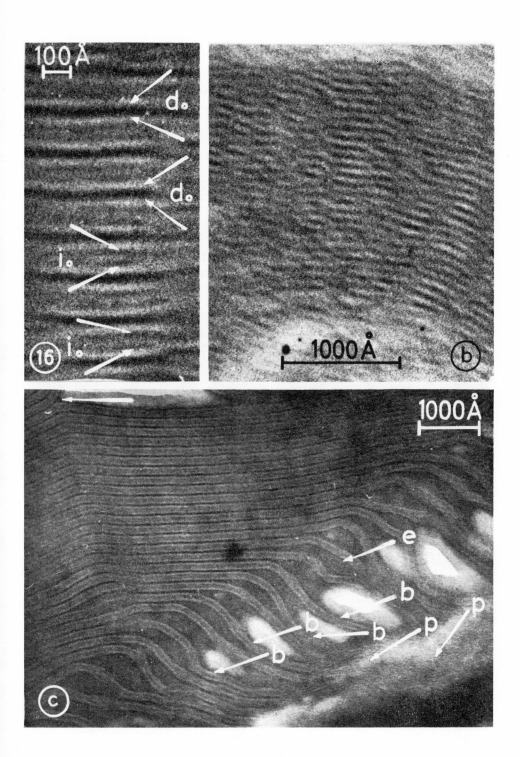

PLATE 240

FIG. 17. Myelin sheath segment from transverse section of fresh rat sciatic nerve extracted with ethanol at 0°C. for 12 hours, prior to fixation with buffered 2 per cent osmium tetroxide solution and embedding in *n*-butyl methacrylate. Notice the residual condensed layer system consisting of a series of dense osmiophilic lines alternating with light spaces with an average period of 46 A. × 660,000.

FIG. 17 *b*. Myelin sheath segment from transverse section of fresh rat sciatic nerve extracted with ethanol at 0°C. for 12 hours, prior to fixation with buffered 2 per cent osmium tetroxide solution and embedding in gelatin. Notice the transitions (arrows) between the layer system with a period of 68 A and an irregular condensed layer system of 30 to 40 A. × 335,000.

FIG. 17 *c*. Same preparation as in Fig. 17 *b* showing structural details of the larger period (67 A) obtained after alcohol extraction of the sheath. × 520,000.

FIG. 17 *d*. Same preparation as in Fig. 17 *b* showing the irregular wavy patterns of the condensed layer system with an average period of 38 A. × 520,000.

FIG. 17 *e*. Low-angle x-ray diffraction pattern of the lipide material extracted from fresh rat sciatic nerve by immersion in ethanol at 0°C. for 12 hours.

FIG. 17 *f*. Low-angle x-ray diffraction pattern of residual dried rat sciatic nerve after extraction with ethanol at 0°C. for 12 hours.

FIG. 17 *g*. Low-angle x-ray diffraction pattern of ethanol extracted nerve fixed with buffered 2 per cent osmium tetroxide and embedded in gelatin.

PLATE 240
VOL. 3

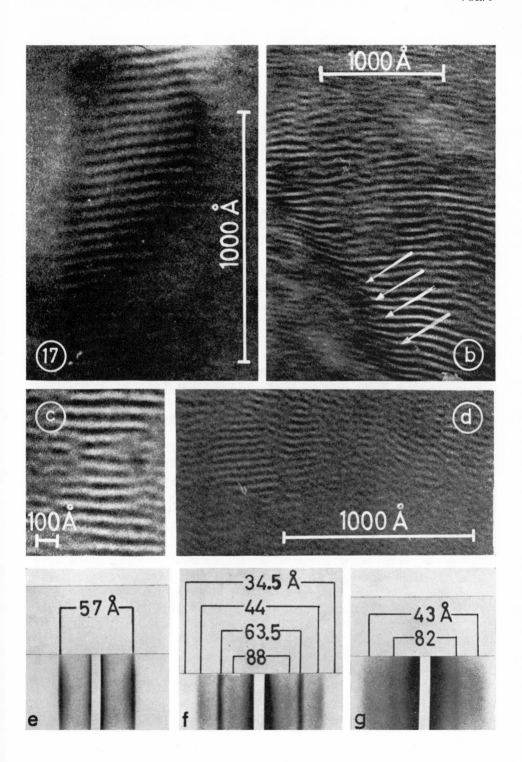

# The Ultrastructure of Cell Membranes and their Derivatives

## By J. D. ROBERTSON

*Department of Anatomy, University College, London*

ELECTRON microscopes have been available to biologists now for less than two decades but progress has been quite rapid as techniques of specimen preparation have evolved. Methods have been found for the fixation, embedding and sectioning of tissues and cells which make it possible now to visualize structures smaller than 50 Å with some assurance that reasonably accurate representations of the patterns of organization of the living structure are being seen, though there are still very severe problems of specimen preparation. Recently a chemical fixative new to electron microscopy ($KMnO_4$) (60) has been applied and an important new embedding technique utilizing epoxide resins (61) (43) found. $KMnO_4$ is particularly suited for the study of cell membranes and membranous cell organelles. Information is now accumulating rapidly about these important structures and it is the purpose of this review to attempt to relate this new information to that derived about cell membranes in other fields. Because of the rapidity with which new information is collecting, many of the electron micrographs included in this paper have not yet been published elsewhere.

The term " cell membrane " has usually been applied by the light microscopist to the thinnest layer which he could resolve at the surface of cells. In fact the thinnest layer which he could see was about $0 \cdot 18 \mu$ or 1800 Å thick. Since the electron microscope makes it possible to see structures more than 100 times thinner than this, it is not surprising that some confusion about terminology has arisen. The electron microscopist looking at the same structure which the light microscopist calls the " cell membrane " may see not one but several things. Strictly speaking if the term were purely an anatomical one, it could include all these structures. However, the term implies more than what has been seen by light microscopy. There is a definite content of physiological meaning, and in most cases electron microscopists have found it easy to eliminate some of the structures lying hundreds of ångström units away from the edge of cytoplasm. For example, in Text-fig. 1 $(a)$ a muscle fibre is shown at about sufficient magnification to give the maximum resolution offered by light microscopy. In $(b)$ the indicated segment of the cell membrane is enlarged to about the degree necessary to give $\sim 50$ Å resolution by electron microscopy. The arrows numbered " 1 " are spaced $\sim 0 \cdot 2$ microns apart and thus everything between them is included in the " cell membrane " as defined by the light microscopist.

The electron microscopist is in fact immediately faced with several problems. First of all the positioning of the arrows is arbitrary.

Reprinted by permission of the author and the Biochemical Society (London) from *Biochemical Symposium No. 16,* 3–43 (1959).

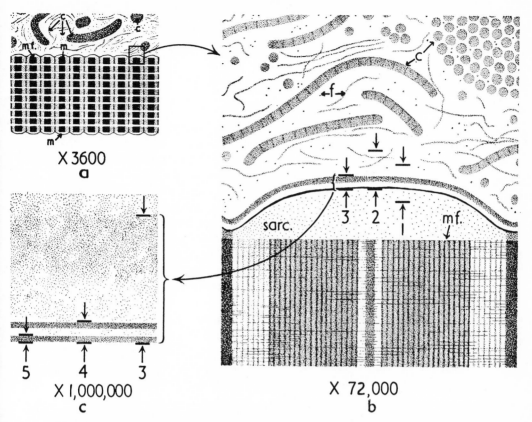

Text-fig. 1. At (*a*) a longitudinal section of a skeletal muscle fibre is shown at a magnification of about 3,600 times. The individual sarcomeres of the myofibrils (mf.) are indicated by the cross bands. The surface membrane (m) of the muscle fibre is indicated as a dense line enfolded slightly at each Z band. The connective tissue outside the muscle fibre contains quite large and much smaller bundles of collagen fibrils (*c*). The smallest collagen fibrils indicated by the dots, although they would be only barely detected by light microscopy, are inserted for convenience of description. N.B. The rectangular area included in (*a*) is enlarged to 72,000 times to indicate the details which are immediately evident in electron micrographs of muscle fibres stained with phosphotungetic acid at fairly low resolution. A single sarcomere of a myofibril (mf.) is indicated. The sarcoplasm (sarc.) is indicated by the light stipple. The connective tissue outside the muscle fibre contains numerous collagen fibrils (*c*) about 500 Å in diameter. These are aggregated in some areas into the large bundles detected by light microscopy. The area between the arrows (3) is enlarged in (*c*) to show the structures visible at a magnification of about 1,000,000 times after fixation with potassium permanganate. The surface membrane complex is included between the arrows (3) and the cell membrane between the arrows (4). The arrow (5) indicates the layer of the cell membrane closest to cytoplasm.

Nevertheless, investigators have not hesitated to place them in the position shown to the left at number " 2 " because the relatively homogeneous appearance of cytoplasm and the sharp discontinuity provided by the lower dense line made this seem reasonable. Obviously much of the material between the arrows when placed in this position could be designated connective tissue because of its content of typical collagen fibrils. A difficulty has arisen, however, in assessing the exact position of the outer arrow. Most electron microscopists would agree that it should be moved down enough to exclude the obvious connective tissue constituents (at least to position 3). But precisely where do the connective tissue elements end and where does the cell membrane begin if indeed there is any sharp boundary? As will be indicated there has been significant disagreement about this point. Most electron microscopists have avoided the question by adopting the practice of light microscopists of calling the thinnest line they could see next to cytoplasm the cell membrane. In the example cited, the outer arrow is either placed as close to the inner arrow as possible or is simply erased and forgotten. This practice has led to difficulties as resolution has improved. In Text-fig. 1 (c) the indicated area in (b) is enlarged further and details now observed at cell surfaces added. The thinnest dense layer next to cytoplasm now is a line $\sim 25\,\text{Å}$ wide. The problem of positioning the outer arrow is again raised and if the usual practice of referring to the thinnest dense line next to cytoplasm as the cell membrane is followed, the arrows would logically be placed in position 5. Indeed, as discussed further on, this has been done. Since present day electron microscopes are quite capable of resolving a unimolecular layer it was clear that eventually this approach would lead to the definition of the cell membrane as a unimolecular layer. Such a definition might, however, be a meaningless morphological abstraction, since it might very well have no physiological significance. It seems more desirable for a biologist to seek a definition of the term cell membrane which has definite operational meaning in both the morphological and physiological sense.

Physiologists, while accepting the term "cell membrane" from morphologists, have to some extent developed their own meaning for it. They have constructed a hypothetical model structure almost entirely on the basis of indirect information. This structure has come to mean a definite aggregate of molecular species which could be expected to perform the various functions required of it. It must be capable of serving as a barrier with certain definite mechanical and physical properties. This hypothetical structure is thicker than a mono-molecular layer and indeed its dimensions are well within the resolution of present day electron microscopes. It may be that there is no unique structure such as the hypothetical "physiological" cell membrane. In different cells greatly different structures might serve. Nevertheless, it is important for electron microscopists to examine carefully the surfaces of cells with this problem in mind, and if there is some structure like the postulated one at the surface of most cells to designate it by the term cell membrane.

It is one of the purposes of this paper to indicate that there is indeed such a structure present at the surfaces of a wide variety of cells and to suggest that the term cell membrane be applied to it.   Furthermore, direct structural evidence will be presented which allows certain general conclusions about the molecular organization of this structure to be drawn in purely morphological terms.   It will be shown that the correct location of the outer arrow in Text-fig. 1 is at 4.   Before proceeding further it seems well to indicate a few of the kinds of structure which have been seen by electron microscopists at the surfaces of cells and the way in which they have applied the term cell membrane to them.

I. *Structures observed at cell surfaces by electron microscopists*

Many observers have seen a single dense line at the surfaces of cells and referred to this as the cell membrane.   For example, Bennett and Porter (7) studying vertebrate skeletal muscle tissue observed a single dense line $\sim 100$ Å thick, at the surface of individual fibres and called it the "sarcolemma".   By this they apparently meant the cell membrane and they, in effect, placed the arrows at either position 4 or 5 in Text-fig. 1 c.   Subsequently Ruska (103) observed in similar material two dense lines at muscle surfaces making a structure $\sim 300$ Å wide to which he applied the term "sarcolemma".   If he meant this term to designate the cell membrane he, in effect, placed the arrows as in position 3 in Text-fig. 1 b.   Robertson (89) observing the same structure in different material used the non-committal term "surface-membrane-complex" since it was not clear at that time, which layer or layers should be called the cell membrane.   Recently Roth (100) has observed a structure at the surface of protozoon cells $\sim 100$ Å thick consisting of two thin dense lines separated by a light zone.   He referred to this whole structure as the cell membrane, in this case placing the outer arrow in Text-fig. 1 c at position 4.   Later the same author (101) observed a structure $\sim 500$ Å thick at the surface of grasshopper spermatids which consisted of an outer fenestrated layer of dense material and a pair of dense lines making a unit $\sim 100$ Å thick next to cytoplasm.   He referred to this entire structure as the cell membrane, in this case placing the arrows in Text-fig. 1 c, roughly in position 3.   Zetterqvist (124) and Sjöstrand and Zetterqvist (115) in their studies of intestinal epithelium recently demonstrated that the minute villi making up the striated border of the epithelial cells were bounded by a structure $\sim 100$ Å wide consisting of a pair of thin dense lines.   This structure was called the cell membrane.   In this instance the arrows in Text-fig. 1 c were placed at position 4.

The intercellular boundaries between parenchymal cells are particularly well suited to the study of cell membranes for here the more obvious connective tissue constituents are excluded.   The so-called "double membrane" forming the boundary between pancreatic acinar cells is typical of such structures.   Double membranes have usually been seen in the past in $OsO_4$ fixed material as structures of indefinite length bordered on both sides by cytoplasm and consisting of two dense layers ~ 100 Å thick separated by a generally structureless light interzone ~ 100–150 Å wide (Text-fig. 2 *a* & *b*). Double membranes of this type have been seen by many observers in many different tissues. They are present not only at intercellular boundaries but inside cells as well. It has been established that nuclear membranes are double membranes (48), that endoplasmic reticulum (81) (75) and the Golgi complex (16) (114) contain double membranes and that mitochondria are double membrane structures (71) (112). Axon-Schwann membranes (41) (87) (22), mesaxons (40) (41) (87) and synaptic membranes (21) (77) (88) are double membranes, though there is now some doubt that the latter are like the usual intercellular type.

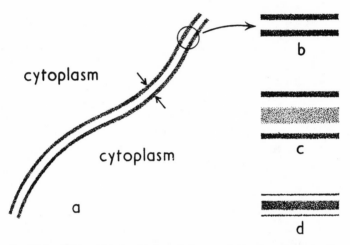

Text-fig. 2. Three different kinds of intercellular membranes are shown as they appear typically in osmic fixed tissues in thin sections. The structure between the arrows in (*a*) is commonly seen at the boundary between two cells. It measures about 250–300 Å across and consists of parallel dense lines bordering the cytoplasm of each apposed cell. The dense lines usually measure less than 100 Å across and are separated by a gap about 100–150 Å wide. In (*b*) the structure is shown at somewhat higher magnification. In (*c*) the type of synaptic membrane complex observed in motor-end plates is shown at the same magnification as (*b*). In this instance the upper dense line bounds axoplasm and the lower dense line sarcoplasm. In this membrane complex two light zones are seen with an aggregate of dense material between them. In (*d*) the type of double membrane observed by Birbeck and Mercer in developing hair cells (13) is shown. Here the dense lines bordering cytoplasm are very much thinner than those shown in (*b*). These dense lines are bordered by light zones ~ 50 Å wide and there is a very dense material between the two light zones.

A special kind of double membrane structure ~ 500–700 Å in overall thickness has been observed between axoplasm and sarcoplasm in motor-end plates (72) (86) (90) (83) (Text-fig. 2 *c*). The central region of these double membranes is occupied by dense material. This entire structure was referred to by Robertson (90) as a synaptic-membrane-complex since it was not clear exactly which layers should be referred to by the term cell membrane.

Birbeck and Mercer (13) working at higher resolution with $OsO_4$ fixed material observed an unusual kind of double membrane structure in developing hair cells (Text-fig. 2 d) resembling somewhat that in Text-fig. 2 c ; its overall width was about the same as in the usual intercellular double membrane and the central material was more dense than in motor-end plates. It appeared then that this structure was like the usual double membranes but the central zone instead of being light was filled by dense material bordered on either side by light zones $\sim 50$ Å wide and dense lines $\sim 30$ Å wide next to cytoplasm. Again it was difficult to be sure which of these layers should be called cell membranes and these authors also used the term " membrane complex " for the whole structure. At one point, however, they referred to the $\sim 30$ Å lines next to cytoplasm as " plasma membranes ", placing the arrows in Text-fig. 1 c at position 5. They commented that these layers were probably too thin to contain the lipid and protein layers usually thought to be present in cell membranes.

Sjöstrand and his collaborators have been concerned with precisely this problem (112) (114) of the location of lipid layers in double membranes. They have assumed that the entire $\sim 100$–$150$ Å wide light zone between the dense lines (Text-fig. 2 b) consists of organized lipid layers. The general problem has been reviewed by Robertson (93). Schmitt and Geshwind (110) have recently reviewed the matter very extensively from the point of view of certain physiological consequences if most of the light zones were occupied by lipid layers. In fact evidence has now been presented by Robertson (94) (98) which supports the view that most of the light zones of double membranes are not occupied by lipid. This matter will be dealt with in detail further on.

It should be clear that there has been lack of unanimity among electron microscopists concerning the nature of the various layers seen at cell surfaces and in double membranes and that no good rational basis has existed for the designation of any one layer or combination of layers by the term cell membrane. It seems appropriate now to consider the hypothetical structure of cell membranes which has been evolved indirectly by physiologists before returning to more recent findings which appear to give a conclusive answer to some of the problems raised in this section.

## II. *Physiological conceptions of cell membrane structure*

Certain conceptions of cell membrane structure have been evolved indirectly by the use of physiological, physical, chemical and biophysical techniques. The idea that lipids were important in cell membrane structure appears to have originated with Overton who in 1895 (69) introduced this conception because of the relative ease with which certain lipoid substances penetrated cells. At first there were no clear ideas as to exactly what kinds of lipid molecules might be present or how they might be arranged.

Plate I

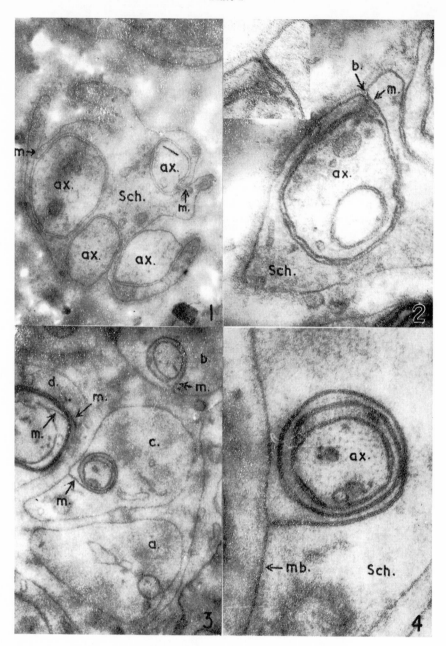

J. D. ROBERTSON. Figs. 1–4.

For legends see p. 10.

Certain deductions were made in 1917 by Langmuir (56) and others (47) about the arrangement of molecules in monomolecular films spread on water surfaces. These are of fundamental importance to modern conceptions of cell membrane structure. Langmuir advanced the idea that lipids at an air-water interface arranged themselves in a monolayer with the polar ends of the molecules in register at the water interface and the non-polar ends in register at the air interface. It was quite logical then in 1925 when Gorter and Grendel (44) found that the total lipid extracted from red cell ghosts when spread in a monolayer occupied twice the area of the membranes of the red cells for them to suggest that the lipid was arranged in the membrane as a bimolecular leaflet with the hydrophilic polar groups at the surfaces and the hydrophobic carbon chains making up the interior as shown in Text-fig. 3. The simplicity of this model, though attractive, was one of its greatest weaknesses since it would be very difficult to imagine its having a sufficient degree of specificity to account for the manifold functions attributed to cell membranes.

In the early 1930's the work of Harvey and Shapiro (50) on the surface tension of intracellular oil droplets in marine eggs and of Cole (15) on the surface tension of starfish eggs made important contributions in the evolution of ideas of cell membrane structure. It was known at this time that in the ranges of pH thought to prevail inside cells (14) most pure lipoid substances gave surface tension values in the range of 5 or more dynes per cm (2). Harvey and Shapiro (50) however,

---

Fig. 1.   Cross section of unmyelinated frog sciatic nerve fibre fixed with $OsO_4$ and embedded in araldite. One Schwann cell (Sch.) is shown with four axons (ax.) embedded in it. Two of these are sufficiently deeply embedded to have mesaxons (m.). The finer details of the double membrane structures are not shown. Mag. × 30,000.

Fig. 2.   Cross section of a portion of an unmyelinated frog sciatic fibre showing a part of the Schwann cell (Sch.) and one axon (ax.) with a mesaxon (m.). The mesaxon is enlarged to the upper left. It shows the details of membrane structure discussed in the text and included in Text-fig. 5. Note the layer of matrix material (b.) extending out from the surface of the Schwann cell and into the mesaxon gap. $KMnO_4$ fixed. Mag. × 70,000.

Fig. 3.   Section of sciatic nerve fibre of two-day-old mouse. Four developing nerve fibres are shown in different stages of the formation of myelin. At " a " a small axon is shown embedded in a relatively large Schwann cell (see Text-fig. 6). This is the earliest stage of development. At " b " a slightly later stage is shown. Note that the mesaxon (m.) connecting the axon with the surface of the Schwann cell is now elongated and wrapped about the axon in a spiral. At " c " (enlarged in Fig. 4) a still later stage is shown in which the mesaxon is more elongated and wrapped spirally around the axon in almost two complete loops. At " d " a later stage is shown in which the loops of the mesaxons have come together and formed a few compact myelin lamellae. Note the two ends of the mesaxon (m.) which are clearly visible. $KMnO_4$ fixed. Mag. × 12,000.

Fig. 4.   Enlargement of " c " in Fig. 3. The ∼75 Å membrane of the Schwann cell (mb.) shows the details indicated in Fig. 2. Two of these membranes in close apposition form the mesaxon which is wrapped spirally about the axon in almost two complete loops. The two membranes of the axon-Schwann membrane are also visible and in some regions the gap is obliterated. $KMnO_4$ fixed. Mag. × 78,000.

Text-fig. 3 appears on page 184.

Plate II

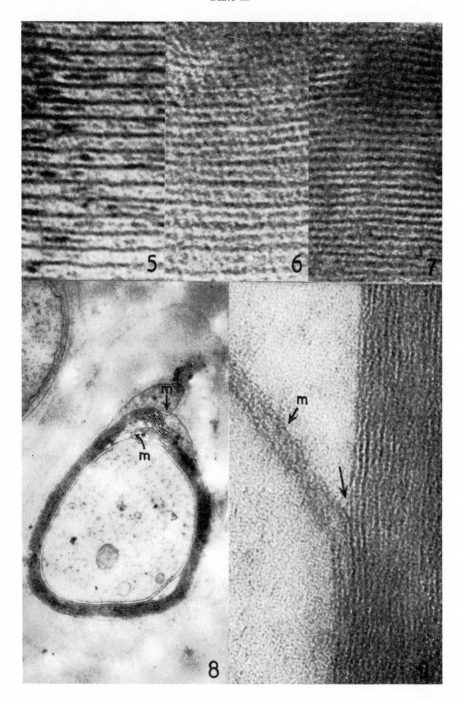

J. D. ROBERTSON.   Figs. 5–9.

For legends see p. 11.

170

calculated values of 0·2 dyne per cm for intracellular oil droplets using a centrifuge microscope technique. Cole (15) had arrived at even lower values by measuring the force required to compress whole starfish eggs and incidentally showed that the cell membrane had elastic and cohesive properties which could not be explained by the assumption that only an interfacial film was involved.

It seemed difficult to explain these low surface tension values if a purely lipid-water interface were concerned. Subsequently Danielli and Harvey (17) showed that these low values were due to the presence of some surface active agent in the cytoplasm surrounding the cells. They concluded that this was protein and that the lipid polar surfaces were covered by at least one protein monolayer. Danielli and Davson (18) then proposed a general model of cell membrane structure consisting of one or more bimolecular leaflets of lipid each polar surface of which had on it a monolayer of protein (Text-fig. 4).

These authors later elaborated this conception into the so-called pauci-molecular theory. This theory was supported by other lines of evidence. In 1936 Schmitt (107) concluded from studies of red cell membranes by polarization microscopy that they contained lipid molecules arranged in smectic mesomorphic leaflets with their carbon chains radially oriented. In 1940 Waugh and Schmitt (118) compared the light reflections of red cell ghosts with those of step films of built up monolayers of barium stearate and concluded that the red cell membrane had an upper limit of thickness of the order of 200 Å with 50–100 Å of this made up of lipoids. The remaining material was thought to represent a non-lipid component of the membrane and perhaps an adherent cytoplasmic stromal constituent.

---

Fig. 5.   Myelin fixed with OsO$_4$ and embedded in methacrylate. The major (heavy) dense lines measure about 25–30 Å in thickness. Less regular lines sometimes appearing thinner or in places thicker bisect the light zones between the major dense lines. The major dense lines are spaced at a period of ~100 Å here. Mag. ×500,000.

Fig. 6.   Myelin fixed with KMnO$_4$ for three hours and embedded in araldite. There is less difference between the major dense lines and the intraperiod lines here but the latter appear lighter. Their thickness is about the same as that of the major dense lines. The major dense lines repeat at a period ~120 Å here. Compare with Figs. 5 and 7 which are printed at about the same total magnification. Mag. ×600,000.

Fig. 7.   Myelin fixed for seven hours with KMnO$_4$. The density of the intraperiod lines is now increased to that of the major dense lines and it appears that the period is halved. Compare with Fig. 6. Mag. ×500,000.

Fig. 8.   Small myelinated fibre fixed with OsO$_4$ and embedded in araldite. Both the outer and inner mesaxons (m) are visible though there is some distortion of the myelin and the axon membrane near the inner mesaxon is partially disrupted. Mag. ×39,000.

Fig. 9.   Outer mesaxon in a fibre fixed with KMnO$_4$ and embedded in araldite. The two ~75 Å component membranes of the mesaxon (m) may be seen in some areas. Note the region (arrow) in which the upper membrane joins the myelin. The outermost major dense line is formed by contact of this membrane with the outermost myelin lamellae above the mesaxon. Mag. ×380,000.

Text-fig. 4 appears on page 184.

Plate III

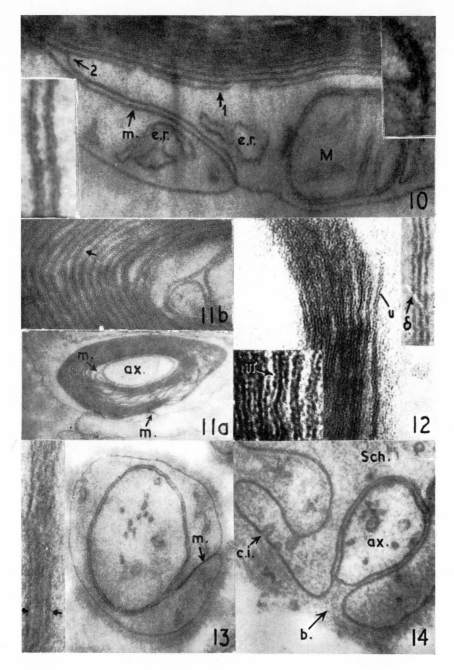

Further support for the general conception of the pauci-molecular theory was provided by certain electrical properties of cell membranes. For example, the value of the electrical impedance of cell surfaces to high frequency alternating current was high relative to that of cytoplasm, as might be expected of this kind of membrane (51). Further, measurements of the electrical capacitance of cell membranes suggested a thickness of 50–100 Å, again compatible with the theory (51).

Several other theories of cell membrane structure have been proposed. Some incorporated the above facts and some did not. These have included suggestions that the membrane was purely lipid, purely

---

Fig. 10.   Portion of the myelin sheath of a frog nerve fibre fixed in permanganate after soaking in distilled water. The outer meso (m.) is to the left. A segment of this is enlarged in the lower inset to show the internal strata of its component membranes. The outer Schwann cell surface appears below. Some components of the endoplasmic reticulum (e.r.) are present in Schwann cytoplasm. Near the meso a large mitochondrion is present to the right, and a portion of its limiting double membrane is enlarged in the upper inset to show the internal strata of its component membranes near the origin of a crista. The myelin period is increased greatly due to a splitting of the intraperiod lines. It is composed of internal compound membranes measuring about 150 Å across as discussed in the text. The outermost layer of the myelin is a simple ~75 Å membrane (arrow 1) like the component membranes of the meso. At the " arrow 2 " the junction of the cytoplasmic surface of this outermost membrane with the cytoplasmic surface of the upper of the component membranes of the meso to make the outermost internal compound membrane is visible. Mag. ×109,000. Insets, ×300,000.

Fig. 11.   (a) Shows a fairly low power view of a section of a myelinated nerve fibre soaked in distilled water before fixation with permanganate. Both the outer and the inner mesos (m.) are visible. The myelin sheath shows distinct alterations which are made clear in the enlarged portion in (b). The myelin period is increased to about 200 Å and it is clear at the unlabelled arrow that this increase is due to a splitting of the intraperiod lines. Internal compound membranes are produced by this process. Mag. (a) ×140,000,   (b) ×230,000.

Fig. 12.   A segment of nerve myelin fixed after soaking in distilled water. The outermost Schwann cell membrane (u.) is visible to the right. The next layer proceeding to the left is again a simple ~75 Å membrane. Each succeeding layer is, however, an internal compound membrane formed by two simple membranes in apposition along their cytoplasmic surfaces at the major dense line. This area is enlarged to the lower left to show the characteristics of the internal compound membrane (π). Compare this with the upper inset which shows an external compound membrane (δ) from an unmyelinated fibre treated with hypertonic Ringer solution. Note the marked increase in the density of the central dense zone in the internal compound membrane as compared with that of the external compound membrane. Mag. ×10,000. Insets, ×350,000.

Fig. 13.   Section of an unmyelinated nerve fibre treated with Ringer solution in which sufficient sucrose was dissolved to increase its molar concentration by a factor of ten, before fixation with permanganate. The gap of the mesaxon (m.) is closed throughout its length. A segment of the mesaxon is enlarged in the inset. This is an external compound membrane. At the unlabelled arrows the apposed outside dense strata of the two Schwann cell membranes making this compound membrane structure are resolved into finer layers. Each measures about 20 Å across, and consists of a pair of dense lines less than 10 Å wide, separated by a light zone of comparable width. The ~75 Å membranes in this region are separated by a gap ~15 Å wide. Mag. ×37,000. Inset, ×480,000.

Fig. 14.   Portion of an unmyelinated fibre consisting of an axon (ax.) partially surrounded by a Schwann cell (Sch.). Fixed without preliminary soaking in any solutions. Note the caveola intracellularis (c.i.) and the hazy dense material extending out from the cell surface for several hundred ångström units. This material extends at the arrow (b) into the axon-Schwann membrane gap. This is the material sometimes referred to as basement membrane material and is probably identical with the gap substance. Mag. ×75,000.

Plate IV

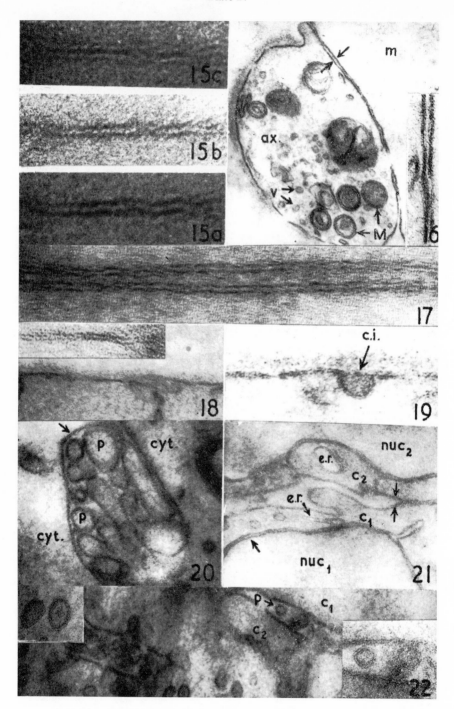

J. D. ROBERTSON.   Figs. 15–22.

For legends see p. 13.

protein with pores of molecular dimensions or a mosaic containing either purely lipid or purely protein in different areas. Mitchison (64) has proposed that red cell membranes are very thick ($\sim 0.5\mu$) and contain highly folded protein chains with the latter contributing the major part of the radially positive intrinsic birefringence. It has also appeared logical to deny the existence of any unique structure common to all cells (123). The latter point of view is perhaps more difficult to refute than any of the others, and in fact if considered in terms of the individual molecules composing the structure is almost certainly correct. For example, the experiments of Mudd and Mudd

---

Fig. 15. (a) Shows a simple $\sim 75$ Å membrane at the surface of a Schwann cell. The membrane here appears to consist of two dense lines over 30 Å thick, separated by a narrow light zone. This micrograph is under focus. (b) The same structure seen closer to exact focus. The dense lines appear thinner and the overall structure more narrow. (c) The same structure over-focused. In this false image a single dense line is seen bounded by two light zones and two dense lines. Mag. × 500,000.

Fig. 16. A portion of the surface of a muscle fibre (m) in a frog neuromuscular spindle is shown. A small nerve ending consisting of a naked axon (ax.) is shown to the left. The axoplasm (ax.) contains vesicular appearing structures (v) and mitochondria (M). The synaptic membrane between the aligned unlabelled arrows is enlarged in the inset to show its internal structure. It measures about 250 Å across and consists of two simple membranes ($\sim 75$ Å) separated by a gap of about 100 Å width. Mag. × 45,000. Inset, × 130,000.

Fig. 17. High magnification micrograph of a segment of the double membrane between two apposed smooth muscle cells in mouse intestine. Note the internal strata of each membrane and the 100 Å gap between the two cell membranes. Mag. × 400,000.

Fig. 18. Surface of a frog muscle fibre. A portion of the cell membrane is enlarged in the inset to show the strata of the $\sim 75$ Å unit membrane. Mag. × 70,000. Inset, × 255,000.

Fig. 19. Portion of the surface of a frog muscle fibre, showing a caveola intracellularis (c.i.). The strata of the $\sim 75$ Å cell membrane are visible. Mag. × 175,000.

Fig. 20. Section of the boundary region between two epithelial cells (cyt.) in frog skin. Numerous finger-like processes (p) of one or perhaps both of the cells lie between them. The internal structure is seen clearly in the membrane bounding the cytoplasm above (arrow) and bounding the processes. KMnO$_4$ fixed. Mag. × 83,000.

Fig. 21. Portion of two glandular epithelial cells in frog pancreas. Portions of two cells ($c_1$ and $c_2$) are shown with the intercellular double membrane (arrows). The double membrane bounding the nucleus (nuc$_1$) of the lower cell shows the internal strata of its component $\sim 75$ Å membranes. Note the extension of the outer membrane of this double membrane into the cytoplasm of cell no. 1. This extension appears much like the double membranes of the endoplasmic reticulum (e.r.) seen in the cytoplasm of both cells. This preparation was soaked in concentrated (6X normal) Ringer solution before fixation in KMnO$_4$. As a result of this the gap of the intercellular double membrane to the right of the unlabelled arrows is closed. Mag. × 76,000.

Fig. 22. This section shows portions of two frog pancreatic aciner cells ($c_1$ and $c_2$). The two cell membranes to the upper right are separated by several hundred ångström units and the gap here is occupied by small finger-like processes (p) of one or both of the cells. This area is enlarged in the lower inset to show the strata of each cell membrane and of the membrane bounding the gap processes. To the left a membrane-bounded area is seen from which finger-like extensions resembling caveolae intracellularis run into the cytoplasm. Numerous membrane bounded bodies are located within this area. Within the cytoplasm of " $c_2$ " several components of the endoplasmic reticulum bounded by unit membranes are seen. One of these is enlarged to the left. Mag. × 67,000. Insets, × 120,000,

(67) in which it was shown that erythrocytes are preferentially wetted by oil and leukocytes by water show that the molecular constituents at the surface of these two types of cells differ. Furthermore, there is a wealth of immunochemical data supporting this conception. This does not mean, however, that no general structural pattern exists. Indeed, it will be shown here that there is a certain pattern common to many cells. It will be seen that many different kinds of cells have at their surfaces a membrane < 100 Å across appearing as two dense lines separated by a light zone. There are reasons to believe that this pattern is of general significance and, at least in the specific case of Schwann cells, that it contains a single bimolecular leaflet of lipid bordered by monolayers of non-lipid material (probably protein and perhaps polysaccharide).

It is now appropriate to examine the evidence on which these statements are based. It happens that much of the evidence for the ideas about cell membrane structure developed in this paper are derived from studies of the ultrastructure of nerve fibres. In order to make this clear it is necessary to deal now with certain general features of nerve fibre structure.

## III. *Peripheral nerve ultrastructure*

### (1) Unmyelinated nerve fibres

It is now known that both unmyelinated and myelinated vertebrate peripheral nerve fibres have essentially the same structural pattern—one being derived by an elaboration of the other. Gasser (39) (40) showed that adult unmyelinated fibres are constructed in the way shown in Text-fig. 5. (The details of membrane structure are added from the author's work (94) (98)). This diagram shows four commonly observed relationships of axons and Schwann cells in adult unmyelinated fibres (Fig. 1, Plate I). In Text-fig. 5 axon (*a*) is merely in apposition with the Schwann cell, the two apposed cell membranes making a double membrane referred to as the axon-Schwann membrane. A segment of this double membrane is enlarged to show its components. It consists of two cell membranes separated by a gap ∼ 150 Å across. Each of the two cell membranes measures ∼ 75 Å across and consists of two dense lines < 25 Å wide, separated by a light interzone (Figs. 2 & 15). Axons (*b*) and (*c*) are almost completely embedded in the Schwann cell. Axon (*d*) is completely submerged and the two enveloping lips of the Schwann cell extending around it are in apposition producing a double membrane connecting the axon with the outside This is referred to as a mesaxon or " meso "*.

* This term was suggested to the author by Prof. Réné Couteaux as a more general term than " mesaxon " which might replace the rather awkward term " surface-connecting-membrane " (87). A " meso " then is a double membrane leading from some included structure to the outside, " mesaxon " being a special kind of " meso " in which the included structure is an axon. The term " meso " might also be used for cytoplasmic structures connected to the outside by a double membrane.

## (2) Myelinated nerve fibres

Fernandez-Moran (27) (28) and Sjostrand (111) were the first to present high resolution micrographs of myelinated nerve fibres. They showed that myelin in sections after $OsO_4$ fixation consisted of dense

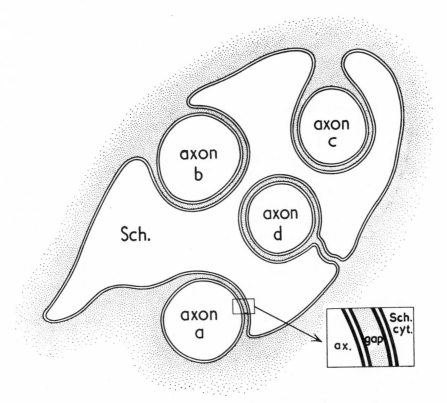

Text-fig. 5.   Diagram of an unmyelinated nerve fibre.   A single Schwann cell (Sch.) is shown with four associated axons.   Axon (a) is merely in apposition with the Schwann cell and axon (b) is partially embedded in it.   Axon (c) is more deeply embedded and axon (d) is completely surrounded.   The two overlapping lips of the Schwann cell extending around axon (d) come together to make a double membrane leading to the outside referred to as a " mesaxon " or by the more general term " meso ".   The stratification of the membrane of the axons and the Schwann cell are indicated in the figure.   A portion of one axon-Schwann membrane is enlarged to the lower right.   The entire Schwann cell is surrounded by a matrix material indicated by the stippling.   This material extends into the gaps of the double membrane and is sometimes aggregated in a layer near the external surface of the Schwann cell as shown to the right.   When this material is aggregated in this fashion, it is referred to as " basement membrane ".

lines $\sim 25$ Å thick repeating radially at a period of $\sim 120$ Å.   Bisecting each light zone between the dense lines there was seen an irregular less dense line (the intraperiod line).   These layers are shown after $OsO_4$ fixation in Fig. 5.   Sometimes the intraperiod line is absent altogether (87).   When present, it is usually a broken line much thinner than the major dense line though sometimes it is thickened into placques or globules.    After KMnO$_4$ fixation (Fig. 6) essentially the same pattern of layers is seen but the intraperiod line is consistently present and much more regular and complete.    It is of about the same thickness as the major dense line but its density after 2–3 hours fixation is lower.    After longer fixation (7–12 hrs.) its density increases so that it becomes indistinguishable from the major dense line (Fig. 7) (29) (94) giving an apparent halving of the period.

In order to understand the significance of these layers it is necessary to consider the embryogenesis of myelin.    At an early stage of development myelinating fibres are constructed like unmyelinated fibres (Text-fig. 6 $a$ and Fig. 3 (a.)).    At a later stage the mesaxon, as shown initially by Geren (41) is elongated and extended around the axon in a simple spiral (Fig. 3 (b. & c.), Fig. 4 and Text-fig. 6 $b$).    Compact myelin is formed as these mesaxon loops elongate and come together along their cytoplasmic surfaces as in Text-fig. 6 $c$ (Fig. 8).    The major dense lines are formed by contact of the inner (cytoplasmic) surfaces of the ~75 Å Schwann surface membranes in the mesaxon and the intraperiod lines by contact of the two outside surfaces.    The two ~75 Å units are usually separated by a gap ~100–150 Å wide between these outside surfaces in the mesaxons of adult fibres.    The gap is either not visible in compact myelin (Fig. 9) or reduced to < 15 Å in width.    The light zones of myelin which probably contain lipid, are the light zones of the ~75 Å Schwann surface membrane (94) (98).

This last point was, until recently, not so obvious.    As indicated above the layers forming the intraperiod lines of myelin are not nearly so constantly fixed by OsO$_4$ as those making the major dense lines.

---

Fig. 23.    This section shows a portion of the outer boundary of a Schwann cell in a frog myelinated nerve fibre.    Note the relationship of the caveola intracellularis (c.i.) to the endoplasmic reticulum (e.r.).    The strata of the Schwann cell membrane may be seen.    Mag. × 104,000.

Fig. 24.    Section of a portion of a connective tissue cell in a frog nerve fibre.    A mitochondrion (M) is identifiable below.    Above this there is a structure (?) bounded by a double membrane superficially resembling a mitochondrion but in which no cristae may be seen.    At the unlabelled arrow the internal strata of the membranes of the structure and of the external membrane of the connective tissue cell may be seen (inset).    Above this double membrane bounded structure, there is another structure bounded by a single membrane.    The latter may represent a microbody.    Mag. × 60,000.    Inset, × 140,000.

Fig. 25.    Section of a portion of the wall of a capillary in a frog nerve fibre.    An endothelial cell nucleus (nuc.) occupies the centre of the field.    The capillary lumen is to the right (arrow l.).    A pericyte (per.) appears to the upper left.    The capillary endothelial cells are characterized by the large numbers of caveoli on their external and internal surfaces and by the circular and oval profiles seen in their cytoplasm.    The endothelium is penetrated by several double membranes which may represent intercellular boundaries.    Caveolae originate from the gaps of these double membranes as well as from the free surfaces of the endothelial cells as shown in the inset enlargements.    Mag. × 12,000.    Insets, × 20,000.

Fig. 26.    Section of a portion of the endothelium of a small frog capillary.    The capillary lumen (l.) lies above the double membrane bounding two endothelial cells (end.).    Note the pericyte (per.) processes below.    One caveolus (c.) appears above and several round or oval profiles are visible within the endothelial cells, Mag. × 50,000,

Plate V

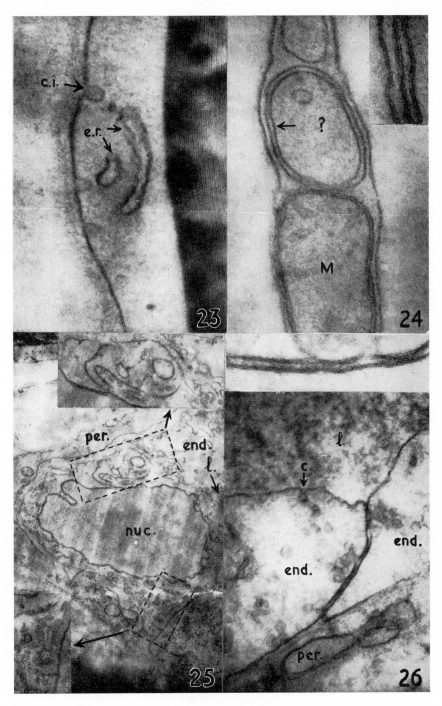

J. D. ROBERTSON.   Figs. 23–26.

For legends see p. 16.

Plate VI

J. D. ROBERTSON. Figs. 27–33.

For legends see p. 17.

Fig. 27 *a*.  Section of the striated border of young mouse intestinal epithelial cells. The microvilli making up the striated border are finger-like extensions of the surface of the epithelial cells.  Note the great concentration of endoplasmic reticulum in the epithelial cell cytoplasm.  There is a zone of cytoplasm of about the same width as the striated border aligned immediately beneath it which is almost completely of endoplasmic reticulum.  One of the microvilli is enlarged in the inset below.  The cell membrane here measures about 100 Å in thickness and shows the strata which are usually observed in cell membranes after permanganate fixation.  However, in this instance the internal stratum is very much more dense and sharp than the external stratum.  Mag. × 16,000.  Inset, × 67,000.

Fig. 27 *b*.  This shows the intercellular boundary between two intestinal epithelial cells like that shown in Fig. 27 *a*.  Here the strata of the ~ 75 Å cell membranes are visible and appear the same as those usually seen elsewhere.  Two small microvilli are present in this region in the gap between the two cell membranes. Each microvillus is itself bounded by a simple membrane.  Mag. × 90,000.

Fig. 28.  A portion of the brush border of a renal epithelial cell in young mouse kidney It may be seen here that the brush border consists of microvilli somewhat similar to those making up the striated border of intestinal epithelium.  However, in this instance the microvilli are larger and much longer.  In the lower part of the section microvilli are seen which are cut transversely, in contrast to the longitudinally cut ones in the central part of the section.  Numerous mitochondria and components of the endoplasmic reticulum are seen in the epithelial cells. In the inset to the lower left a region showing transected microvilli is enlarged. Here the characteristics of the cell membrane may be seen.  The usual ~ 75 Å structure consisting of a pair of dense lines bordering a light zone is visible. The dense layer next to cytoplasm appears slightly more dense than the outer layer and is like the structure seen at the striated border in the intestine.  In the lower inset to the right the intercellular boundary between two epithelial cells is shown.  The usual stratification is seen in the  ~ 75  Å cell membranes. Mag. × 78,500.  Insets, × 110,000.

Fig. 29.  Section of young mouse liver showing portions of two glandular cells, and the intercellular boundary, to the lower left.  A segment of this is enlarged in the inset to the left.  Each cell membrane shows the usual stratification.  The liver cells show components of the endoplasmic reticulum and mitochondria.  Note the mitochondrion to the lower right in which a crista extends all the way across and thus divides the central membrane bounded material into two portions. Mag. × 20,000.  Inset, × 251,000.

Fig. 30.  Section of portion of eosinophil in young mouse intestine.  Note the large eosinophilic granules consisting of a granular material bounded by a  ~ 75 Å membrane bisected by a central dense band.  A segment of the surface membrane of the eosinophil is enlarged to the upper left.  It has the usual strata characteristics of cell membranes and measures about ~ 75 Å across.  Mag. × 48,000. Inset, × 115,000.

Fig. 31.  Portion of the surface membrane of a frog red blood cell showing the usual strata of the ~ 75 Å cell membrane.  Mag. × 160,000.

Fig. 32.  Portion of a motor nerve ending on frog skeletal muscle. Sarcoplasm (sarc.) lies to the right.  It contains components of the endoplasmic reticulum (e.r.) and mitochondria (M).  A terminal axon (ax.) lies to the left; this is surrounded by a layer of Schwann cytoplasm (Sch.) everywhere except in the region in which it is in direct relationship to the muscle fibre.  Here Schwann cytoplasm is absent and the axon and muscle membranes are in apposition with a separation of about 400–500 Å.  Each membrane measures about 75 Å across and so the synaptic membrane complex measures about 550–650 Å across.  The gap between the membranes sometimes contains cytoplasmic processes (p.) of unknown origin. Junctional folds (j.f.) of the muscle surface occur less frequently than in lizard nerve endings and are not well shown in transverse sections such as this.  The terminal axoplasm contains numerous vesicular appearing bodies measuring 300–500 Å in diameter and bounded by a  ~ 75 Å membrane.  The junctional fold below is enlarged in the inset to show the membrane relationships. Mag. × 19,000.  Inset, × 66,500.

Fig. 33.  Enlargement of one of the mitochondria such as that shown in Fig. 29, in which the central membrane bounded material is divided into two divisions. It is as if a crista extended all the way across the mitochondrion.  Mag. × 59,000.

When the $\sim 75$ Å units making the Schwann surface membrane are not in contact along their outside surfaces, $OsO_4$ fixation usually reveals only the dense layer next to cytoplasm. $KMnO_4$ on the other hand, consistently fixes both layers regardless of whether they are in contact.

### (3) Certain physiological implications

This deficiency of $OsO_4$ fixation was partly responsible for a long standing controversy of physiological significance (110) which has only recently been resolved (98). It was apparent to some that the lipid layers in double membranes probably would appear partially as light zones. This was based on the assumption that relatively poorly reactive lipid carbon chains are responsible for the light zones in myelin (111). Sjöstrand and his collaborators (112) (114) assumed that the major portion of the light zones of intercellular and other double membranes were representative of compact lipid layers. Others (75) (104) assumed that all of the observed light zone between the dense lines represented a space between two cell membranes. Neither viewpoint was entirely correct.

Recently Frankenhaeuser and Hodgkin (35) and Ritchie and Straub (85) have presented electrophysiological evidence which could best be interpreted by assuming that most of the light zones of certain double membranes (i.e. the mesaxons of unmyelinated nerve fibres) were available as pathways for ionic current flow. If Sjöstrand's assumption were correct there might not be enough unbound water in the light zones for this to be true. Partly on this basis these physiological conceptions have been questioned in a recent review (110).

---

Fig. 34.  Enlargement of a mitochondrion in a frog muscle fibre. The details of the unit membrane structure do not show clearly here but the origin of one of the cristae by an inward folding of the inner membrane may be seen clearly at the arrow. Mag. $\times 115,000$.

Fig. 35.  Portion of the Schwann cell surrounding an axon in a frog nerve fibre after soaking in distilled water before fixation. The section is near a node of Ranvier and only a few myelin lamellae are present. One internal compound membrane may be seen at the arrow near the mesaxon (m.). Note the row of vesicles (v.) or tubules which are in contact with one another. The membranes bounding these structures retain their individuality despite their intimate contact with one another. Mag. $\times 104,000$.

Fig. 36.  Mitochondrion from frog muscle showing internal cristae obliquely sectioned. A portion of the double membrane bounding the mitochondrion is enlarged above to show the strata of the two 75 Å membranes of which it is composed. The gaps of mitochondrial double membranes usually measure about 100 Å or less across. Mag. $\times 52,000$. Inset, $\times 154,000$.

Fig. 37.  Section of a terminal axon in a frog neuromuscular spindle. The axon is completely devoid of a Schwann cell covering in this region and is bounded by the usual $\sim 75$ Å membrane. It is embedded in a granular matrix material and the axoplasm contains numerous vesicular appearing bodies resembling those seen in motor endings. Note the concentrically lamellated body present in the axoplasm. This consists of concentric double membranes and is referred to by the term " target body ". Mag. $\times 85,000$.

Plate VII

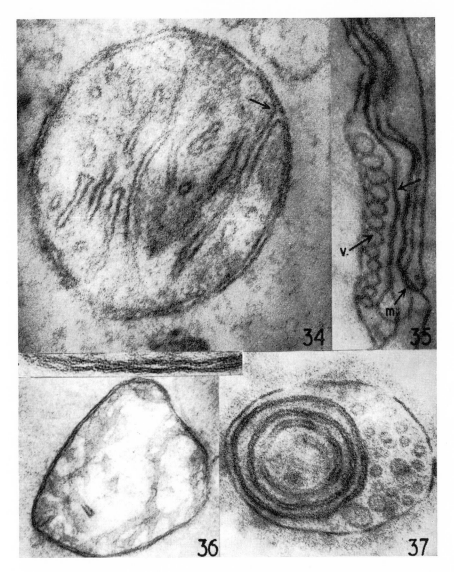

J. D. ROBERTSON.   Figs. 34–37.

For legends see p. 18.

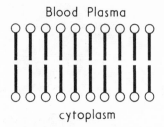

Blood Plasma

cytoplasm

Text-fig. 3. Hypothetical structure of the red cell membrane advanced by Gorter and Grendel (44). The cytoplasm is here bounded by a single bimolecular leaflet of lipid. The polar ends of the lipid molecules are indicated by light circles and the non-polar carbon chains by dense bars.

# EXTERIOR

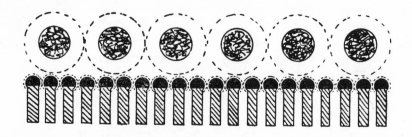

# LIPOID

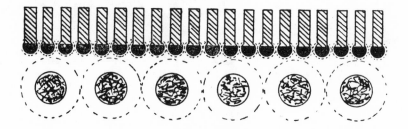

# INTERIOR

Text-fig. 4. This diagram taken directly from Danielli and Davson (19) illustrates the pauci-molecular theory of cell membrane structure. A layer of lipid of unknown thickness bounded externally by monolayers of phospholipid molecules was proposed. The polar ends of the phospholipid molecules indicated by the dark semi-circles in the diagram, were thought to be associated closely with monolayers of a globular protein.

**184**

It is now clear that only a relatively small fraction of the light zones of double membranes is occupied by the lipid components of the individual membranes. Most of the light zone is actually a highly hydrated gap which should be available for ionic current flow. In order to make these points clear, it is necessary to consider the molecular structure of myelin in more detail, and take into account some experimentally induced alterations in the structure of nerve fibres.

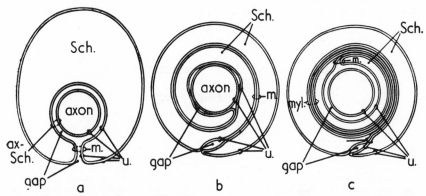

Text-fig. 6. Three stages in the development of nerve myelin are indicated. The earliest recognized stage is shown in (a). Here a single axon is embedded in a Schwann cell (Sch.). The enveloping lips of the Schwann cell come together around the axon to form a double membrane known as the mesaxon (m.). There is usually a small gap between the Schwann cell membranes (u.) forming the mesaxon, which is continuous with the gap between the axon and the Schwann cell membranes making up the axon-Schwann membrane (ax-Sch.). At a later stage of myelination represented by (b) the mesaxon is elongated in a spiral around the axon and its central gap is largely obliterated. The gap of the axon-Schwann membrane is also partially obliterated. At a later stage (c) the mesaxon is elongated further and the cytoplasmic surfaces of the spiral mesaxon loops come together to form the major dense lines of compact myelin (myl.).

## IV. *Molecular structure of myelin*

The earliest histological studies of nerve myelin led to the suggestion that some lipid constituent was present and later a protein, " neuro-keratin " was found (25) (57). As mentioned above it was well known that lipid molecules tend to aggregate at air-water interfaces with their polar hydrophilic surfaces lined up at the water interface and their hydrophobic hydrocarbon chains arrayed laterally at the air surface (56) (47). It soon became evident from X-ray diffraction studies that lipid molecules dispersed in water tend to aggregate as two such molecular monolayers with their hydrocarbon chains interlocked making a bimolecular leaflet like that in Text-fig. 3. At higher concentrations such bimolecular leaflets tend to line up with one another along their polar surfaces making a multilayered aggregate in the so-called smectic state giving regular X-ray diffraction patterns (9) (10) (109). The thickness of the water layers between the leaflets may exceed that of the leaflets themselves when the lipid is in relatively low concentration (108).

Lipid water model systems also display the peculiar cylindrical bodies known as myelin forms. If, for example, a mixture of lecithin and water is placed under a light microscope, long slender worms about $1-2\mu$ in diameter and of indefinite length are seen growing out of the lipid aggregates into the water. These are birefringent. Their intrinsic double refraction is negative with respect to the long axis of the worms (37). This suggests that they contain bimolecular leaflets running parallel to their long axis. If nerve myelin is damaged the same kind of worms are seen growing out of its surface in aqueous media, suggesting an essentially similar molecular structure.

## MYELIN   SHEATH   STRUCTURES
### (RADIAL   DIRECTION)

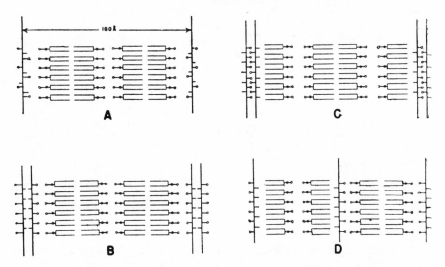

Text-fig. 7.   Diagram taken from Schmitt, Bear & Palmer (109) showing four arrangements of bimolecular leaflets of lipid and monolayers of protein which could satisfy the X-ray diffraction data available on myelin in 1941. In A two bimolecular leaflets of lipid are shown bounded by monolayers of protein making a structure about 180 Å across repeating radially in myelin. In B two extra monolayers of protein are inserted. In C a different arrangement of both lipid and protein layers is shown and in D still another possible arrangement is indicated. Other possibilities existed but these four were chosen at that time for illustration.

The polarization optical studies of W. J. Schmidt on nerve myelin (105) led him to postulate that it is composed of layers of radially oriented lipid molecules and tangentially oriented protein molecules, though it was possible only to speculate about the exact constitution of the layers. In view of what was known about lipids in aqueous systems it might have been reasonable to deduce that the lipid molecules were present in bimolecular leaflets and the protein molecules disposed along the hydrophilic surfaces of the leaflets with their axes perpendicular to the radial axis of the nerve fibre, though Schmidt conceived of more bulky layers than this.

The X-ray diffraction studies of Schmitt, Bear and Clark (106) provided the first evidence for this thesis, since a radial repeating unit ~170–185 Å across was detected. Subsequently studies by Bear, Palmer and Schmitt (5) (109) showed that extracted mixed peripheral nerve lipids formed systems of bimolecular leaflets with an average spacing ~60–70 Å and the hypothetical molecular models of the repeating unit shown in Text-fig. 7 were proposed (5).

Later studies by Elkes and Finean (23) and Finean (30) have focused attention on the type of model shown in Text-fig. 8. This is a variant of models A and B in Text-fig. 7. Finean inserted an extra layer of material in the middle of the repeating unit because of work (23) (31) which indicated that under certain conditions the myelin period shows a strong tendency towards halving. This could best be explained if there were present at the mid-position some material having an X-ray scattering power similar to that bounding the unit cell but differing in some way. He called this material the " difference factor ". Model D in Text-fig. 7 with certain alterations conceivably could satisfy Finean's requirements for the " difference factor ". However, this model like model C in essence proposes that the side chains of protein molecules can form an association with the non-polar ends of lipid molecules which is stronger than or as strong as that formed by the non-polar ends of two lipid molecules in apposition. Since so many protein side chains have polar groups this seems unlikely. Furthermore, other objections to these models exist as will be brought out below. However, Finean's model fits the electron microscope observations better than any of the others.

If Finean's conceptions of the molecular structure of myelin are to be extrapolated to the Schwann cell surface it is of primary and crucial importance to decide exactly which of the layers seen in the electron micrographs of sections of myelin correspond to the ~170–185 Å X-ray repeating unit. Taking into consideration the formation of myelin, it is reasonable to suppose that the two ~75 Å unit membranes united in each myelin lamella or mesaxon make this repeating unit. The fact that this unit when observed alone in the mesaxon of developing fibres measures ~150 Å and when in compact myelin ~120 Å is easy to reconcile with the ~170–185 Å unit in fresh myelin since the structure seen by electron microscopy is dehydrated and somewhat shrunken by the preparatory procedures.

Finean (31) has obtained quantitative information about the degree of shrinkage involved in the preparation of myelin. He obtained diffraction patterns from one of Sjöstrand's $OsO_4$ fixed methacrylate embedded nerve fibres, which indicated a fundamental spacing of 148 Å, a reduction of ~25–30 Å from the fresh state. The same material

when sectioned and examined in the electron microscope shows a
spacing of ~ 120 Å.   This further reduction is easily accounted for
by shrinkage induced by heating in the electron beam.     This work
has been repeated and extended recently by Fernandez-Moran and
Finean (29).   It appears then that it is reasonable to consider the

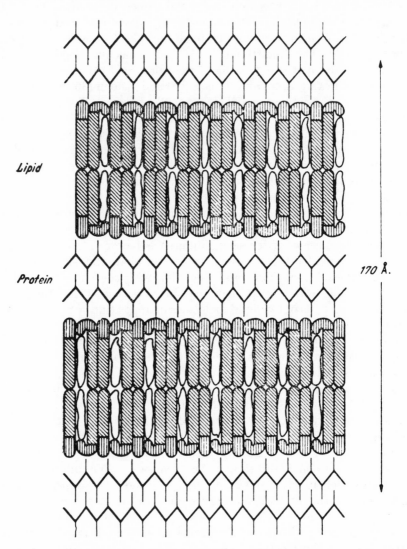

Text-fig. 8.   Diagram taken from Finean (34) indicating his conception of the arrangements of the lipid bimolecular leaflets and the protein monolayers in the radially
repeating unit of myelin.   The non-polar portions of the lipid molecules are
indicated by diagonal lines, and the polar portions by vertical lines.   Cholesterol
molecules are inserted between every other lipid molecule without cross-hatching.
The backbone chains of the protein monolayers are indicated by the zig-zag lines
and the side-chains by the related vertical lines.   According to this model each
bimolecular leaflet of lipid is bounded on its polar surface by a monolayer of
protein.

~ 120 Å repeating lamellae observed in myelin by electron microscopy to represent the repeating structure detected by X-ray diffraction (93).

The first observation by electron microscopy of radially repeating layers in myelin was made by Fernandez-Moran (27) using $OsO_4$ fixed frozen dried nerve fibres. Dense lines were seen repeating at a period of ~ 70–80 Å. It is now clear either that both the major dense lines and the intraperiod lines appeared the same in these early preparations or that the intraperiod lines were not seen and the lamellae were greatly compressed in sectioning. The former is more probable. Fernandez-Moran (28) and Fernandez-Moran and Finean (29) have now reinvestigated this matter and found that the true period in $OsO_4$ fixed frozen dried material is about the same as that found in methacrylate embedded material.

After fixation with $KMnO_4$ heavy dense layers are seen again repeating radially at a period of ~ 120 Å but the intraperiod lines are much more prominent as discussed above. Examination of the junctions of the mesaxons with compact myelin in Figs. 8 and 9 (Plate II) and in Text-fig. 6 c make it clear that the major dense lines and intraperiod lines in both $OsO_4$ fixed and $KMnO_4$ fixed myelin represent precisely the same layers.

An interesting corollary of this conclusion is that the densities observed in electron micrographs of myelin are probably not entirely due to " staining " of the underlying structure since the electron scattering power of Os and Mn, considering their atomic numbers, should be quite different. It is probable that an important part of the observed densities are due to the underlying structure, though in evaluating this statement the exact state of focus of the micrographs must be considered (99).

It is possible on the basis of all the above information to make certain definite and important deductions about the molecular structure of Schwann cell membranes. It has been shown that each of the repeating units seen by electron microscopy is in fact simply two Schwann cell membranes in contact along their outside surfaces. It is therefore possible to extrapolate what is known about the molecular structure of myelin directly to Schwann cell membranes. In Text-fig. 9 a a mesaxon and a few layers of myelin are shown with the molecular structure of each layer indicated to the right (b) simply by superposition of a drawing derived from that of Finean (33) shown in Text-fig. 8. If Finean's model is correct then it follows from the structural arrangement that the Schwann cell membrane, as indicated in the figure, consists of a single bimolecular leaflet of mixed lipids the hydrophilic surfaces of which are covered by monolayers of non-lipid material. The latter may be protein on the cytoplasmic side and possibly polysaccharide, glycoprotein or protein on the outside.

Other possible models exist as indicated in Text-fig. 7. Finean's model is related to those in Text-fig. 7 A and B. Those in Text-fig. 7 C and D can be eliminated by the electron microscopical evidence. Model D is not possible partly because the single monolayer of protein at the intraperiod position could not be split symmetrically. This condition must be met because each half of the periodic unit is, after all, the same membrane. Model C could be split symmetrically but the resulting membranes would have hydrophobic outer surfaces. In fact

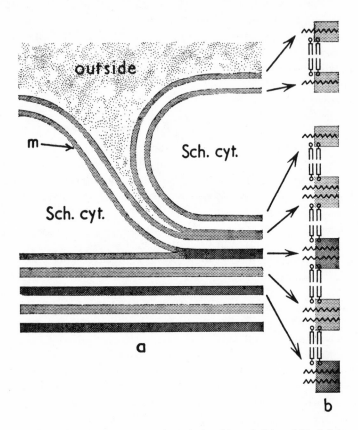

Text-fig. 9. This diagram illustrates the relationships of the enfolded Schwann cell membrane in a mesaxon (or meso) of an adult myelinated fibre. The two cell membranes come together along their outside surfaces to form the outermost myelin lamella. The inside surfaces of the mesaxon loops are in apposition at the major dense lines in compact myelin. Three complete repeating units of myelin are indicated in (a). The molecular structure of the outer two repeating lamellae is indicated in (b). At the top the molecular structure of the Schwann cell membrane is indicated. The molecular diagrams are based on Finean's model shown in Text-fig. 8. The stippling superimposed on the molecular model indicates the densities which are observed after permanganate fixation.

these surfaces are hydrophilic as will be made clear by the effects of hypotonic solutions on myelin considered below. Two additional monolayers of protein could be added to this model to circumvent this objection but the inverted arrangement of the lipid molecules within each membrane though distinctly possible, appears improbable. It thus seems most likely that the molecular structure given in Text-fig. 9 *b* is correct.

The molecular model of Schwann cell membrane structure deduced by the above reasoning is very much like the one proposed by Danielli and Davson on different grounds (18) (19) (Text-fig. 4). It differs however, in two ways. First the Danielli–Davson model requires that both the non-lipid layers be protein. The present model requires that only one of these layers be protein. The other may be a different kind of material, perhaps polysaccharide. Secondly, the Danielli–Davson model did not infer any particular number of lipid layers in the membrane. The present model limits the number of lipid layers to a single bimolecular leaflet. Since some of the conclusions reached above are based on experiments in which alterations were brought about in myelin these will now be presented briefly.

### V. *Alterations in nerve fibres brought about by hypotonic and hypertonic solutions*

It has recently been found by Finean and Millington (34) using X-ray diffraction techniques that if nerve fibres are soaked in hypotonic solutions the myelin period increases from ~170–190 Å to ~270 Å and that this change is reversible. It had previously been found by Finean (32), again using X-ray techniques, that myelin tends to break up into ~150 Å layers after freezing and thawing. It might have been deduced that the increase in the period after soaking in hypotonic solutions was due to some such alteration as this, though no deductions about the exact nature of the ~150 Å layers could have been made.

This problem has now been investigated by electron microscopy, and it has been found that after soaking in hypotonic solutions, myelin does indeed break up into layers ~150 Å across (Figs. 10–12, Plate III). Each of these layers consists of two Schwann cell membranes in apposition along their inside (cytoplasmic) surfaces. They appear as a central dense line ~40 Å thick bordered on each side by a light zone ~35 Å wide and dense lines ~20 Å wide. These ~150 Å membranous structures are referred to as " internal compound membranes ". Their central dense line is the major dense line of compact myelin. Evidence for this interpretation is contained in Figs. 10–12. In Fig. 10 the outer mesaxon and Schwann cell surface membranes of a myelinated fibre are shown with the outer few myelin layers. The latter are dissociated by the water treatment into internal compound membranes and the gap of the mesaxon is opened except at the outer end. Note that the outermost myelin layer proceeding inward from the Schwann cell surface is a simple ~75 Å membrane while the succeeding layers are the thicker internal compound membranes. This outermost ~75 Å membrane and the upper ~75 Å membrane of the mesaxon join at the unlabelled arrow along their cytoplasmic surfaces to make the outermost internal compound membrane (see

Text-fig. 10).   The gap of the mesaxon is open, through the spiral, deep
into the myelin.   The dense layers bordering the internal compound
membranes then represent the outside surfaces of the Schwann cell
surface membrane, which in intact myelin are in contact along the
intraperiod line.

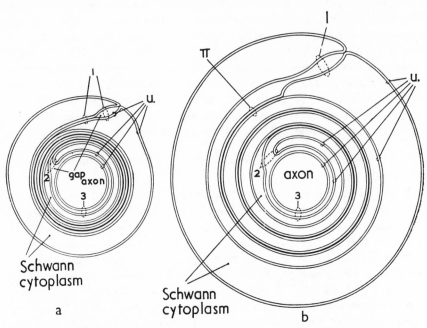

Text-fig. 10.   These two diagrams illustrate the effects on the structure of the myelin
     sheath of soaking fibres in hypotonic solutions ;  (a) is comparable to (c) in
     Text-fig. 6.   The outer and inner mesos (mesaxons) are shown at 1 and 2.   The
     axon-Schwann membrane is shown at 3.   A definite gap is present between the
     component membranes of the latter but the gap is only present in a part of the
     outer meso; throughout most of its length it is in the external compound mem-
     brane form.   In (b) the myelin lamellae are separated throughout the spiral by a
     restoration of the gaps between the unit membranes of the primitive meso from
     which it was formed during development.   (Text-fig. 6.)   The inner (cytoplasmic)
     surface of the cell membranes united during development to form the major
     dense lines of myelin remain united during this swelling process.   The two cell
     membranes united along their cytoplasmic surfaces form an internal compound
     membrane ($\pi$).   Note that the outer end of the mesos in both diagrams remain
     in contact.   While this is not invariably found in the sections thus far examined
     it occurs rather frequently.

Fig. 11 shows a myelinated fibre at low power after soaking in water.
Both the inner and outer mesaxons are visible.   The inner mesaxon
is enlarged above and the internal compound membranes of the
myelin are visible.   In Fig. 12, a portion of another myelinated fibre
soaked in water is shown.   The outer Schwann surface membrane is
seen to the right (u.).   This is separated from the outermost layer
of myelin by a thinner layer of Schwann cytoplasm than in Fig. 10.
The first layer of myelin is again a single $\sim 75$ Å simple membrane,
and the succeeding layers internal compound membranes.   The

lower inset shows the membranes at higher magnification. These observations all support the interpretation presented in Text-fig. 10.

Two important conclusions may be drawn from these findings. First, the outside surfaces of the Schwann cell membrane are hydrophilic since water clearly enters the myelin structure preferentially along their surfaces. This is one reason, as mentioned above, for rejecting the molecular model shown in Text-fig. 7 C. Second, the inner (cytoplasmic) surface of the $\sim 75$ Å Schwann cell membrane probably differs chemically from the outer in some important way because, when in contact in myelin, the inner surfaces do not so easily separate. The membrane is therefore an asymmetric structure. This is in accordance with Finean's " difference factor " concept.

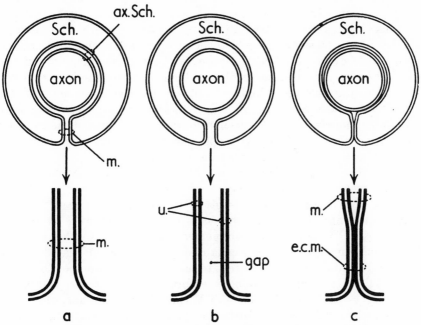

Text-fig. 11. Effects of hypotonic and hypertonic solutions on the double membranes of unmyelinated nerve fibres. (a) Unmyelinated nerve fibre after soaking in isotonic Ringer solution before fixation. The gap of the axon-Schwann membrane (ax. Sch.) formed by the apposition of the Schwann cell (Sch.) membrane with that of the axon measures about 100–150 Å in width and that of the meso (m.) about the same. After soaking in hypotonic solutions before fixation the gap between the unit membranes (u.) is definitely widened as in (b). After hypertonic solutions the gap is closed as in (c). This applies to both the axon-Schwann membrane and the meso. In the regions in which the gap between the cell membranes is closed an external compound membrane (e.c.m.) is produced.

The effects of hypotonic and hypertonic solutions on the double membranes of unmyelinated fibres give further insight into the nature of Schwann cell surfaces. Mesaxons and axon-Schwann membranes fixed in the fresh state or after soaking in isotonic Ringer solution (Text-fig. 11), consist of two $\sim 75$ Å cell membranes separated by a

gap ~ 100–150 Å wide.   After soaking in water, the gaps are distinctly
widened (Text-fig. 11 b).   After soaking in hypertonic solutions, the
gaps are collapsed in many areas and the two cell membranes are
separated by only ~ 15 Å or less (Text-fig. 11 c & Fig. 13, Plate III).
This effect is obtained after soaking in 4N or more Ringer solution
or somewhat higher concentrations of normal Ringer to which sucrose
has been added.   This behaviour of the gap substance is like that of a
highly hydrated gel and its collapse in hypertonic solutions is perhaps
a syneresis phenomenon.

In Fig. 14, Plate III, a distinct layer of amorphous material is seen
surrounding the Schwann cell, extending out from the cell membrane
for several hundred ångström units.   This material apparently extends
into the double membrane gaps and is probably identifiable both as
basement membrane material and gap substance.   Such material
as this is well known to be PAS positive.   Recently Abood and Abul-
Haj (1) have presented new histochemical evidence suggesting that a
thin layer of polysaccharide is present in this location around the
surfaces of myelinated nerve fibres.   This supports the idea that the
gap substance may be a highly hydrated polysaccharide gel.   If this
is correct, the outer layer of the Schwann surface membrane may
contain a monolayer of polysaccharide which is retained in the compact
myelin structure.   This   concept   would   account   for   Finean's
" difference factor " if the inside is protein.

A further point in support of the conception that the Schwann
surface membrane has monolayers of different substances coating its
outside and inside surfaces, is given by the appearance of the unmyelinated fibre double membranes after treatment with hypertonic
solutions.   The upper inset enlargement in Fig. 12 is another example
of a double membrane with a collapsed gap like that in Fig. 13.   Such
double membranes are referred to as " external compound membranes ".   External compound membranes, like internal compound
membranes, consist of two ~ 75 Å cell membranes and they also
measure ~ 150 Å across.   However, in the former case, the outside
surfaces of the cell membranes are in contact and in the latter the
inside surfaces are in contact.   (These two related but fundamentally
different kinds of membrane structures are compared in Text-fig. 12.)
The lower inset of Fig. 12, Plate III, shows an internal compound
membrane at the same magnification as the external compound membrane to the upper right.   Both were fixed and treated photographically in the same way.   Note the pronounced difference in the densities
of the central dense zones.   This, like the difference in the densities
of the major dense lines and intraperiod lines of myelin again leads to
the idea that different chemical substances are present in these two
locations.

It is of considerable interest that external compound membranes
occur normally in certain cases.   The axon-Schwann membranes and
mesaxons of the juxta-terminal myelin region of Nodes of Ranvier (92)

(95) (96) (98) (121) have gaps which are constantly closed, though the gaps are open over the unmyelinated part of the node. This fact may provide a morphological basis for saltatory conduction if open gaps are necessary for ionic current flow (35) (53) (85). Interestingly, external compound membranes also occur normally in young developing nerve fibres.

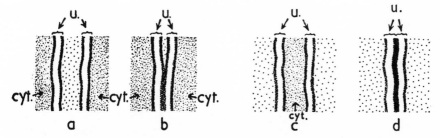

Text-fig. 12.   The diagram compares the structure of external compound membranes (b) with that of internal compound membranes (d) ; (a) shows a double membrane bounded on both sides by cytoplasm (cyt.). The two cell membranes (u.) are separated by gap substance. In (b) the gap is collapsed, and the two cell membranes (u.) in apposition form an external compound membrane. (c) Hypothetical stage in the evolution of an internal compound membrane showing two cell membranes (u.) separated by a thin layer of cytoplasm (cyt.) and bounded externally by gap substance to the right and left. The internal compound membrane is produced by condensation or removal of the cytoplasm (cyt.). The central dense zone of internal compound membranes after permanganate fixation is very much more dense than that of external compound membranes, after similar fixation.

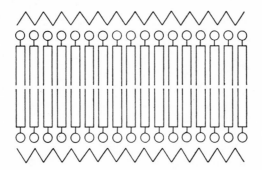

Text-fig. 13.   This figure illustrates the molecular structure of Schwann cell membranes deduced from all of the evolved information. According to this conception the cell membrane consists of a single bimolecular leaflet of lipid with the polar surfaces of the lipid molecules covered by monolayers of non-lipid material. The open circles indicate the polar ends of the lipid molecules. The non-polar portions are indicated by the tuning-fork configuration. The non-lipid layers are indicated by the zig-zag lines.

It should be clear now that the $\sim 75$ Å triple layered membrane structure is an entity which is constantly present in Schwann cells after $KMnO_4$ fixation, and that it is quite stable, resisting violent osmotic effects before fixation. Furthermore, the evidence concerning the junctions of mesos with compact myelin in material fixed either in $OsO_4$ or $KMnO_4$ suggests that the structure seen is not a fixation artifact without meaning. Reasons have been given for supposing that this ~ 75 Å cell membrane structure consists of molecular layers like those shown in Text-fig. 13. It is now important to decide whether this membrane structure is peculiar to Schwann cells or is of more general occurrence. In an effort to answer this question a survey of several tissues in several different animals has been conducted and will now be considered.

## VI. *Cell membranes and membranous organelles*

1.—Cell membranes—The following types of cells were included in a general survey and micrographs of a few representative samples are shown in Figs. 15–36 (Plates IV–VII). In all of the types of tissue cells listed, the surface membranes and the membranes of cell organelles were of the ~ 75 Å triple layered type characteristic of Schwann cells.

[i]  Frog—(*a*) skin (Fig. 20, Plate IV), (*b*) intestinal epithelium, (*c*) liver, (*d*) pancreas (Figs. 21–22, Plate IV), (*e*) muscle (Figs. 16, 18, 19, Plate IV, 34, 36, Plate VII), (*f*) nerve (Figs. 2, Plate I, 9, Plate II, 10–14, Plate III, 15, 16, Plate IV, 23, Plate V, 32, Plate VI, 35 & 37, Plate VII), (*g*) red blood cells (Fig. 31, Plate VI), (*h*) connective tissue cells (Fig. 24, Plate V) (*i*) endothelial cells (Fig. 26, Plate V).

[ii]  Cat—(*a*) liver, (*b*) kidney, (*c*) skeletal muscle.

[iii]  Mouse—(*a*) nerve (Fig. 4, Plate I), (*b*) skeletal muscle, (*c*) smooth muscle (Fig. 17, Plate IV), (*d*) intestinal epithelium (Fig. 27 *a* & *b*, Plate VI), (*e*) liver (Fig. 29, Plate VI), (*f*) kidney (Fig. 28, Plate VI), (*g*) fibroblasts, (*h*) endothelial cells, (*i*) eosinophils (Fig. 30, Plate VI).

[iv]  Crayfish—nerve.

[v]  Crab—muscle.

Observations by others working in this laboratory have shown the same unit in chick embryonic cells (Bellairs (6)), locust nerve tissue (Gray (45)) and mouse cornea (Whitear (120)). The unit is seen most clearly after $KMnO_4$ fixation, but has been seen also after $OsO_4$ fixation though as discussed above the structure is less consistently well fixed by $OsO_4$. Roughly the same unit has been reported by others in several other tissues fixed with either $OsO_4$ or $KMnO_4$ though interpretations have differed. These include hair follicle cells (Birbeck and Mercer (13)), tissue culture cells and amoebae (Mercer (62)), grasshopper spermatids and a protozoon ciliate (Roth (100) (101)), mouse intestinal mucosa (Zetterqvist (124) and Sjöstrand and Zetterqvist (115)). Roth gave a figure of 100 Å for the comparable unit in grasshopper spermatids. Similarly Sjöstrand and Zetterqvist (115) gave a figure of 100 Å for mouse intestinal epithelial cells. It is not clear whether these figures should be considered significantly different from 75 Å because methods of calibration and measurement as well as slight fixation differences might account for the discrepancy (e.g. the fixative used in most of these examples was $OsO_4$).

The findings on mouse intestinal epithelial cells (124) (115) after $OsO_4$ fixation have been checked in this laboratory using $KMnO_4$ fixation, but without controlled feeding of the animals. Roughly the same three layered structure is seen on the papillary extensions of the epithelial cells toward the gut lumen with this different technique (Fig. 27 a, Plate VI). The outer dense layer is, however, less clear than the inner. Measurements in the order of 100–120 Å were commonly found. The surface membrane of the same cells away from the gut lumen in the intercellular double membranes had the usual appearance seen in the other cells and measured $\sim 75$ Å (Fig. 27 b, Plate VI). Changes in this membrane were detected by Sjöstrand and Zetterqvist (115) after feeding, and it may be that its dimensions and to some extent fixation characteristics are altered during absorbtion of foodstuffs. This probably implies a transitory alteration in the general structural pattern during physiological activity. It is important in this connection that the non-absorptive surfaces show the usual $\sim 75$ Å unit consistently.

2.—Membranous cell organelles—It is not within the scope of this paper to deal in detail with all the membranous cell organelles which have been described and no effort is made to cover the field. However, a few general statements will be made about the most prominent of these. The emphasis is placed on what are believed to be the important underlying ideas. The endoplasmic reticulum, nuclear membrane, Golgi complex, mitochondria, microbodies and so-called " microvesicular " bodies will be dealt with briefly.

(a) *Endoplasmic Reticulum (ER)*. This important cell organelle from which the microsome fraction of tissue homogenates is thought to be derived, was first described by Porter and Thompson (82) in tissue culture cells. It appeared at low magnification in these greatly flattened cells as an irregular reticular network of interconnected fibrils and vesicles confined to the endoplasm of the cells. The term " endoplasmic reticulum " (ER) was therefore applied to it. At higher magnification in thin sections the apparent fibrils were later seen to be membranous tubules sometimes expanded into sac-like vesicles (75) (81). Later, by the use of thin sectioning techniques it was found that tissue cells fixed *in situ* showed membranous as well as tubular and vesicular elements, and that no particular localization with regard to ecto- or endoplasm was demonstrable. The membranes of components of the ER show the same $\sim 75$ Å unit structure seen in cell surfaces (Fig. 17, Plate IV).

The cytoplasmic surfaces of the ER membranes sometimes appear rough in $OsO_4$ fixed material due to attached small dense granules $\sim 100$–150 Å in diameter. These were described clearly by Sjöstrand and Hanzon (114). Similar granules sometimes lie free in the cytoplasm. Palade (73) has studied these granules further and Palade and Siekevitz (76) have succeeded by the use of deoxycholate in separating them from the ER membrane fragments appearing in the microsome fraction of homogenates. Chemical analysis showed them to be very high in RNA content. On this basis they are considered to be the principal basophilic component of the cytoplasm. Some of the membranes of the ER do not have associated granules. These smooth components are referred to as the "agranular reticulum".

Some (11) (68) (119) prefer to use the term "ergastoplasm" for the ER structures. This term was invented by Garnier (38) and applied originally to basophilic areas in cytoplasm thought to be responsible for protein synthesis. Palade (73) argued that the term should not be applied generally to the ER system because this is not all basophilic. Others (116) prefer to use still another term "cytomembrane", designating the different kinds of elements by prefixing letters of the Greek alphabet. The term endoplasmic reticulum, despite certain inadequacies is most widely used.

The ER system in some form has been found in every variety of cells studied except erythrocytes (75). Largely because of the tissue culture findings it is believed by some that all these membranous, tubular and vesicular elements are interconnected, but some isolated vesicles may be present in cytoplasm free of the system. The term "Golgi complex", as used by electron microscopists, includes a system of fairly closely packed layers of the membranes and vesicles near the nucleus, and it is believed by some that this system is a part of the ER (55) (24) although positive evidence for this is lacking.

The nuclear membrane was first found by Hartman (48) (49) to be a double membrane. It has been found in this laboratory that this double membrane consists of two ~75 Å units separated by a gap ~150 Å wide (Fig. 21, Plate IV). It is interrupted by a variable number of openings ~500 Å across (117). By means of these openings nucleoplasm and cytoplasm are in continuity (Text-fig. 14). Occasionally the outer component membrane of this double membrane is extended into the cytoplasm as a tubule (Fig. 21) (24) (91). On evidence of this kind Watson (117) has concluded that the nuclear membrane is a part of the system of membranes composing the endoplasmic reticulum.

Taking all of the above conceptions into account the ER has been referred to as the "circulatory system of the cell" (104). Palade and Siekevitz (76) have presented evidence that pancreatic secretion granules may be present within tubules or vesicles of the ER since they are separated from cytoplasm by a membrane. Sometimes the gaps of the ER double membranes are relatively small and resemble those of intercellular double membranes. It is intriguing that this kind of double membrane gap in Schwann cells has not been observed to close in response to treatment with hypertonic solutions as have those of intercellular membranes and mitochondria (99). Perhaps the gap substance or the character of the unit membrane surfaces here is different.

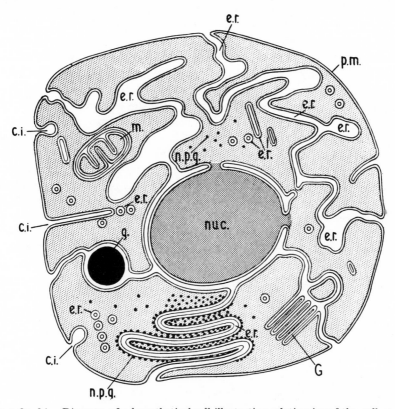

Text-fig. 14.   Diagram of a hypothetical cell illustrating relationsips of the cell membrane to various cell organelles.   The cell membrane is shown as a pair of dense lines separated by a light interzone.   The invaginations of the cell surface known as caveolae intracellularis (c.i.) are indicated in several areas.   Some of these extend for a considerable distance into the cell and they may connect with the endoplasmic reticulum (e.r.).   The nuclear membrane is composed of flattened sacs of the endoplasmic reticulum, and by means of the nuclear pores nucleoplasm (nuc.) is in continuity with cytoplasm.   The Golgi apparatus (G) is here shown as a modified component of the endoplasmic reticulum.   Secretion granules (g.) are shown as dense aggregates contained within membranes of the endoplasmic reticulum.   Nucleo-protein granules (n.p.g.) are shown scattered through the cytoplasm and in some regions attached to the cytoplasmic surfaces of membranes of the endoplasmic reticulum.   In some regions the endoplasmic reticulum is shown as tubules, either in longitudinal section or cross-section.   It is not clear on present evidence how many of these round membranes are transected tubules and how many, if any, represent isolated vesicles.   One mitochondrion (m.) is shown with its cristae formed by invagination of its inner membrane.

If it is accepted that the ER is indeed a continuous intracellular system of interconnected channels, the lumina of which sometimes contain secretory granules the conception of its being a kind of intracellular " circulatory system " is not unreasonable (Text-fig. 14). The important question then arises of whether or not the system is connected with the outside by continuity of its component membranes with those of the outside cell surface. If this is the case secretion, phagocytosis, pinocytosis and other processes may not involve the passage of large aggregates of material directly out of or into the cytoplasm by means of a physical separation of membrane fragments as some have asserted (70) (8) (65). Instead secretion, for example, might involve passage of single molecules through the cell membrane at perhaps widely separated loci with later aggregation into large secretion granules which pass along the channels of the ER to the outside. Phagocytosis would be essentially the reverse of this process and pinocytosis simply a special case of phagocytosis.

This question of whether or not the ER is a closed system is one of the most fundamental unsolved problems in tissue ultrastructure. Numerous specific instances other than the above may be cited in which the surface membranes of single cells are enfolded upon themselves forming intracellular double membranes. For example, the basal surfaces of renal epithelial cells were shown by Sjöstrand and Rhodin (112) to be greatly enfolded to form " cytomembranes ". Palade and Siekevitz (76) have demonstrated enfoldings of a similar but less extensive nature in pancreatic acinar cells. In the case of renal epithelial cells it is now clear that the enfolded cell membranes represent the boundaries between closely packed evaginations of the cells (65) (79). Similar folds at the cell surfaces occur in cells of the choroid plexus (63) (80). In fact it is possible to look upon the cell as a complex aggregate of evaginations and folds of nucleocytoplasm extending out from the nucleus. Text-fig. 14 presents this hypothetical viewpoint diagramatically. Epstein (24) has recently presented evidence bearing importantly on this point. He believes that his micrographs establish a direct connection between the membranes of the ER, nuclear membranes and the cell surface membrane in Rous sarcoma cells. The connection between the ER and the nuclear membrane is quite clear. Unfortunately, however, the connection with the outer surface membrane is not at all clear since the membranes are sectioned very obliquely at the crucial region. His findings, though suggestive, are not acceptable as proof of this very important relationship. The matter of whether or not the ER is a closed intracellular system of membranes, remains to be settled by conclusive evidence which may be derived from serial sections.

The commonly observed goblet-shaped enfoldings of the surface membranes of many cells called " caveolae intracellularis " by Yamada (122) (e.g. Schwann cells (20) (Fig. 23, Plate V), endoneurial cells (91), endothelial cells (70) (65) (Figs. 25, 26, Plate V), pulmonary epithelial cells (54) and muscle cells (66) (Fig. 19, Plate IV)) are difficult to assess. These measure $\sim 300$–$500$ Å in diameter and are like those shown in Fig. 23. Obviously they could represent the beginnings of tortuous tubular channels connecting with the ER system. This, however, has not been proven. Sometimes, particularly in endothelial cells, these enfoldings seem to extend into the cytoplasm for considerable distances in sections. Beyond their origin they are sometimes narrowed to < 300 Å in width. It has been suggested in the case of endoneurial cells (91) that some of these represent the beginning of tubular channels running completely through the cell, but again no real proof of this has been presented. They may simply represent blind pockets which extend for variable distances into cells and increase the available membrane surface. In the case of endothelial cells the number of caveolae is very large (Fig. 25, Plate V) and it may be that these channels as well as the intercellular gaps are involved in capillary permeability (78).

Palade (70) and Moore and Ruska (65) have interpreted such flask-shaped membrane invaginations in endothelial cells in an entirely different way. They considered them to represent stages in a process of micro-pinocytosis (58) whereby droplets of water were engulfed into the cell by a " pinching-off " of portions of the cell membrane (called " cytopempsis " by Moore and Ruska (65)). This process was assumed to be reversed on the other side of the cell and fluid transport then accomplished without the necessity for any substance to pass directly through the cell membrane. Bennett (8) has elaborated this idea and extended it to other cells. He proposed that in phagocytosis after " pinching-off " the cell membrane was dissolved in cytoplasm.

This conception is obviously extremely important and possibly correct. It is certainly true that cell membranes can undergo the required " pinching-off " process (e.g. in cell division). It is easy to see how this might occur if the presumed protein layers in the membrane are caused to contract. There is, however, no positive direct evidence that the reverse of this process (i.e. coalescence) occurs between aggregates of lipids and proteins organized into the $\sim 75$ Å unit membrane structures. If purely lipid droplets were concerned such coalescence would, of course, be expected. Hodge et al. (52) have presented evidence suggesting that coalescence of vesicles occurs in plant cells, and it seems probable that these vesicles were bounded by membranes though this was not clearly shown. On the other hand, it is an observed fact that Schwann cell membranes which are often covered by numerous flask-shaped surface invaginations may contact one another either on their inside or outside surfaces without coalescence (99) (Fig. 35, Plate VII). While it is conceivable that local environment changes could bring about such " coalescence " as well as the supposed " pinching-off ", this matter should certainly be studied further before conclusions are drawn. An adequate serial section study would be very useful. In the meantime it seems well to treat the " micro-pinocytosis " (or " cytopempsis ") idea as a stimulating conception based almost entirely on speculations. Perhaps it is worth pointing out before leaving this matter, that the mere fact that pinocytosis occurs in tissue culture cells cannot be used as evidence in favour of the

" pinching-off " conception.   The droplets of liquid observed by light microscopy to be engulfed into the cell may either carry with them an enfolding of the cell surface invisible by light microscopy or simply enter the ER system if the latter does open to the surface.

(b) *Microbodies and Microvesicular Bodies.*   Microbodies (84) (12) (102) are supposedly discrete organelles existing independently in cytoplasm.   In size they resemble mitochondria.   However, they are bounded by a single rather than a double membrane and cristae are not present.   This single membrane is an ~ 75 Å unit membrane like that seen at cell surfaces and elsewhere.   The membrane surrounds a material often more dense than the surrounding cytoplasm.   These structures are frequently seen in both the axons and Schwann cells of normal nerve fibres.   Their origin and function is unknown.

So-called " microvesicular " bodies have recently been described by De Robertis (22) in adrenal cortical cells, and similar structures referred to as " compound vesicles " have been seen in plant cells by Sager and Palade (104).   These structures resemble ones seen in nodal axoplasm to be described separately and similar structures seen in this laboratory by Bellairs (6) in embryonic nerve tissue. Neither their origin or function in nerve tissue is clear.   It appears that the apparent " vesicles " may represent tubular invaginations of the limiting membrane (104), and in this sense they may be related to " microbodies ".

(c) *Mitochondria.*   Palade (71) and Sjöstrand (113) were the first to present high resolution micrographs of mitochondria.   Both investigators showed that these cytoplasmic organelles are limited by double membranes and that double membranes sometimes run partially across the structures between the bounding membranes. Sjöstrand believed that these two types of double membranes were independent of one another in the fully developed structure (Text-fig. 15 b).   Palade believed that the transverse membranes represented folds of the inner of the two bounding membranes and introduced the term " cristae mitochondrialies " for them (Text-fig. 15 a).   Obser-vations by others (e.g. (16)) and by the author (Fig. 34, Plate VII) have supported Palade's conception.   It seems that the cristae some-times represent linear folds superficially rather like the rugal folds in the colon.   Sometimes they may occur as finger-like extensions of the inner layer of the bounding double membrane though this point is not well established.   Occasionally the substance bounded by the inner membrane of mitochondria is divided into two compartments as in Figs. 29 and 33 (Plate VI), (26).   Occasionally dense accretions are seen in the matrix surrounded by the bounding double membrane (84).

It is of considerable interest that the double membranes of which mitochondria are composed show the ~ 75 Å unit membrane structure (Fig. 10, Plate III, Figs. 34 and 36, Plate VII).   This was first reported by Freeman (36) and by Low (59) though not clearly demonstrated.

The membranes are in every way similar in appearance to those seen in cell surfaces, mesaxons and axon-Schwann membranes.  They are separated by a gap substance ~ 100 Å thick.  Apart from the relative smallness of the gap the mitochondrial double membranes do not differ at present levels of resolution from those of the double membranes of the endoplasmic reticulum, nuclear membranes, etc.

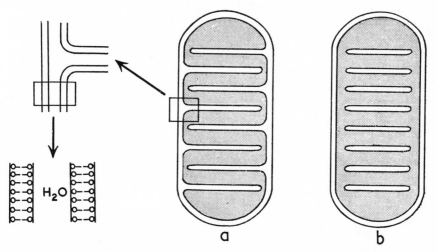

Text-fig. 15.   (a) and (b) indicate the pattern of organization of mitochondria.   (a) represents the viewpoint of Palade, and (b) that of Sjöstrand.   The rectangle indicated in (a) is enlarged to show the details of membrane structure discussed in the text though not to scale.   The probable molecular structure of each of these membranes is indicated below.   The gap between the membranes is probably highly hydrated.   The width of the gap is exaggerated in this drawing.

Occasionally structures like mitochondria but without cristae are seen in cells.  These are like that in Fig. 24 (Plate V).  The gap of the double membrane bounding such structures is wider than that of mitochondria and in one instance the author has traced one of these bodies out to the cell surface.  It proved to be an enfolded cell process. Either such structures are not mitochondria or they represent a stage in the formation of mitochondria from the cell surface (42). There is some evidence accumulating in this laboratory suggesting that the latter may be the case.  Recently Bang and Bang (3) have shown in a serial section study that some mitochondria are not such discrete structures as might be supposed.  They showed that some apparently transected spherical bodies seen in sections actually were very elongated, contorted structures which seemed related to the cell surface.  Quite frequently in this laboratory small (diameter ~ 500 Å) finger-like evaginations of cell surfaces ("p." in Text-fig. 16 a) have been observed next to invaginations (caveolae) ("c." in Text-fig. 16 a) of comparable size.  Such observations lead to some speculations about the origin of mitochondria which may be worth mentioning.  If such an evagination were to extend down into one of the invaginations, the beginning of one of the mitochondria-like bodies such as that in Fig. 24 would be formed ("t.M." in Text-fig. 16 a). It would only be necessary to expand this structure and fold the inner membrane into cristae to obtain a structure like a mitochondrion (" M." in Text-fig. 16 a).   The connection with the cell surface might then be retained as a double membrane tubule of sublightmicroscopic dimensions (Text-fig. 16 b) or it might pinch off.   Such double membrane bounded tubular structures ~500 Å in diameter have been seen near cell surfaces ("t." in Text-fig. 16 a) but they have not been seen connected with mitochondria.   They could easily have been missed however, if they are sufficiently tortuous, and should be sought particularly in serial sections before it is concluded that they do not exist. It might be mentioned that such "tails" on mitochondria would not prevent rather extensive migrations about the cell.

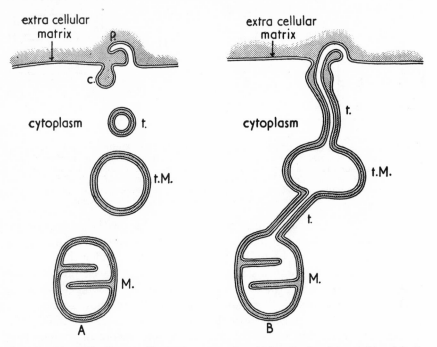

Text-fig. 16.   This diagram illustrates a way in which mitochondria might originate
        from cell surfaces.   To the left there is shown a segment of the surface of a
        muscle fibre in which structures which have been directly observed have been
        drawn.   To the right these structures are related speculatively.

While studying the effects of hypertonic solutions on the double membranes of nerve fibres (97) (99), it was noted that the gaps of mitochondrial double membranes were sometimes closed in the same way that the gaps of the double membranes of the intercellular type were closed.   In the same cells the gaps of the double membranes of the endoplasmic reticulum and nuclear membranes remained open. A distinct structural difference was observed between two cell membranes in contact along their outside surfaces as compared with two in contact along their inside (cytoplasmic) surfaces. Mitochondrial double membranes after closure of the gaps between the unit membranes resemble the former. They are like external compound membranes. This suggests that the gap substance of the mitochondrial double membranes is somewhat similar to that of the intercellular membranes and it may be taken to infer that this gap is bounded by layers like the outside layers of the ~75 Å unit membranes bounding cells. This may be a very important point in considering the origin of mitochondria and is entirely compatible with the above hypothesis.

Beams *et al.* (4) have described a type of concentrically lamellated structure in snail tissues which they called " concentrically lamellated mitochondria ". Such structures as this have been described also by the author in crayfish synaptic axoplasm (88). Fig. 37 (Plate VII) shows such a " target-like " body in axoplasm in a frog neuromuscular spindle. These bodies might result if a double membrane sac were pushed in upon itself repeatedly. In the sense that they may be derived from a single double membrane structure they are like mitochondria. On the other hand, each concentric double membrane may be independent. Because of their distinctive appearance it may be better to consider these structures separately. Hence the author prefers to call them " target bodies ".

VII. *Conclusion*

The aims of this review have been limited and no effort has been made to cover the many aspects of tissue ultrastructure now being explored. The emphasis has been placed exclusively on cell membranes and membranous cell organelles. It has been pointed out that structures are now being seen at the surfaces of cells which are remarkably close to what one would expect to see from indirect evidence about membrane structure. It has been shown that a three-layered structure, ~75 Å thick, consisting of two dense lines ~20 Å thick bordering a light central zone is seen at the surface of a number of dissimilar cells. In the special case of Schwann cells it was shown that this unit composed half of each myelin lamella. Reasons were given for believing that the lamellae of the myelin sheath repeating at a radial period of ~120 Å are identical with the fundamental repeating unit in fresh nerve fibres deduced by X-ray diffraction. If this is correct it seems reasonable to assume that the ~75 Å unit represents one bimolecular leaflet of lipid, the polar surfaces of which are covered by monolayers of non-lipid material. Since it was shown that this structural pattern is common to many cells it seems clear that it may be generally present. Such a concept is in keeping with the paucimolecular theory of Davson and Danielli (19).

No effort has been made to discuss at length the obvious possibility that the observed structures represent artifact. Indeed, it seems certain that artifact is present to some degree. However, there are many reasons for believing that the observed membrane and myelin sheath structures are not entirely false. Essentially the same structural pattern in myelin and to some extent at the surfaces of cells has been observed independently by different investigators using two different fixation methods. The cell surface membrane structures are simply and directly related to the layered structures seen in myelin and these are compatible with those deduced from X-ray diffraction patterns and polarization optical analyses made on fresh nerve fibres. On the basis of these facts alone it seems reasonable to believe that the observed structures are, within certain obvious limits, representative of a pattern of molecular structure existing in living cells. This is not to say that the individual molecules responsible for the pattern have been seen; probably only a skeleton is left in the sectioned material and indubitably the underlying molecules are profoundly altered or even removed. It is believed merely that the residual pattern is closely representative of the original structures at the molecular level. This representation, if no more direct than that of a photographic image of its object, is none the less valid. Only further investigation can settle this ever present question of the degree of artifact.

It is hoped that the observations and discussions presented here, while in no way complete, will serve to indicate certain trends in the development of tissue ultrastructure and to focus attention on some of the most important general problems awaiting investigation.

## REFERENCES

1. Abood, L. G. & Abul-Haj, S. K. (1956). *J. Neurochem.* **1**, 119.
2. Adam, N. K. (1941). *The Physics and Chemistry of Surfaces*, Oxford Univ. Press.
3. Bang, B. G. & Bang, F. B. (1957). *J. Ultrastructure Research*, **1**, 138.
4. Beams, H. W. & Tahmisian, T. N. (1954). *Exp. Cell Res.* **6**, 87.
5. Bear, R. S., Palmer, K. J. & Schmitt, F. O. (1941). *J. cell & comp. Physiol.* **17**, 355.
6. Bellairs, R. Unpublished observations.
7. Bennett, H. S. & Porter, K. P. (1955). *Amer. J. Anat.* **93**, 61.
8. Bennett, H. S. (1956). *J. biophys. & biochem. Cytol.* **2**, No. 4, Suppl. 99.
9. Bernal, J. D. (1937). *Nature, Lond.* **129**, 277.
10. Bernal, J. D., Crowfoot, D. & Fankuchen, I. (1940). *Phil. Tran. Roy. Soc. A.* **239**, 135.
11. Bernhard, W. & Rouiller, C. (1956). *J. biophys. & biochem. Cytol.* **2**, No. 4, Suppl. 73.
12. Bernhard, W. & Rouiller, C. (1956). *J. biophys. & biochem. Cytol.* **2**, No. 4, Suppl. 355.
13. Birbeck, M. S. E. & Mercer, E. H. (1957). *J. biophys. & biochem. Cytol.* **3**, 223.
14. Chambers, R. & Pollack, H. (1927). *J. gen. Physiol.* **10**, 739.
15. Cole, K. S. (1932). *J. cell. & comp. Physiol.* **5**, 483.
16. Dalton, A. J. & Felix, M. D. (1957). *Soc. exp. Biol. Sympos. No.* 10, Cambridge Univ. Press, p. 148.
17. Danielli, J. F. & Harvey, E. N. (1935). *J. cell. & comp. Physiol.* **5**, 483.
18. Danielli, J. F. & Davson, H. (1935). *J. cell. & comp. Physiol.* **5**, 495.
19. Davson, H. & Danielli, J. F. (1943). *The Permeability of Natural Membranes*, Cambridge Univ. Press.

20. De Robertis, E. D. P. & Bennett, H. S. (1954). *Exp. Cell Res.* **6**, 543.
21. De Robertis, E. D. P. & Bennett, H. S. (1955). *J. biophys. & biochem. Cytol.* **1**, 47.
22. De Robertis, E. D. P. (1957). *Exp. Cell Res.* **12**, 575.
23. Elkes, J. & Finean, J. B. (1953). *Exp. Cell Res.* **4**, 69.
24. Epstein, M. A. (1957). *J. biophys. & biochem. Cytol.* **3**, 851.
25. Ewald, A. & Kuhne, W. (1874–77). *Verhandl. Naturlist. Med.* **1**, 457.
26. Fawcett, D. W. (1955). *J. Nat. Cancer Inst. Suppl.* **15**, 1475.
27. Fernandez-Moran, H. (1950). *Exp. Cell Res.* **1**, 309.
28. Fernandez-Moran, H. (1954). *Progress in Biophysics*, **4**, 112.
29. Fernandez-Moran, H. & Finean, J. B. (1957). *J. biophys. & biochem. Cytol.* **3**, 725.
30. Finean, J. B. (1953). *Exp. Cell Res.* **5**, 202.
31. Finean, J. B. (1954). *Exp. Cell Res.* **6**, 283.
32. Finean, J. B. (1955). *Exp. Cell Res.* **9**, 181.
33. Finean, J. B. (1956). *Biochemical Problems of Lipids, Proc. 2nd Int. Conf. (Ghent)*, ed. G. Popjak & E. le Breton. Butterworths Scientific Pub., Lond.
34. Finean, J. B. & Millington, P. F. (1957). *J. biophys. & biochem. Cytol.* **3**, 89.
35. Frankenhaeuser, B. & Hodgkin, A. L. (1956). *J. Physiol.* **131**, 341.
36. Freeman, J. A. (1956). *J. biophys. & biochem. Cytol.* **2**, No. 4, Suppl. 353.
37. Frey-Wyssling, A. (1953). *Submicroscopic Morphology of Protoplasm*, Elsevier Publishing Co., London.
38. Garnier, C. J. (1900). *J. Anat. et Physiol., Paris* **36**, 22.
39. Gasser, H. S. (1952). *Cold Spring Harbor Sympos. Quant. Biol.* **7**, 32.
40. Gasser, H. S. (1955). *J. gen. Physiol.* **38**, 709.
41. Geren, B. B. (1954). *Exp. Cell Res.* **7**, 588.
42. Geren, B. B. & Schmitt, F. O. (1954). *Proc. Nat. Acad. Sci.* **40**, 863.
43. Glauert, A. M., Rogers, G. E. & Glauert, R. H. (1956). *Nature, Lond.* **178**, 803.
44. Gorter, E. & Grendel, R. (1925). *J. exp. Med.* **41**, 439.
45. Gray, G. Unpublished observations.
46. Hall, B. V. (1954). *Proc. V Ann. Conf. Nephrotic Syndrome, N.Y.* The National Nephrosis Foundation Inc.
47. Harkins, W. D. (1917). *J. Amer. chem. Soc.* **37**, 354.
48. Hartman, J. F. (1952). *Anat. Rec.* **112**, 340.
49. Hartman, J. F. (1954). *Anat. Rec.* **118**, 19.
50. Harvey, E. N. & Shapiro, H. (1934). *J. cell & comp. Physiol.* **5**, 255.
51. Höber, R., (1945). *Physical Chemistry of Cells and Tissues*, The Blakiston Co., Philadelphia.
52. Hodge, A. J., McLean, J. D. & Mercer, F. V. (1956). *J. biophys. & biochem. Cytol* **2**, 597.
53. Hodgkin, A. L. (1958). *Proc. Roy. Soc. B.* **148**, 1.
54. Karrer, H. (1956). *Exp. Cell Res.* **10**, 237.
55. Lacy, D. (1957). *J. biophys. & biochem. Cytol.* **3**, 779.
56. Langmuir, I. (1917). *J. Amer. chem. Soc.* **37**, 1848.
57. Le Baron, F. N. & Folch, J. (1956). *J. Neurochem.* **1**, 101.
58. Lewis, W. H. (1931). *Bull. Johns Hopkins Hosp.* **49**, 17.
59. Low, F. N. (1956). *J. biophys. & biochem. Cytol.* **2**, No. 4, Suppl. 337.
60. Luft, J. H. (1956). *J. biophys. & biochem. Cytol.* **2**, 799.
61. Maaløe, O. & Birch-Andersen, A. (1956). *Bacterial Cytology, Sympos. No. 6, Soc. of General Microbiology.* Ed. Spooner, E. T. C., & Stocker, B. Cambridge Univ. Press, p. 268.
62. Mercer, E. H. (1957). Paper delivered at *IXth Int. Cong. for Cell Biol.* St. Andrews, Scotland.
63. Millen, J. W. & Rogers, G. E. (1956). *J. biophys. & biochem. Cytol.* **2**, 407.
64. Mitchison, J. M. (1952). *Soc. exp. Biol. Sympos. No.* 6, Cambridge Univ. Press, p. 105.
65. Moore, D. H. & Ruska, H. (1957). *J. biophys. & biochem. Cytol.* **3** 261.

66. Moore, D. H. & Ruska, H. (1957). *J. biophys. & biochem. Cytol.* **3**, 457.
67. Mudd, S. & Mudd, E. B. H. (1931). *J. gen. Physiol.* **14**, 733.
68. Oberling, Ch. & Rouiller, C. (1956). *Annales d'Anatomie Pathologique*, **1**, 401.
69. Overton, E. (1895). *Vjschr. neturf. Ges. Zurich*, **40**, 159.
70. Palade, G. E. (1953). *J. app. Phys.* **24**, 1424.
71. Palade, G. E. (1953). *J. Histochem. & Cytochem.* **1**, 188.
72. Palade, G. E. (1954). *Anat. Rec.* **118**, 335.
73. Palade, G. E. (1955). *J. biophys. & biochem. Cytol.* **1**, 59.
74. Palade, G. E. (1956). *J. biophys. & biochem. Cytol.* **2**, 171.
75. Palade, G. E. (1956). *J. biophys. & biochem. Cytol.* **2**, No. 4, Suppl. 85.
76. Palade, G. E. & Siekevitz, P. (1956). *J. biophys. & biochem. Cytol.* **2**, 671.
77. Palay, S. & Palade, G. E. (1955). *J. biophys. & biochem. Cytol.* **1**, 69.
78. Pappenheimer, J. R., (1953). *Physiol. Rev.* **53**, 387.
79. Pease, D. C. (1955). *J. Histochem. & Cytochem.* **3**, 295.
80. Pease, D. C. (1956). *J. biophys. & biochem. Cytol.* **2**, No. 4, Suppl. 203.
81. Porter, K. R. (1953). *J. exp. Med.* **97**, 727.
82. Porter, K. R. & Thompson, H. P. (1947). *Cancer Res.* **7**, 431.
83. Reger, J. (1957). *Exp. Cell Res.* **12**, 662.
84. Rhodin, J. (1954). *Correlation of Ultrastructural Organization and Function in Normal and Experimentally Changed Proximal Convoluted Tubule Cells of the Mouse Kidney.* Aktiebolaget Godvil, Stockholm.
85. Ritchie, J. M. & Straub, R. W. (1957). *J. Physiol.* **136**, 80.
86. Robertson, J. D. (1954). *Anat. Rec.* **118**, 346.
87. Robertson, J. D. (1955). *J. biophys. & biochem. Cytol.* **1**, 271.
88. Robertson, J. D. (1955). *Exp. Cell Res.* **8**, 226.
89. Robertson, J. D. (1955). *J. biophys. & biochem. Cytol.* **2**, 369.
90. Robertson, J. D. (1956). *J. biophys. & biochem. Cytol.* **2**, 381.
91. Robertson, J. D. (1956). *Proc. Stockholm Cong. Elec. Micro.* Almqvist & Wiksell, Stockholm, p. 197.
92. Robertson, J. D. (1956). *J. Physiol.* **135**, 56.
93. Robertson, J. D. (1957). *Progress in Neurobiology II. Ultrastructure and Cellular Chemistry of Neural Tissue* (Ed. Waelsch, H.). N.Y., Paul B. Hoeber, Inc.
94. Robertson, J. D. (1957). *J. Physiol.* **137**, 6.
95. Robertson, J. D. (1957). *J. Physiol.* **137**, 8.
96. Robertson, J. D. (1957). *Anat. Rec.* **127**, 357.
97. Robertson, J. D. (1957). *J. appl., Phys.* **28**, 1372.
98. Robertson, J. D. (1957). *J. biophys. & biochem. Cytol.* **3**, 1043.
99. Robertson, J. D. (1958). *J. biophys. & biochem. Cytol.* In press.
100. Roth, L. E. (1956). *J. biophys. & biochem. Cytol.* **2**, No. 4 Suppl., 235.
101. Roth, L. E. (1957). *J. biophys. & biochem. Cytol.* **3**, 816.
102. Rouiller, C. & Bernhard, W. (1956). *J. biophys. & biochem. Cytol.* **2**, No. 4 Suppl., 355.
103. Ruska, H. (1954). *Z. Naturforsch.* **96**, 358.
104. Sager, R. & Palade, G. E. (1957). *J. biophys. & biochem. Cytol.* **3**, 463.
105. Schmidt, W. J. (1937). *Z. Wissersch. Mkr.* **54**, 159.
106. Schmitt, F. O., Bear, R. S. & Clark, G. L. (1935). *Radiology*, **25**, 131.
107. Schmitt, F. O. (1936). *Cold Spr. Harbor, Sympos. Quant. Biol.* **4**, 7.
108. Schmitt, F. O. & Palmer, K. J. (1940). *Cold. Spr. Harbor Sympos. Quant. Biol.* **8**, 94.
109. Schmitt, F. O., Bear, R. S. & Palmer, K. J. (1941). *J. cell & comp. Physiol.* **18**, 39.
110. Schmitt, F. O. & Geschwind, N. (1957). *Progress in Biophysics*, **8**, 165.
111. Sjöstrand, F. S. (1953). *Experientia*, **9**, 68.
112. Sjöstrand, F. S. & Rhodin, J. (1953). *Exp. Cell Res.* **4**, 426.
113. Sjöstrand, F. S. (1953). *Nature, Lond.* **171**, 30.
114. Sjöstrand, F. S. & Hanzon, V. (1954). *Exp. Cell Res.* **7**, 393.

115. Sjöstrand, F. S. & Zetterqvist, H. (1956).   *Proc. Stockholm Cong. Elec. Micro.*
     Almqvist & Wiksell, Stockholm, p. 150.
116. Sjöstrand, F. S. (1956).   *Int. Rev. Cytol.* **5,** 455.
117. Watson, M. L. (1955).   *J. biophys. & biochem. Cytol.* **1,** 257.
118. Waugh, D. F. & Schmitt, F. O. (1940).   *Cold Spring Harbor Sympos. Quant. Biol.*
     **8,** 233.
119. Weiss, J. M. (1953).   *J. exp. Med.* **98,** 607.
120. Whitear, M.   Unpublished observations.
121. Uzman, B. G. (1957).   *J. biophys. & biochem. Cytol.* **3,** 589.
122. Yamada, E. (1955).   *J. biophys. & biochem. Cytol.* **1,** 445.
123. Young, J. Z. (1953).   *Quart. J. micro. Soc.* **94,** 399.
124. Zetterqvist, H. (1956).   *The Ultrastructural Organization of the Columnar Epithelial
     Cells of the Mouse Intestine.*   Thesis.   Karolinska Institutet, Stockholm.

# FINE STRUCTURE ANALYSIS OF CHLOROPLASTS

A. Frey-Wyssling and E. Steinmann

*Department of General Botany, Swiss Federal Institute of Technology*

The chloroplasts of higher plants are composed of a colorless stroma in which are embedded little green disks called grana. In general, the size of the grana is at the resolving limit of the light microscope. In the fluorescence microscope, only the grana appear red, and thus all of the chlorophyll is concentrated here. Besides their pigments, chloroplasts also contain a high concentration of lipid which composes one-third of their weight (Frey-Wyssling, 1949). It is probable that the lipid is not free but bound to protein as lipoprotein. However, the lipoprotein bonds must be weak because the lipids are easily extracted in fat solvents or released as myelin figures under mild detergent action (Weber, 1933). As the grana are selectively stained by Rhodamin B – a lipid reagent – they must be rich in lipoprotein. During isolation of chloroplasts the lipid and protein components can separate while drying on an electron microscope grid. The lipids form semifluid myelin masses which inundate the other objects (grana, macromolecules) on the grid and appear in the electron microscope as thin incrustations (Frey-Wyssling and Mühlethaler, 1949). On the other hand, proteins appear either as folded skins or as isolated spherical macromolecules. The separation of lipid and protein can be prevented by isolating the chloroplasts in sucrose solution or phosphate buffer (Granick and Porter, 1947). The structures seen then in the electron microscope are lipoprotein, and chloroplasts isolated in this fashion are surprisingly liable to swelling. We have used this property in the following fine structure analysis of the grana and stroma.

## FINE STRUCTURE OF THE GRANA

The grana are cylindrically stacked over each other within the stroma (Strugger, 1950, 1951), each granum forming a system of lamellae (Frey-Wyssling and Mühlethaler, 1949) as suggested in the diagram of Figure 1a. In vivo, the grana stacks are easily recognized in profile views of the chloroplast, but it has not yet been possible to obtain thin sections which in the electron microscope show the picture outlined in Figure 1a. The grana obviously move during fixation and it is to be hoped that freeze-drying methods will provide better results. On the other hand, the lamellar nature of individual grana is

Translated by D. Branton and reprinted by permission of A. Frey-Wyssling and the publisher from *Vierteljahrschrift der Naturforschende Gesselschaft* (Zürich), **98**, 20–29 (1953).

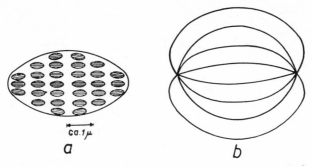

FIGURE 1. Profiles of chloroplasts. (a) Distribution of the grana. (b) Balloon-like swelling of the chloroplast (after Strugger, 1951).

recognizable in cross sections of tulip chloroplasts (Fig. 2), and the grana can be disintegrated into about 70 Å thick lamellae by ultrasonication (Steinmann, 1952a). The unusually large (over 1 $\mu$) grana isolated from *Aspidistra* chloroplasts could be disintegrated into over thirty such lamellae (Fig. 3; Steinmann, 1952b).

The grana of *Aspidistra* (Fig. 5) also show that its elementary lamellae are composed of macromolecular double layers. When distilled water is slowly added to chloroplast material suspended in a 1.0 M sucrose solution, the grana swell (Fig. 6), break apart (Fig. 7), and grow into long strands (Figs. 8 and 9). These changes are distinctly visible in the phase-contrast microscope. Since the strands appear red in the fluorescence microscope, their derivation from the chlorophyll-containing grana is certain. In the electron microscope (Figs. 10 and 11) they appear as chains of vesicles, collapsed and folded by drying. Thus, elementary lamellae of the grana are swollen into vesicles. Figure 3, as well as Figures 14 and 15 which show spinach chloroplasts ground in 5 percent formaldehyde, illustrates that slightly swollen elementary lamellae slide off their stacks during drying. Thus, Figures 3, 14, and 15 show the lamellae in surface view. Disruption of the grana is far less distinct in sucrose solution or phosphate buffer.

Upon further swelling, each elementary lamella balloons, but such swollen vesicles of one granum remain attached to one another and form the long chains illustrated in Figures 10 and 11.

The elementary lamellae must therefore have been composed of two layers before swelling. Measurements of the elementary lamellae are difficult to make, but if they are correct at 70 Å (Steinmann, 1952a, b) each of the hypothetical layers would be only 35 Å thick. This corresponds to the thinnest unit in the elementary lamellae of rods of the retina which Sjöstrand (1949) has described. Such thin layers have approximately the same diameter as a dehydrated protein particle of one Svedberg unit (S) (cf. Frey-Wyssling, 1953, Tab. XV, S 141). However, one must take into account that the macromolecular spherical molecule may be flattened during drying. One can therefore assume somewhat larger particles, such as the 4 S hemoglobin particles which are about 55 Å in diameter. It is therefore probable that bimolecular elementary

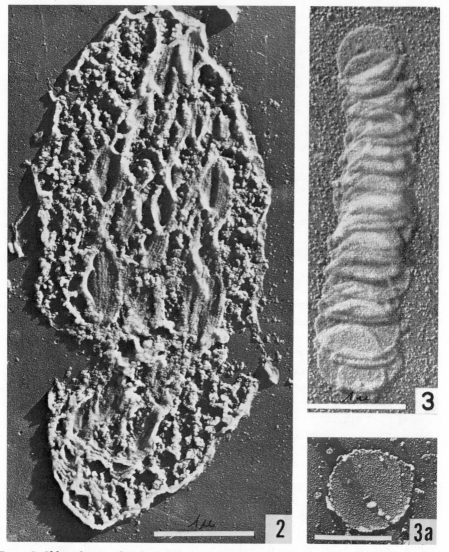

PLATE I. Chloroplasts in the electron microscope. The white bar on each photo indicates 1 $\mu$.
FIGURE 2. Cross section through a tulip chloroplast in the electron microscope. $\times$ 27,000 (from Steinmann, 1952a).
FIGURE 3. Disintegrated *Aspidistra* granum showing the elementary lamellae. $\times$ 27,000 (from Steinmann, 1952b).
FIGURE 3a. An elementary lamella from an *Aspidistra* chloroplast fixed 17.5 hours in 1% $OsO_4$ and then sonicated. On the right it is obvious that the elementary lamella is composed of two layers. $\times$ 21,000 from Steinmann, 1952a).

lamellae measure over 100 Å in the hydrated state, so that the following diagram of their structure can be suggested (Fig. 4).

The hypothesis that the elementary lamellae are composed of spherical macromolecules is supported by electron micrographs, the best of which regularly show a fine granulation (Fig. 3a); this granulation is also observable in

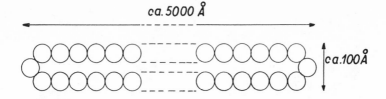

FIGURE 4. Diagram of the molecular organization of an elementary lamella (cross section).

Thomas's (1952) micrographs. Unfortunately the exact size of these granules cannot be measured precisely.

It is certain that the globules, which compose the elementary grana lamellae, are smaller than 100 Å in diameter. They must therefore contain less than 24 S and have a molecular weight less than 400,000. They cannot, therefore, be identical with Stoll's (1936) chloroplastin, which has a molecular weight of 5 million and contains 420 chlorophyll molecules.

Because the macromolecules of grana are chlorophyll chromoproteids with dimensions similar to those of hemoglobin molecules, other comparisons should be made. The hemoglobin molecule has a molecular weight of 68,000 (4 S) and contains 4 heme irons (Granick, 1948). Furthermore, the concentration of hemoglobin molecules in red blood cells is so great that a closely packed solution results (Jung, 1950). In this respect they are very different from the grana particles.

In the grana there are about 9 chlorophyll molecules per Svedberg unit (Frey-Wyssling, 1953), so that one 4 S particle must contain 36 chlorophylls. If a chlorophyll-chromoproteid exists in the grana, it must be far richer in pigment than hemoglobin. Furthermore, this proteid does not exist in a concentrated solution but is anchored in a coherent bimolecular film. It is probable that the grana lipids are incorporated into or associated with these macromolecules to form lipochromoproteids. Since the pigment and lipid are easily extracted from the chloroplasts, their attachment to the protein must be weak, and it is probable that these components are near the outer surface of the bimolecular layer. Also, because of their ability to form vesicles, one must conclude that the lipochromoproteid lamellae must have semipermeable characteristics. It would not be easy, therefore, to extract pigment and lipid molecules from the inside of the elementary lamellae.

## FINE STRUCTURE OF THE STROMA

Particles larger than those of the grana lamellae can be seen in many pictures (Figs. 3, 11). These must originate from the stroma. In fact the section in Figure 2 shows that the stroma has a granular structure.

The stroma is even more liable to swelling than are the grana. Figure 12 is an electromicrograph showing a spinach chloroplast isolated in 0.5 M sucrose. In spite of the fact that this medium is supposed to preserve chloroplast morphology, the plastid membrane is swollen and its surface bumpy. This is not due to incipient formation of myelin figures since separation of protein

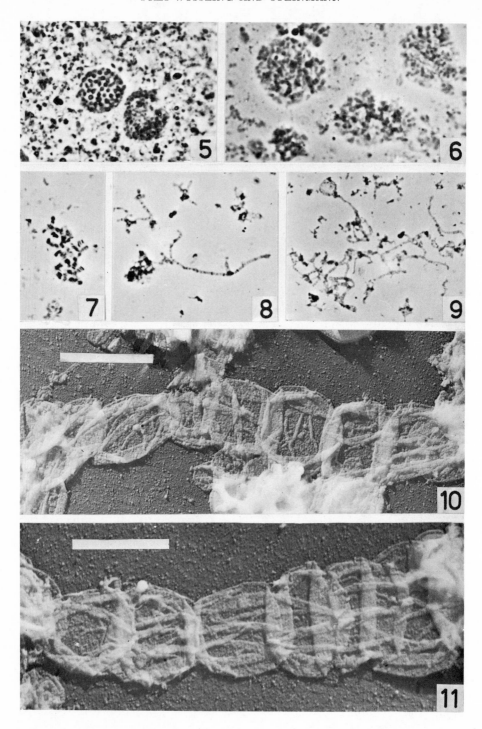

and lipid by saponification does not occur in a neutral sucrose solution. It is plainly the lipoproteid which swells.

This swelling is extremely irregular and it is not known which factors determine whether it occurs slowly or explosively. Figure 13 shows another spinach chloroplast which (as in Fig. 12) was also isolated in 0.5 M sucrose. On one side the stroma is swollen to form three large vesicles, whereas on the other side only incipient bumps are visible. The surface of the vesicle is coagulated or denatured as a result of contact with the suspending medium. As a result of drying during specimen preparation these vesicles collapse and their skins lie in folds.

The vesicles formed by swelling of the stroma during chloroplast preparation attain many different sizes but their surfaces always form a continuous skin which then collapses into folds. They are thus easily distinguished from myelin figures which lie flat on the support film, sometimes covering enclosed grana (Frey-Wyssling and Mühlethaler, 1949). Sometimes one of these vesicles covers an entire chloroplast like a cap, and subsequently collapses in folds, simulating a chloroplast membrane. We described it as such in 1949 in this journal but now believe this precipitation membrane is not a chloroplast envelope but an artifact.

This should not by any means be taken as positive evidence against the existence of a plastid envelope. The cross section in Figure 2 shows a marked thickening at the plastid surface which, to be sure, is clearly bordered only at the outer side. On the other hand, it has yet to be demonstrated that the observed precipitation membrane represents the denatured, swollen plastid surface film.

That no grana are visible in the swollen plastids illustrated in Figures 13 and 16 is due perhaps to the fact that the grana protein are also swollen and participate in the swelling of the vesicle or the formation of the precipitation membrane.

The vesicles described here have often been seen (cf. Kausche and Ruska, 1940; Menke, 1940; Algera et al., 1947). All workers always note their very variable diameter. Menke was the first to identify them correctly as "protein lamellae." Because shadowing techniques had not yet been perfected in 1940, the folds in these lamellae, which demonstrate their vesicular origins, could not be observed.

---

PLATE II. *Aspidistra* chloroplasts.

FIGURE 5. Intact *Aspidistra* chloroplasts in a (granaaufschlamung). Isolation medium: 1 M sucrose. Phase contrast, oil immersion. × 1,100.

FIGURE 6. Slightly swollen *Aspidistra* chloroplasts. Medium: 0.5 M sucrose. Phase contrast, oil immersion. × 1,100.

FIGURE 7. A row of grana from *Aspidistra* chloroplasts. Stroma swollen. Medium: 1 M sucrose and subsequent addition of 1% $OsO_4$. Phase contrast, oil immersion. × 1,100.

FIGURES 8 AND 9. *Aspidistra* grana swollen in distilled water. Fixation in 1% $OsO_4$. Phase contrast, oil immersion. × 1,100.

FIGURES 10 AND 11. *Aspidistra* grana swollen in distilled water. Fixed in 1% $OsO_4$, shadowed with chromium and observed in the electron microscope. The white bar on the micrograph indicates 1 $\mu$. Figure 10, × 26,000; Figure 11, × 27,000.

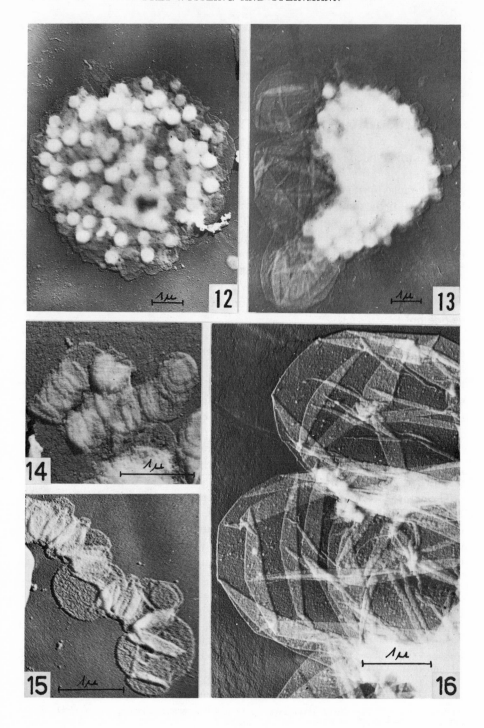

As a result of studies on swelling, using potassium thiocyanate and other salts which strongly induce swelling, Strugger (1951) noted ballooning of the stroma in the light microscope (Fig. 1b). He was of the opinion that the lamellae which appeared following his treatments must previously have existed in the chloroplast stroma as a carrier for the grana. Such a carrier membrane would be visible in cross sections of the chloroplast, but neither the electron micrograph in Figure 2 nor any other investigation in the electron microscope shows any trace of such a lamellae.

We have also investigated KCNS-treated maize chloroplasts, a prime example showing balloon-like swelling. The lamellae prepared in this way (Fig. 16) appear the same as those shown in Figure 13. It is therefore reasonable that here again a precipitation membrane is formed by contact of stroma protein with the suspension medium. The swelling phenomena illustrated in Figure 1b may thus be understood as resulting from formation of a precipitation membrane at the plastid surface, diffusion of suspending medium through this membrane, and formation of a second precipitation membrane within the first. Unprecipitated protein would contribute to swelling these two membranes apart, and the process would repeat itself, in the fashion of Liesegang rings, until the suspension medium had fully penetrated the chloroplast from both sides.

Although it is clear that some sort of layered structure exists in the grana-free chloroplasts of the Zygnematales (Frey-Wyssling and Steinmann, 1948; Steinmann, 1952a), evidence of such a layering in higher plant chloroplasts has so far been restricted to the grana.

The stroma protein can apparently become stringy so that chromidia-like strands develop. Thomas, Bustraan, and Paris (1952) observed such strands in spinach chloroplasts, using their preparation techniques which involve grinding the leaves in phosphate buffer, pH 6.0, centrifuging, transferring to 10 percent sucrose, and finally lipid digestion. We have not observed such strands in our experiments. The published photographs appear to show that the protein aggregates, visible in their Figure 3, are stuck together in linear fashion by a second kind of protein. The authors named the granulations in these strands "chromidia" and called the portions holding the chromidium particles together "interchromidia." They note that the chromidia scattered electrons 1.4 times as strongly as the interchromidia (Bustraan, Goedheer, and Thomas, 1952). It is therefore probable that two kinds of proteins exist in the stroma.

---

PLATE III. Chloroplasts in the electron microscope. Chromium shadowing.

FIGURE 12. Spinach chloroplast isolated in 0.5 M sucrose. Initiation of stroma swelling. No chloroplast membrane.

FIGURE 13. As in Figure 12, swelling on one side.

FIGURES 14 AND 15. Spinach grana from leaves cut in 5% formaldehyde. FIGURE 14. Grana broken into elementary lamellae (compared with Fig. 3). FIGURE 15. Individual elementary lamellae somewhat swollen.

FIGURE 16. "Stroma lamellae" from maize chloroplasts, appearing in the electron microscope as vesicular skins. Prepared according to Strugger in 0.6 M KCNS and then fixed in 1% $OsO_4$.

## SUMMARY

The chlorophyll-containing grana of chloroplasts are composed of elementary lamellae which appear to be bimolecular layers of protein (Fig. 4).

The chlorophyll-free stroma is composed of a globular lipoprotein macromolecule which can easily be seen in the electron microscope. This stroma protein is unusually liable to swelling, and forms a precipitation membrane upon contact with aqueous solutions (Figs. 13 and 16). The membrane which Strugger identified as a "carrier lamellae," and which is frequently observed during the balloon-like swelling of chloroplasts, may be such a precipitation membrane.

## REFERENCES

Algera, L., Beyer, J. J., v. Iterson, W., Karstens, W. K. H., and Thung, T. H. Some data on the structure of the chloroplast, obtained by electron microscopy. *Biochim. Biophys. Acta,* 1: 517, 1947.

Bustraan, M., Goedheer, J. C., and Thomas, J. B. On the electron scattering power of protein structure in the spinach chloroplast. *Biochim. Biophys. Acta,* 9: 499, 1952.

Frey-Wyssling, A. Morphological aspects of the lipo-proteins in chloroplasts. *Disc. Faraday Soc.,* No. 6, p. 130, 1949.

————. Submicroscopic morphology of protoplasm. 3rd ed. Amsterdam and New York, 1953.

————, and Mühlethaler, K. Über den Feinbau der Chlorophyllkörner. *Vierteljahrsschrift Naturf. Ges.* (Zürich), 94: 179, 1949.

————, and Steinmann, E. Die Schichtendoppelbrechung grosser Chloroplasten. *Biochim. Biophys. Acta,* 2: 254, 1948.

Granick, S. The structural and functional relationships between heme and chlorophyll. *Harvey Lectures* (Springfield, Ill.), 44: 220, 1948.

————, and Porter, K. R. The structure of the spinach chloroplast as interpreted with the electron microscope. *Amer. J. Bot.,* 34: 545, 1947.

Jung, F. Strukturprobleme am roten Blutkörperchen. *Naturw.,* 37: 229, 1950.

Kausche, G. A., and Ruska, H. Zur Frage der Chloroplastenstruktur. *Naturw.,* 28: 303, 1940.

Menke, W. Untersuchungen über den Feinbau des Protoplasmas in dem Universal-Elektronenmikroskop. *Protoplasma,* 35: 115, 1940.

Sjöstrand, F. S. An electron microscope study of the retinal rods of the guinea pig eye. *J. Cell. Comp. Physiol.,* 33: 383, 1949.

Steinmann, E. Contribution to the structure of granular chloroplasts. *Experientia,* 8: 300, 1952a.

————. An electron microscope study of the lamellar structure of chloroplasts. *Exp. Cell. Res.,* 3: 267, 1952b.

Stoll, A. Zusammenhänge zwischen der Chemie des Chlorophylls und seiner Funktion in der Photosynthese. *Naturw.,* 24: 53, 1936.

Strugger, S. Weitere Untersuchungen über die Vitalfärbung der Plastiden mit Rhodaminen. *Flora,* 31: 324, 1937.

————. Über den Bau der Proplastiden und Chloroplasten. *Naturw.,* 37: 166, 1950.

————. Die Strukturordnung im Chloroplasten. *Ber. deutsche bot. Ges.,* 64: 69, 1951.

Thomas, J. B. A note on the occurrence of grana in algae and in photosynthesizing bacteria. *Proc. Acad. Sci.* (Amsterdam), C 55: 207, 1952.

Thomas, J. B., Bustraan, M., and Paris, C. H. On the structure of the spinach chloroplast. *Biochim. Biophys. Acta,* 8: 90, 1952.

Weber, F. Myelinfiguren und Sphärolithe aus Spirogyra-Chloroplasten. *Protoplasma,* 19: 455, 1933.

# A MACROMOLECULAR REPEATING UNIT OF

# MITOCHONDRIAL STRUCTURE AND FUNCTION

Correlated Electron Microscopic and Biochemical

Studies of Isolated Mitochondria and Submitochondrial

Particles of Beef Heart Muscle

## H. FERNÁNDEZ-MORÁN, M.D., T. ODA, M.D.,
## P. V. BLAIR, Ph.D., and D. E. GREEN, Ph.D.

From the Mixter Laboratories for Electron Microscopy, Neurosurgical Service, Massachusetts General Hospital, Boston, and The Department of Biophysics, University of Chicago; and the Institute for Enzyme Research, University of Wisconsin, Madison. Dr. Fernández-Morán's present address is Department of Biophysics, University of Chicago. Dr. Oda's present address is Department of Pathology, Okayama University Medical School, Okayama, Japan

ABSTRACT

A repeating particle associated with the cristae and the inner membrane of the external envelope has been recognized and characterized in beef heart mitochondria by correlated electron microscopic and biochemical studies. Many thousands ($ca.$ $10^4$ to $10^5$) of these particles, disposed in regular arrays, are present in a single mitochondrion. The repeating particle, called the elementary particle (EP), consists of three parts: (1) a spherical or polyhedral head piece (80 to 100 A in diameter); (2) a cylindrical stalk (about 50 A long and 30 to 40 A wide); and (3) a base piece (40 × 110 A). The base pieces of the elementary particles form an integral part of the outer dense layers of the cristae. The elementary particles can be seen in electron micrographs of mitochondria $in$ $situ$, of isolated mitochondria, and of submitochondrial particles with a complete electron transfer chain. Negative staining with phosphotungstate is only one of several techniques that can be used for reproducible demonstration of the repeating particles and underlying subunit organization of mitochondrial membranes. A particulate unit containing a complete electron transfer chain can be isolated from beef heart mitochondria. The isolated unit approximates in size that of the elementary particle $in$ $situ$. The molecular weight of the particle $in$ $situ$ is calculated to be $1.3 \times 10^6$. Evidence is presented for identifying the isolated unit with the elementary particle visualized $in$ $situ$. The elementary particle of the mitochondrion is believed to be a prototype of a class of functional particles or macromolecular assemblies of similar size found in association with membranes generally.

INTRODUCTION

The pioneering electron microscope studies of Palade (53, 54) and Sjöstrand (67, 68) established more than a decade ago the distinctive fine structure of the mitochondrion as essentially that of an elongated subcellular body bounded by a membrane consisting of two layers. The external layer

Reprinted by permission of H. Fernández-Morán and The Rockefeller University Press from the *Journal of Cellular Biology*, **22**, 63–100 (1964).

is considered to be the limiting membrane, while regular infoldings of the inner membrane form numerous internal ridges termed "*cristae*" by Palade. During the same period the mitochondrion was identified as the locale of citric cycle oxidations, electron transfer, and oxidative phosphorylation (49, 65). The concept of the mitochondrion as an organized system in which there was a precise arrangement of the many enzymes involved in the sequential reactions underlying mitochondrial function (32, 36, 50) became firmly established in biochemical thinking.

Large scale isolation of stable mitochondria (33, 51) under conditions which do not impair their main enzymic activities has made these highly organized, membranous organelles available for chemical analysis. Equally important, there are multiple, exact criteria by which the functional integrity of the mitochondrion can be evaluated. Of all the specialized lamellar systems, mitochondria appeared, therefore, to be particularly well suited for a study of correlations between biochemical function and ultrastructure (23–25, 37).

Respiratory energy transformations have been shown to take place in the organized membrane structures of the mitochondrion. The mitochondrial membranes contain the different multi-enzyme complexes involved in these transformations; these complexes are arranged in highly ordered arrays (33, 37, 40, 51). Although the first phase of the fine structural analysis of the mitochondrion (53, 54, 67) established the base line for a correlation of structure and function (4, 14, 65, 79, 80), the shortcomings of the preparative techniques and of the resolution of the electron microscope limited the extent of meaningful correlation. With mitochondria, as with other lamellar systems (18, 68, 78), it is now apparent that the submicroscopic patterns of sectioned specimens fixed with osmium tetroxide reveal merely a general structural framework consisting essentially of lipoprotein. Thus, in the mitochondrial membranes only certain stereotyped, uniform features of the "osmium-stained" smooth membranes are seen, with no indications of the specific enzymic complexes and other constituents. The mitochondrion is a lamellar system in which the biochemical and enzymic properties are better characterized than is the ultrastructure.

Recent improvements in preparative techniques, particularly that of negative staining applied to the study of virus ultrastructure (7, 8), have made possible the examination of biological systems in far greater detail than could heretofore be achieved in sectioned material. Fortunately, mitochondria (both those seen *in situ* and after isolation), by virtue of their ultrathin membranes, are particularly suitable for application of many of these new techniques which do not necessarily require sectioning (16, 23).

Three years ago, we applied these techniques, including negative staining and improved low temperature methods which yield better morphological and histochemical preservation in sectioned material (20–23), to the study of mitochondria. These techniques, combined with improved high-resolution electron microscopy, revealed for the first time the presence of a characteristic polyhedral or round structural unit, 80 to 100 A in diameter, as a basic component of mitochondrial membranes (23, 25, 26). This finding casts a new light on our views of the organization of the mitochondrion. Recognition of this repeating particulate subunit, which we designated "elementary particle" (EP), was the starting point for a program of biochemical isolation.

In essence, the experimental approach of our studies correlating structure with function involved fragmentation of mitochondria into subunits. The mitochondrion was, in effect, treated as a chemical entity capable of stepwise disassembly into its component parts (and reassembly into the original unit) (40). This approach, from a biochemical point of view, has already led to the discovery of new electron transfer components such as coenzyme Q, and of proteins containing non-heme iron and copper. The study of electron transfer in intact cells and in particles containing the respiratory chain (as exemplified by the studies of Chance and his collaborators (9, 10) has been of great value in promoting understanding of the over-all kinetics and the sequence of oxidoreduction of the spectroscopically visible components of the respiratory chain. A third approach involved reconstitution of a fully functional electron transfer particle from its purified segments and from the highly purified and independent component parts (37, 44, 45).

Studies on the stepwise degradation of the mitochondrion into particles of decreasing complexity have led to the recognition of three basic components of mitochondrial organization: (1) the particulate electron transfer chain; (2) the insoluble network composed of structural protein and lipid; and (3) the "solubilizable" dehydrogenase complexes. This was the biochemical picture at the time when the collaborative effort of our two laboratories began.

Sonic irradiation dissociates mitochondria into a particulate structured fraction and a soluble fraction; this resolution makes it clear that there cannot be a single mitochondrial subunit which is all-embracing, but rather several subunits depending upon the function under consideration. We are particularly concerned here with the subunit that contains the complete electron transfer chain—the apparatus for the transfer of electrons from succinate and DPNH to molecular oxygen

We have worked mainly with mitochondria prepared from beef heart muscle, because they are relatively stable and can be isolated on a large scale; an additional advantage of heart mitochondria over liver mitochondria is their higher density of cristae per unit volume with a correspondingly greater oxidative rate. By careful comminution of beef heart mitochondria in a sucrose medium, well defined fractions were prepared, one of which (ETP) contains particles with an essentially intact electron transfer chain, divested of the primary dehydrogenating enzyme complexes. The capacity for both electron transfer and oxidative phosphorylation was retained in an analogous particle (ETP$_H$). Electron microscopic studies of these submitochondrial fractions by standard osmium fixation and thin sectioning techniques (14, 33, 79, 80) indicated that the double-membraned structure was preserved in specimens of ETP$_H$, whereas only a single-membraned structure was observed in ETP. More extensive correlation of fine structure with function, however, could not be achieved in these early investigations.

Concentrating on the electron transfer particle (ETP) as the primary unit of mitochondrial function, Green and his colleagues (33, 37, 40) succeeded in isolating and characterizing eleven oxidation-reduction components of the electron transfer chain. At least nine proteins with oxidation-reduction groups participate in the terminal electron transfer process. Approximately 30 per cent of the total dry weight of the mitochondrion and of the ETP is accounted for by lipids, the bulk of which (95 per cent) is phospholipid (29 b). Green and Oda (38) tentatively assumed, from preliminary data, that the structural unit of

ETP was a cylindrical particle about 445 A long and 100 A in diameter, with a particle weight of the order of 4.3 million.

Three developments have pointed to a downward revision of the estimated value proposed (38) as the molecular weight of the repeating unit of the electron transfer particle: (1) the demonstration by Fernández-Morán (23, 25) that the membrane structure of isolated mitochondria and subfractions appeared to be built up of paired arrays of the 80 to 100 A particles, noted above, separated by a "middle" or mesolayer of variable width; (2) the isolation by Green et al. (12, 13, 39) of a structural protein, devoid of oxidation-reduction groups, accounting for 60 to 70 per cent of the total mitochondrial protein; (3) the resolution of the electron transfer chain into four complexes functionally independent (44, 45), each of high purity, and the reconstruction of the original particle with essentially undiminished activity by recombination of the four complexes carried out by Hatefi and his colleagues (30, 44, 45). The postulated molecular weight of $4.3 \times 10^6$ for the electron transfer chain was hardly compatible with the dimensions of the 80 to 100 A repeating unit seen by Fernández-Morán. The observation that a large proportion of the total protein of the mitochondrion was not concerned with the electron transfer process per se suggested the possibility that the electron transfer particle as isolated could be resolved into a fraction containing structural protein and a fraction containing the electron transfer chain. The latter unit would have a calculated molecular weight of 1 to $2 \times 10^6$; this value would bring the size of the unit better into line with the dimensions of the repeating particle seen by the electron microscope. The particle weight of the reconstructed electron transfer chain (from the four purified complexes) was estimated to be $1.4 \times 10^6$ on a protein basis, calculated from the known particle weights of each of the four constituent complexes (established from composition and ultracentrifuge data). These developments made the conclusion inescapable that the molecular weight of the unit of electron transfer had to be no more than 1 to $2 \times 10^6$ and led us to a program directed toward isolation of a unit of electron transfer of molecular weight less than that of ETP. Indeed, such a particle has been isolated (5). It contains the complete electron transfer chain with all the components in the same molecular ratios as those found in the mitochon-

**221**

drial electron transfer chain. Increase in activity and increase in concentration of the oxidation-reduction proteins per unit weight run parallel throughout all but the last stage in the purification. The molecular weight of the particle at the highest purity level attained is $1.4 \times 10^6$ on a protein basis (this would correspond to a molecular weight of $2 \times 10^6$ for the lipoprotein complex). The particle reconstructed from the four isolated complexes has a molecular weight that corresponds closely to that of the integrated particle isolated directly from the mitochondrion.

In consequence of these developments, we have elected to designate the particle obtained both by isolation and by reconstruction as the elementary particle, and we have postulated that the isolated or reconstructed elementary particle corresponds to the repeating particle with a head piece of 80 to 100 A, a stalk, and a base piece, seen in electron micrographs.

After the initial phase was completed, resulting in a definition of the basic structural parameters of the new repeating particle and the establishment of its relationship to the mitochondrial membranes, it remained to be established that the visualized particle is a *bona fide* constituent of the membrane system. Mitochondria from a wide variety of sources were examined and the preparative procedures for the electron microscopic examination were carefully checked for the possibility of artifact formation. In addition, a complete set of particles was examined ranging in size from the mitochondrion to the individual complexes; an internal control of artifact formation thus became available since only particles with a complete electron transfer chain could be expected to constitute the repeating unit.

The present communication will deal specifically with: (1) the electron microscopic evidence of the existence of a repeating particle in whole mitochondria and in those submitochondrial particles that have intact electron transfer chains; (2) the isolation and properties of the particles; (3) the experimental basis for identifying the isolated or reconstituted particle with the repeating particle visualized by the electron microscope. Preliminary accounts of facets of the present study have been reported elsewhere (23–27, 34).

## MATERIALS AND METHODS

MATERIALS: In the course of extensive correlative studies, mitochondria from many sources were examined either *in situ* or after isolation from heart muscle, retina, liver, pancreas, and brain of the rat, mouse, beef, chicken, and guinea pig; but the principal effort was directed to the study of isolated beef heart mitochondria.

ISOLATION OF MITOCHONDRIA: Large scale isolation of mitochondria from beef heart muscle was carried out under conditions that minimized contamination by other cell particulates and by myosin (5, 11). Suspensions in 0.5 M sucrose (kept at 0 to 5°) conformed to the most rigorous standards for preservation of mitochondrial structure and activity. Two alternative preparative procedures were used. In the first procedure ground beef heart muscle homogenized in 0.5 M sucrose at pH 7.0 and the mitochondrial fraction is separated from other structures and compounds by differential centrifugation. In turn, the mitochondrial fraction is refractionated; a heavy fraction containing only intact whole mitochondria with well preserved cristae is collected. For ease of presentation the details of this preparative procedure are summarized in Table I. In the second procedure ground beef heart muscle was suspended in 0.66 M sucrose and treated with Nagarse proteinase according to the method of Hagihara (43). In the Hagihara method the use of the high speed blendor is eliminated. The proteolytic enzyme attacks the myofibrils and connective tissue and thus releases mitochondria from the muscle mass.

We have found no recognizable difference in the purity or integrity of the mitochondria prepared by the two procedures outlined above. Both types of preparations were used for electron microscopy of intact mitochondria. Freezing of the suspensions was avoided and generally no more than 8 to 24 hours intervened between the preparation of the mitochondria and examination by electron microscopy.

ELEMENTARY PARTICLES: The detailed procedure for the isolation of elementary particles has been described in the companion article by Blair *et al.* (5). A summary of the preparative procedure is given in Table II. It should be pointed out that elementary particles isolated from the standard preparation of mitochondria in 0.25 M sucrose are equally as satisfactory as those prepared from mitochondria that had been purified more rigorously for good electron microscopy.

The mitochondrial suspensions which served as the starting point for the isolation of EP had "theoretical" P/O ratios (the value was two for succinate and three for pyruvate plus malate). Furthermore, they showed all the characteristics of intact mitochondria: non-reduction of external cytochrome $c$ or DPN$^+$, non-oxidation of external DPNH, non-oxidation of citrate or isocitrate, low rate of oxidation for succinate and negligible ATPase activity.

Essentially the isolation of the elementary particle

222

involves a quantitative separation of the mitochondrial subunits; this separation is achieved by ammonium sulfate fractionation of mitochondria that have been frozen in presence of 0.3 per cent KCl washed with 0.9 per cent KCl, and finally "solubilized" with a mixture of cholate and deoxycholate. The insoluble structural protein fraction sediments at low concentrations of ammonium sulfate; the floating fraction containing the elementary particle separates at about 0.5 saturation; the soluble fraction (not precipitated by 0.5 saturation) contains some of the primary dehydrogenase complexes and cytochrome $c$.

When the procedure outlined in Table II is repeated, the elementary particle thus obtained is stripped further of contaminating structural protein and is correspondingly enriched with respect to the oxidation-reduction components. Thus, the cytochrome $a$ content of the one-cycle material is about 2.8 m$\mu$moles per mg of protein and of the two-cycle material as high as 4.2 m$\mu$moles per mg of protein.

For ultracentrifugal and x-ray scattering analyses,

TABLE I

*Method for Large Scale Preparation of Mitochondria in 0.5 M Sucrose*

1. Suspend 3200 gm of ground beef heart muscle in 9.6 l. of 0.5 M sucrose containing 0.02 M $K_2HPO_4$ (final volume *ca.* 13 l.).
2. Adjust pH to 7.0 with N KOH and filter the suspension through cheese cloth (double layer). The filtered residue is resuspended in 9.6 l. of 0.5 M sucrose containing 0.02 M phosphate buffer of pH 7.0.
3. Homogenize in macro Waring blendor for 1 min. with the rheostat setting at 60. Neutralize the suspension with N KOH to pH 7.0.
4. Two fractions are removed after centrifugation at 0–5°: $R_1$—after centrifugation for 20 min. at 1600 $g$ (13-liter refrigerated centrifuge); $R_2$—after centrifugation at 50,000 $g$ in the Sharples continuous centrifuge.
5. $R_2$ is resuspended in 1 l. of a mixture 0.5 M in sucrose and 0.01 M in phosphate (pH 7.0); the homogenized suspension is centrifuged at 15,000 $g$ for 20 min. The residue consists of a well packed as well as a loosely packed layer. The two layers are separated, suspended in about 500 ml of the sucrose-phosphate medium, and the homogenized suspensions are recentrifuged at 15,000 $g$ for 20 min. The suspension prepared from the well packed residue layer on centrifugation yields a predominantly well packed layer topped by a small layer of loosely packed material. Only the well packed material is resuspended in 0.5 M sucrose and this suspension constitutes the final mitochondrial preparation.

TABLE II

*Summary of the Procedure for Isolation of Elementary Particles from Beef Heart Mitochondria*
(Blair *et al.*, 5)

1. Standard large scale isolation of beef heart mitochondria by the method of Crane *et al.* (9). Suspension medium—0.25 M sucrose.
2. Freezing of mitochondria in a mixture containing 0.3% KCl and 0.17 M sucrose and then washing the thawed mitochondria in 0.9% KCl. Residue resuspended in 0.66 M sucrose to a final sucrose concentration of 0.3 M.
3. Mitochondria exposed to deoxycholate (0.3 mg per mg protein) and cholate (0.3 mg/mg protein) at pH 8.0 (0.02 M Tris buffer) and fractionated with saturated ammonium sulfate. The first fraction at 33 per cent saturation was discarded; the second at 50 per cent saturation (floating pellet) was retained.
4. Floating pellet diluted to 0.5 mg of protein per ml in 0.25 M sucrose and sedimented at 30,000 RPM (4 hours). Pellet resuspended in buffered 0.25 M sucrose; the suspension was clarified by sonic irradiation. Insoluble material was removed by centrifugation. The clear supernatant solution contains a fine suspension of the elementary particles.

the suspension of elementary particles (two cycles of treatment; 20 mg of protein per ml) was "solubilized" with $1.5 \times 10^{-3}$ M sodium phosphotungstate in presence of 0.2 per cent $\alpha$-tocopherol (to minimize lipid peroxidation). The particles were separated into a tightly packed sediment which was discarded, and a translucent liquid precipitate which was used for physical measurements as well as for electron microscopy.

COMPLEXES OF THE ELECTRON TRANSFER CHAIN: The four complexes that make up the electron transfer chain were prepared by the following procedures: succinic-coenzyme Q reductase by the method of Ziegler and Doeg (81), or of Tisdale et al. (75 a); DPNH-coenzyme Q reductase by the method of Hatefi et al. (47); QH$_2$—cytochrome reductase by the method of Rieske, Zaugg, and Wharton (61); and cytochrome oxidase by the method of Griffiths and Wharton (42) or that of Wharton and Tzagoloff (77). These four complexes interact to form a reconstituted elementary particle under the conditions specified by Hatefi et al. (44, 45) and by Fowler and Richardson (30).

ELECTRON TRANSFER PARTICLE: The electron transfer particle with phosphorylating properties (ETP$_H$) was prepared from heavy beef heart mitochondria by the method of Smith and Hansen (69).

## METHODS OF ELECTRON MICROSCOPY

A variety of complementary methods was applied in the course of the correlated studies of mitochondria.

The principal preparation procedures used can be classified as follows:

1. Modified negative staining techniques requiring minimal preparative manipulations were mainly used. These techniques do not involve sectioning, but only extension or surface spreading of whole mitochondria and mitochondrial membranes.

2. Thin sectioning of mitochondria by standard and modified techniques for fixation and embedding.

3. Cryofixation and related low temperature preparation techniques. Most of the results described in this report were obtained with methods of group 1, which will be described in greater detail.

## 1. Preparation of Mitochondria by Modified Negative Staining Techniques

(a) Isolated mitochondria suspended in microdroplets of a sucrose solution containing 0.1 to 1 per cent potassium phosphotungstate (pH 7.2) are sandwiched between carbon-coated plastic films, or impermeable single-crystal graphite, or mica lamellae in vacuum-tight microchambers of special design (20–25). When used in combination with low-intensity microbeam illumination and controlled specimen cooling (0° to −130°C), this technique for electron microscopy of wet or partly hydrated biological systems yielded the first useful pictures of the regular mitochondrial membrane particles (23). Cytochrome $c$ can be used instead of phosphotungstate to enhance contrast through "negative staining" by embedding flattened mitochondrial membrane

FIGURES 1 and 2 a   Thin sections of isolated beef heart mitochondria, "Nagarse" preparations (0.66 M sucrose); osmium fixation, low temperature embedding in methacrylate stained with Pb(OH)$_2$. Note regularity of cristae and preservation of fine structure. Fig. 1 $\times$ 180,000; Fig. 2 a, $\times$ 130,000.

FIGURE 2 b   Enlargement of Fig. 2 a demonstrating particulate subunit structure in dense outer layers of each crista. $\times$ 650,000.

FIGURE 3   Enlarged segment of loop of a crista in a specimen similar to that shown in Fig. 2 a. Clearly visible array of globular subunits about 70 to 80 A in diameter. $\times$ 500,000.

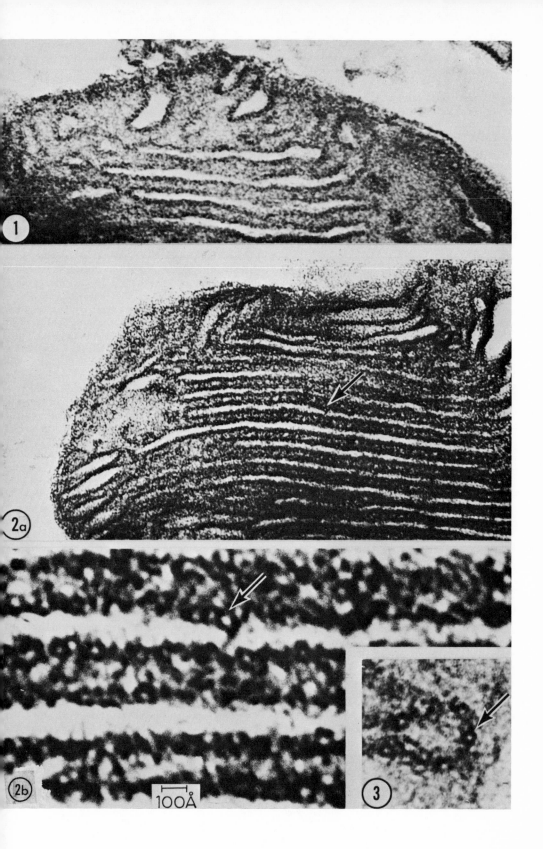

in the ultrathin liquid layers (*ca.* 500 to 1000 A) which are enclosed between the microchamber film "windows." Since this technique essentially yields negative staining of wet specimens without most of the usual drying artifacts, it is proving to be indispensable for studies of labile membrane structures and lipoprotein systems under conditions approaching the native hydrated state.

(*b*) *Surface cell-film method* was used in combination with positive or negative staining and related variants of our original technique (16) for spreading mitochondria (either as isolated or *in situ*) on a liquid surface to form an ultrathin layer. This can be picked up directly on a specimen grid and examined directly or after suitable staining and shadow-casting. The best results were obtained by using the valuable modification introduced by D. Parsons (55, 56) which embodies the advantages of negative staining–embedding. This simple method was carried out by inserting a clean glass needle or a freshly cleaved mica surface into the specimen of native tissue or the mitochondrial suspension without prior fixation. The needle or mica surface coated with the specimen was then dipped slowly into a 1 to 2 per cent sodium- or potassium phosphotungstate solution at pH 7.2, preferably cooled to 0° to 4°, and ultra-filtered (using 10 m$\mu$ Millipore filters). The mitochondrial membrane specimen spreads out into an exquisitely preserved ultrathin layer floating on the liquid surface. This coherent surface film (only a few hundred A thick and even less in certain areas) is picked up directly on a thin Formvar specimen support, carrying with it a tenuous phosphotungstate layer. Upon drying (preferably in a cold chamber at 0°–4°), this phosphotungstate film forms an amorphous embedding matrix of high electron opacity, and provides both protection against surface tension artifacts and excellent negative contrast. These spread-cell preparations are ideally suited for high resolution electron microscopy of mitochondrial membranes and related lamellar systems, provided the specimens are examined immediately under appropriate conditions to reduce irradiation damage and contamination. Thus, remarkable integrity of the fine structure of the membrane system of an entire mitochondrion is obtained which compares favorably with that observed in the best ultrathin sections. This simple technique is susceptible of further refinement by spreading the specimens against constant pressure, spreading on undercooled liquid surfaces, or on clean mercury surfaces, etc. Also, by spreading the native mitochondria on solutions of buffered formalin, glutaraldehyde, osmium tetroxide, or potassium dichromate (0.1 to 2 per cent) the effects of prior fixation can be studied in detail.

(*c*) *Microdroplet cross-spraying techniques* (23, 24) were used routinely in the study of mitochondrial membranes and isolated particles requiring minimal exposure to reagents, and a high degree of reproducibility. With the use of a special multiple-spraying device with suitably arranged separate capillaries for specimens and reagents, it is possible to obtain controlled, brief interaction of microdroplets of the specimen with microdroplets of 1 to 2 per cent potassium phosphotungstate at pH 7.2, uranyl acetate, or other heavy metal solutions. The cross-sprayed microdroplets collide and interact very rapidly shortly before impinging on the specimen grid. The twofold advantage is hereby gained of imposing predetermined spatial and temporal constraints on the specimen-reagent system during a highly reproducible preparative process. This method has to be contrasted with the standard negative staining procedure by which the PTA reagent is mixed with the specimen, and can produce variable degrees of modification before being sprayed and dried on the support. Moreover, as a result of the small size and relatively high speed of the cross-sprayed microdroplets, there is a favorable concurrence of rapid specimen cooling and limited drying to achieve a unique degree of preservation of the most labile structures (24). Finally, this technique is easily carried out and permits rapid processing of a large number of specimens. In the present studies it was used for examination of all critical specimens, and to investigate the effects of fixation agents and heavy metal solutions on the fine structure of native mitochondrial components.

Interesting results were obtained in the study of isolated EP (Fig. 20) by combining positive or negative staining of cross-sprayed microdroplets with subsequent shadow-casting at an extremely low shadowing angle (using platinum, or platinum-carbon

FIGURE 4  Negatively stained beef heart mitochondrion; isolated in 0.5 M sucrose, and prepared by surface spreading on 1 per cent potassium phosphotungstate at pH 7.2 without prior fixation. Partly intact whole mount of flattened mitochondrial membranes showing regular arrangement of repeating particulate components. $\times$ 62,000.

FIGURE 5  Profile view of cristae with arrays of elementary particles (EP) in enlarged segment of Fig. 4. Polyhedral head pieces of the elementary particles are attached by stalks to the continuous dense outer layers of the cristae. $\times$ 420,000.

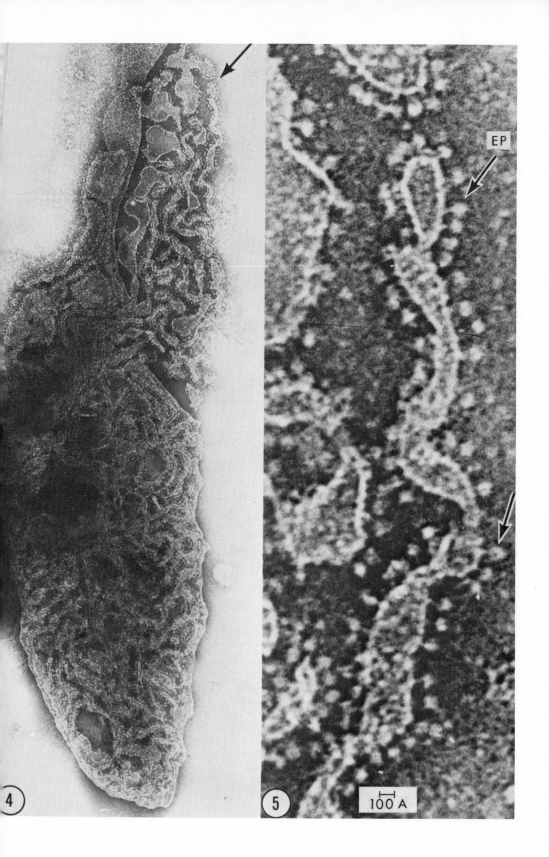

evaporation in a vacuum system with liquid nitrogen cold-trap). The resulting reproducible "surface decoration" patterns may provide information on the underlying subunit structure of isolated EP.

For attainment of highest resolution the carbon-coated, fenestrated specimen films (29) were used without the normal ultrathin film supports (cast from 0.05 per cent Formvar solutions in ultrafiltered ethylene chloride). Instead, extremely thin embedding supports bridging the holes of the fenestrated film (ca. 100 to 1000 A in diameter) were obtained by the addition of very dilute (0.01 to 0.05 per cent) sodium silicate, gelatin, or gum arabic solutions to the specimen, preferably applied through microdroplet cross-spraying (24).

## 2. Thin Sectioning Techniques

In addition to the standard osmium fixation or glutaraldehyde fixation procedure followed by methacrylate or Araldite embedding and thin sectioning, the following two variants proved useful in the study of mitochondrial fine structure:

a. Negative staining—embedding of ultrathin sections. Fresh tissues or mitochondrial suspensions (either unfixed and dried, or partially fixed by formalin vapor, or by ultraviolet irradiation) were sectioned without embedding by a diamond knife mounted on a Moran-Leitz ultramicrotome. When these coherent ultrathin sections were collected directly on a 1 to 2 per cent buffered phosphotungstate solution (pH 7) and picked up on filmed specimen grids, the fine structure of mitochondria and other lamellar systems showed up in striking negative contrast images. This favorable result is simply due to permeation of the "unsupported" ultrathin section by the "phosphotungstate glass" which acts as an "embedding" medium of high density and permits enhanced contrast and resolution. Despite its inherent limitations (mainly caused by drying artifacts), this interesting and simple approach has proved to be of value as a control procedure for the evaluation of negative staining in sectioned material. The results will be reported in a separate publication.

b. Ultrathin frozen sections of fresh tissues (24) prepared by cutting the frozen tissue with a diamond knife in a cryostat (at $-30°$ to $-180°C$) can also be examined directly without thawing by embedding the sections in vitrified heavy metal layers. A liquid nitrogen cooling device and appropriate low temperature methods of electron microscopy are required to implement this technique. However, numerous technical problems still remain to be solved before this method can be used routinely.

For thin sectioning of suspensions and pellets of isolated mitochondria and submitochondrial fractions (ETP), the technique described earlier (29 a) for examination of oriented Tobacco Mosaic Virus gels proved very useful. The pellets or suspensions were sucked into thin plastic capillaries (0.1 to 0.2 mm internal diameter). The specimen capillaries were cut into short segments which could then be stained, dehydrated, and embedded. Extraction and dehydration or embedding artifacts were considerably reduced, particularly when using low temperature preparation techniques.

c. Cryofixation and related low temperature techniques (19–23), including low-temperature dehydration and embedding in methacrylate after standard osmium fixation, were used primarily for control purposes in these studies.

ELECTRON MICROSCOPY: A Siemens Elmiskop I was used, operating mainly at 80 kv (also at 40, 60, and 100 kv for selected specimens). Improved pointed filaments (20) of single-crystal tungsten with a tip radius of 1 to 10 $\mu$ were used routinely with the double condenser system of the Elmiskop to provide intense microbeam illumination of high coherence and low angular divergence. With this arrangement, the image brightness (with a 2 to 10 $\mu$ spot size, beam current 2 to 8 $\mu$a at 80 kv) was adequate for direct observation of image detail at the highest electron optical magnifications. Using clean multiple objective apertures of copper or platinum (50 $\mu$), the astigmatism of the objective lens could be readily corrected under direct observation and reduced to less than 0.2 micron; for high resolution studies, the measured

FIGURE 6   Isolated beef heart mitochondrion embedded in thin phosphotungstate (PTA) layer. Prepared by microdroplet cross-spraying procedure involving only brief interaction of mitochondrial suspension in 0.5 M sucrose with 1 per cent PTA. Notice characteristic paired arrays of elementary particles in profiles of fragmented cristae, which are readily distinguishable from the envelope of the mitochondrion. × 120,000.

FIGURE 7   Enlarged segment of crista in a specimen similar to that shown in Fig. 6. Demonstration of three parts of the elementary particle: head piece, stalk, base piece. Invariant association of the arrays of head pieces EP with the underlying dense layer of crista. Segmentation and knob-like proturberance of dense layer at point of attachment of stalk × 600,000.

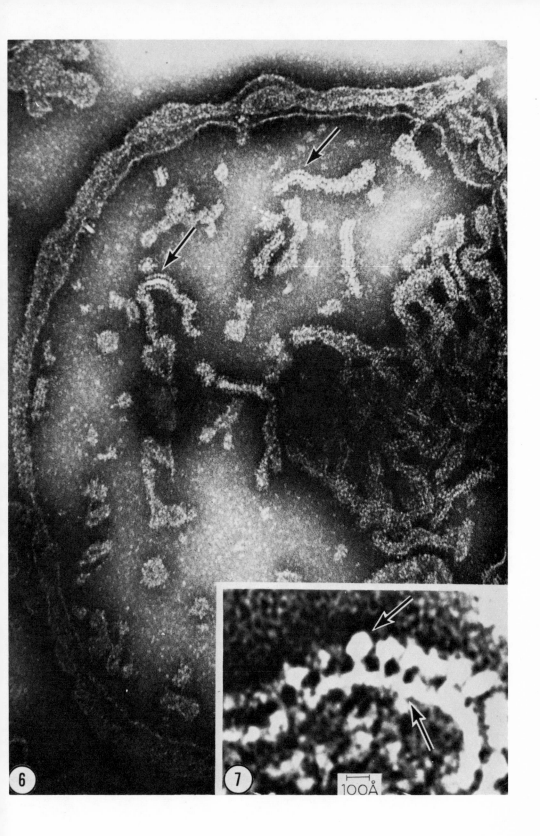

astigmatism of the objective lens was 0.1 $\mu$ or less. The higher efficiency of the pointed filament enabled us to use special Ilford High Resolution Plates as a routine (8 to 15 seconds exposure at 80,000 to 100,000 electron optical magnifications) for recording satisfactory electron micrographs which can be subsequently enlarged to yield higher useful magnifications than ordinary plates (22, 24). Conversely, it was also possible to obtain microbeams (0.5 to 2 $\mu$ in diameter) of extremely low intensity by using the new pointed filaments under appropriate conditions, and by providing the double condenser system (CII) with apertures of 50 to 100 $\mu$. This arrangement proved to be essential in examining certain highly labile membrane constituents. In fact, useful micrographs from these specimens could be recorded only on high-speed emulsions (e.g. 35 mm Tri X Kodak, sensitized with gold thiocyanate solutions) by first focusing on adjacent specimen areas, and then rapidly shifting the low-intensity microbeam to the preselected site. Irradiation damage and specimen contamination could be considerably reduced by using improved specimen cooling devices (Leisegang liquid nitrogen stage with special shielding apertures) in combination with low-intensity electron optics (19–24). For all critical measurements, calibration of the microscope was carried out at the time of recording the electron micrographs, using a diffraction grating replica carefully adjusted for the same specimen position. Ferritin molecules of uniform size (118 to 120 A diameter), prepared by density gradient ultracentrifugation and used by J. W. Anderegg and F. Fischback for x-ray scattering studies, were frequently used as an internal calibration reference for certain specimens. However, in all of these experiments particular care was taken to guard against possible contamination with apoferritin or modified ferritin particles by running parallel controls without addition of ferritin or other calibration markers. The observations described here are based on the evaluation of more than 3,000 plates and films, in which an average resolution of 10 to 20 A was consistently achieved.

## BIOCHEMICAL METHODS

The companion paper by Blair *et al.* (5) gives a full description of the methods of assay of the enzymic activity of mitochondria and submitochondrial particles and of the analytical methods used in quantifying the components in these particles.

## RESULTS

### Electron Microscopy of Isolated Mitochondria

Isolated beef heart mitochondria prepared as described in the section on Methods showed good preservation of form and fine structure. Routine checks were made for contamination of mitochondrial preparations with myofilaments, ribosomes, and other extraneous particulate material by systematic examination of pellets of isolated mitochondria. None of these contaminants were found in our standard preparations.

Since mitochondria are essentially fluid-filled vessels with an involuted internal membrane system of a few molecules in thickness, they are, in principle, well suited for direct examination without sectioning. Once the internal fluid has been removed, the collapsed and distended mitochondrial membranes can be permeated by buffered solutions of phosphotungstate and supported by negative staining embedding. The embedded layers are thin enough for high-resolution electron microscopy.

Disruption, dissociation, and spurious rearrangements of the delicate membrane structures must be taken into account as possible causes of artifacts. Various methods of negative staining were used to control the possibility of artifact formation. We have had no indication that the structures which are the principal subject of the present communication are products of a particular type of preparative procedure. On the con-

FIGURE 8  Enlarged portion of crista from specimen shown in Fig. 4. Notice characteristic knob-like structure of the base piece at the insertion point of each EP stalk. The base piece subunits and underlying regular segmented arrangement of dense layer discernible in both profile and surface view of crista. $\times$ 600,000.

FIGURE 9  Segment of negatively stained crista in a PTA spread-cell preparation of beef heart mitochondrion. The regular know structures demarcating the base piece of each elementary particle form an integral part of the dense layer of the crista. Penetration of PTA between two apposed dense layers of the crista may account for the central dense band of the "mesozone" region. $\times$ 650,000.

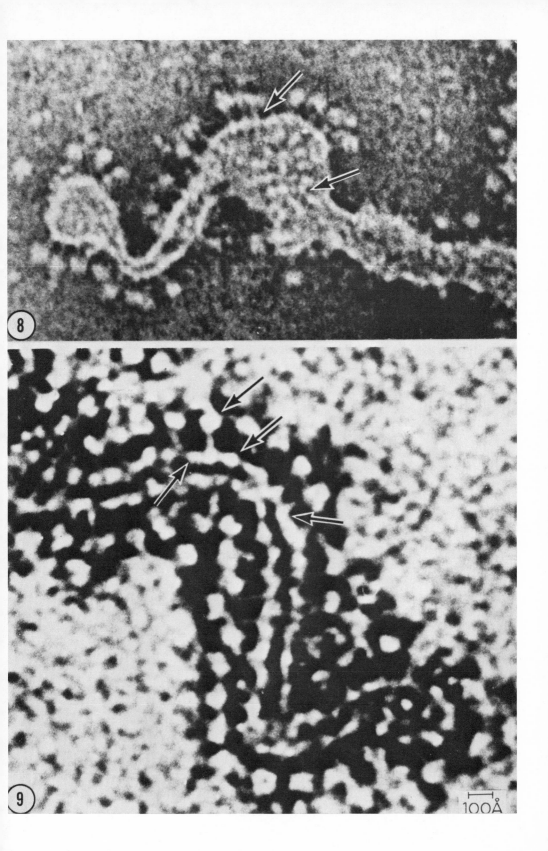

trary, a wide range of preparative procedures has been used successfully for the visualization of these structures.

In view of the large number of electron micrographs presented in this communication, we have prepared an Index summarizing all the essential structural items to be discussed in the section on Results and the corresponding figures to be examined in these contexts.

FINE STRUCTURE OF ISOLATED MITOCHONDRIA IN SECTIONS: Preparations fixed with osmium tetroxide and dehydrated and embedded at low temperatures (Figs. 1 to 3) reveal a degree of preservation of fine structure of the membranes which compares favorably with that found in the best preparations of retinal mitochondria (22–25). In both types of preparations, the electron opaque layers of the cristae show characteristic granular or globular subunits about 70 to 80 A in diameter. This particulate subunit structure of the mitochondrial membranes is also regularly encountered in sectioned preparations fixed with glutaraldehyde or formalin and stained with uranyl or lead acetate. Apposing membranes of adjacent mitochondria (in sections of pellets) exhibited a regular pattern with a period of 100 to 160 A. Such patterns were first described by Pease (57). The typical angular configurations of the cristae, previously noted by Revel et al. (59), are particularly noticeable in preparations treated at low temperatures. There is a formal resemblance between the cristae in osmium-fixed and negatively stained preparations in respect to the dense layers. In both cases, the structured elements are localized in these two layers and it is only in the electron opaque layers that a regularity of structural pattern is recognizable. The possibility must be borne in mind that the material present in the particles associated with the cristae in the negatively stained preparations may become incorporated into the thicker electron opaque layers of the osmium-fixed preparations.

THE ELEMENTARY PARTICLES: In whole membrane mounts of negatively stained mitochondria, all of the visible membrane surfaces appear to be covered with uniform particles having diameters the order of 80 to 100 A (cf. Figs. 4 to 7). The vast numbers of these particles—as well as their regularity and periodicity—are the most remarkable features. When first observed (23, 25), this repeating structural entity was designated the "elementary particle" (EP). In typical negatively stained preparations (Figs. 4 to 10), the elementary particles are arranged in recurring arrays associated with the cristae and with the inner membrane of the external mitochondrial envelope. Examination of whole-mount specimens reveals approximately 2,000 to 4,000 particles per square micron. If a fairly uniform distribution is assumed, the total number would be of the order of 10,000 to 100,000 elementary particles per mitochondrion depending on the size and type of mitochondrion. The average distance separating two adjacent particles was found to be about 110 to 115 A. If the particles are assumed to be spheres, 100 to 120 A in diameter, they would account for 10 to 15 per cent of the total mitochondrial volume. Similar estimates have been made by Smith (70, 71) for the volume occupied by these particles in insect sarcosomes.

As seen best in paired arrays along a crista, each elementary particle consists of the following three recognizable components: a head piece, a stem or stalk, and a base piece which is the region of attachment of the stalk to the crista. The head piece is the most conspicuous portion, being polyhedral and asymmetric by virtue of the stem region (Figs. 5 to 12, 13 a to c). The measured diameter in micrographs of freshly prepared specimens is about 80 to 100 A (cf. Figs. 4 to 12). The ratio between the long and short axes of the asymmetric head piece comes to values of 1.2 to 1.4. When mitochondria are fixed with aldehydes (formaldehyde, glutaraldehyde), and the resulting preparation treated with iodine or dichromate, the head often appears surrounded by a "halo" of granular components (20 to 30 A diameter) delimiting the periphery.

FIGURE 10 Electron micrograph of negatively stained beef heart mitochondrial membranes recorded with low-intensity microbeam illumination, and specimen cooling (−80°) to reduce irradiation damage. Under these favorable conditions, the dense substructure of the EP head pieces can be more frequently observed in suitably oriented specimens. Notice larger size of detached EP. Specimen cooled and examined immediately after preparation by cross-spraying technique. × 360,000.

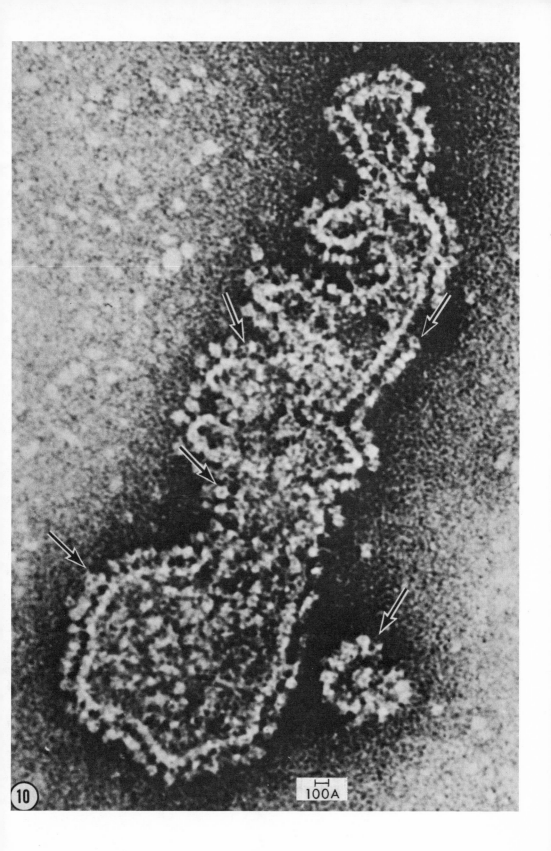

The head piece exhibits a characteristic, electron opaque core which can be demonstrated consistently, providing special precautions are taken (Figs. 10 to 12, 13 a to d). The visualization of this electron-opaque region of the head is influenced by exposure of the specimen to the intense electron beam. The apparent fading away of the dense central region while the head piece is being observed with electron optics at high magnification has been repeatedly noted. The head core is therefore best recorded when low-intensity, microbeam illumination is used at relatively low electron optical magnifications ($\times$ 10,000 to 20,000). For observations at higher electron optical magnifications ($\times$ 40,000 to 80,000), the stage containing the specimen is cooled with liquid nitrogen (19, 23–26) to avoid deterioration and fading of the image. As demonstrated in through-focus series (Figs. 11 a, b and 12 a, b), the electron opaque core of the head piece is of variable width (ca. 20 to 60 A). The core shows up best against a low contrast background such as is achieved by embedding the specimen in dilute (0.1 to 0.3 per cent) phosphotungstate solutions. In many ways the electron opaque core of the head piece resembles the corresponding electron opaque core seen in electron micrographs of cytochrome oxidase (annular forms of the complex). The electron opaque core has been consistently observed also in preparations treated with uranyl acetate or dichromate and in specimens fixed with formalin or glutaraldehyde (Fig. 13 d).

The stem or stalk region appears to have variable size and configuration depending on the type of negative staining. When the specimen is prepared by microdroplet cross-spraying with a very brief period of interaction with phosphotungstate, the stalk seems to be very short (Fig. 10) and the head piece seems to be wedged directly within the mesoregion of the crista. In these cases, the elementary particles assume a teardrop formation (cf. Fig. 7). In spread cell preparations, the stalk is seen to be well developed (Figs. 5, 8) and is approximately 20 to 40 A wide and 40 to 50 A long. At the point of attachment of the stalk to the crista a characteristic knob-like formation, approximately 40 to 50 A in diameter, is regularly seen.

An invariant feature of all the electron micrographs examined is the correlation between the arrays of head pieces of the elementary particle and the electron opaque layer of the crista to which the head pieces are attached by stalks (cf. Figs. 7 to 9, and 15). We consider the dense layer to be an expression of the end-to-end alignment of the base pieces of the elementary particles. The segmentation of this dense layer in the form of recurring knobs parallels the periodicity of the head pieces and the stalks. Since the average distance between the head pieces is about 115 A, the same distance must be assigned to the width of a base piece if the dense layer is assumed to be made up of fused base pieces. The thickness of the dense layer is 40 to 50 A. The third dimension of the base piece would have to be 115 A to be consistent with the assumption of a continuous layer.

ELEMENTARY PARTICLES IN SUBMITOCHONDRIAL FRAGMENTS: The same type of repeating particulate structure is regularly observed in submitochondrial fragments (ETP) obtained by sonication (cf. Figs. 14 and 15). The particles are an intrinsic feature of the mitochondrial membranes even when the mitochondrion has been disrupted. In fact, the presence of elementary particles both in intact mitochondrial membranes and in mitochondrial fractions was the starting point for the biochemical isolation. The three parts of the elementary particle (head

---

FIGURES 11 a and b, and 12 a and b   Electron micrographs selected from through-focus series of negatively stained cristae prepared and examined under same experimental conditions as described in legend for Fig. 11. Even under such favorable conditions, the electron opaque core with indications of substructure can be reproducibly demonstrated only in certain EP head pieces (arrows). Figs. 11 a, b, $\times$ 750,000; Figs. 12 a, b, $\times$ 450,000.

FIGURES 13 a to d   Inset enlargements showing electron opaque core in head pieces of selected elementary particles. Experimental conditions as described in legends for Figs. 10 and 11. Figs. 13 a to c, specimens stained with 1 per cent potassium phosphotungstate without prior fixation. Fig. 13 d, specimen fixed with 2 per cent glutaraldehyde at pH 7.2 prior to staining with 1 per cent uranylacetate. Magnifications: Fig. 13 a, $\times$ 1,250,000 Figs. 13 b to d, $\times$ 950,000.

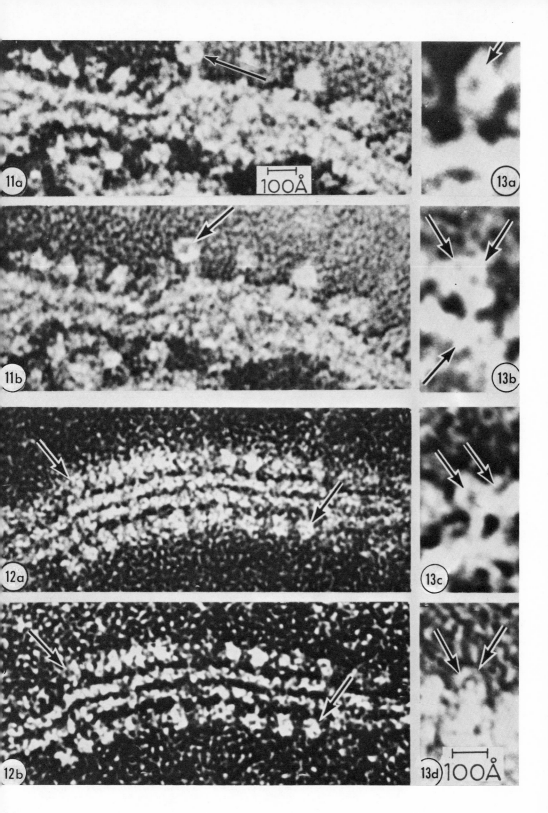

piece, stalk, and base piece) have the same relative dimensions in the submitochondrial fragments as they do in the intact mitochondrion.

We have frequently used ferritin as a reference particle for estimation of size. On the basis of careful measurement of the diameters of specially graded ferritin particles which show up as spherical units with an electron-opaque core, we have assigned a value of 118 A which is in good agreement with the unpublished x-ray data of J. W. Anderegg and F. Fischback. The head piece of the elementary particle is remarkably similar to ferritin, although the average diameter is slightly less than that of ferritin and the electron opaque core is less pronounced.

In many preparations of mitochondria and submitochondrial fractions, completely detached particles are observed near the membranes. If these particles are, in fact, detached elementary particles, their size would be significantly larger than that of the head piece (approximately 120 to 140 A in diameter compared to 80 to 100 A). These detached particles are larger than those of ferritin.

VISUALIZATION OF THE ELEMENTARY PARTICLE BY ALTERNATIVE TECHNIQUES: Mitochondria (in situ and after isolation) have been fixed and stained with a variety of reagents (including buffered solutions of osmium tetroxide, formaldehyde, glutaraldehyde, potassium permanganate, uranyl acetate, potassium dichromate, silicotungstate, potassium iodide, sodium bromide, and cadmium iodide). Examination of such treated preparations has consistently revealed essentially the same type of particulate structure. The following types of variation in the experimental conditions were also explored: interaction of the mitochondrion with the fixing reagent prior to staining for different times and at various temperatures; cooling of the specimen during observation; electron microscopy of partially hydrated

mitochondrial specimens in vacuum-tight microchambers (20, 22–24) and related techniques. Visualization of the subunit structure was not significantly affected by such variations. Positive results were also obtained in the examination of specimens prepared by ultrathin sectioning after cryofixation, by negative staining combined with ultrathin sectioning, and by embedding in gelatin and other water-soluble media. These results will be described in detail in a separate communication.

BIOCHEMICAL RESULTS

ELEMENTARY PARTICLE AND THE UNIT OF ELECTRON TRANSFER: Full evidence has already been presented (5) that the components of the electron transfer chain as well as electron transfer activity (as measured by succinoxidase and DNPH oxidase activities) are concentrated some 2.6 times during isolation of the elementary particle from mitochondria. In presenting the results that follow, we shall adopt the conclusion of Blair et al. (5) that the elementary particle is, in fact, the intact electron transfer chain stripped completely from the primary dehydrogenase complexes and largely, if not completely, from the structural protein-lipid network. We shall now consider the experimental evidence that bears on the molecular weight of the isolated elementary particle and on its probable molecular dimensions. This information is essential to answer the question of the identity of the isolated elementary particle with the counterpart particle seen in the cristae of intact mitochondria.

MOLECULAR WEIGHT OF THE ELEMENTARY PARTICLE FROM ANALYTICAL DATA: The cytochrome a content of the elementary particle isolated by processing through two cycles of exposure to the cholate-deoxycholate mixture, followed by fractionation with ammonium sulfate,

FIGURE 14  Electron micrograph of negatively stained preparation of the electron transfer particle (ETP)—a submitochondrial fraction. Elementary particle arrays closely resemble those in intact cristae; average dimensions of head piece and other components of EP same as those for corresponding structures in EP of intact mitochondria; apposition of two dense layers to form a single fused central layer. Specimen preparation as described in legend for Fig. 6. × 600,000.

FIGURE 15  Negatively stained segment of crista from isolated whole mitochondrion (enlargement of Fig. 6). Specimen preparation conditions are essentially the same as for specimen shown in Fig. 14. Note identity of form and arrangement of elementary particles in crista of intact mitochondrion and in the electron transfer particle (ETP). × 660,000.

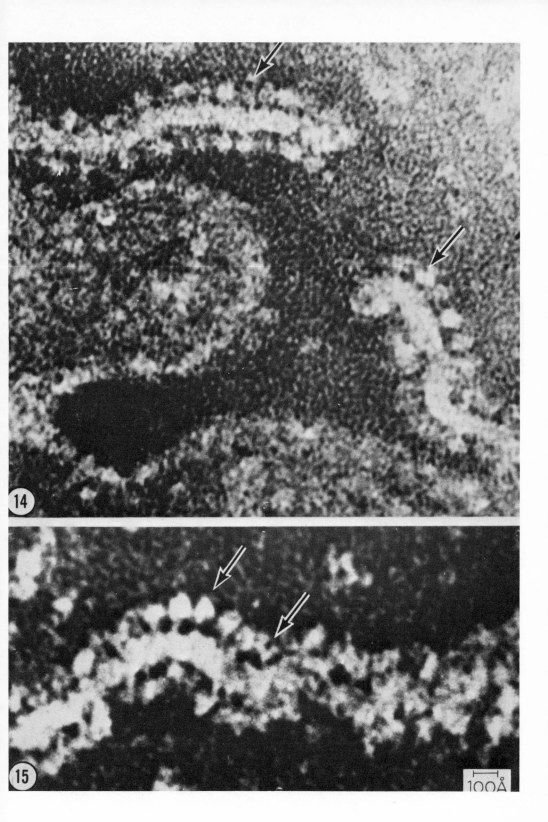

TABLE III

*Minimal Molecular Weights of the Four Complexes of the Electron Transfer Chain at the Highest Purity Levels Achieved*

| Complex | Designation | Molecular weight | |
| --- | --- | --- | --- |
| | | Protein basis | Lipoprotein (30 ‰ lipid)* |
| I | DPNH–coenzyme Q reductase* | 550,000 | 786,000 |
| II | Succinic–coenzyme Q reductase‡ | 208,000 | 297,000 |
| III | QH$_2$–cytochrome $c$ reductase§ | 200,000 | 285,000 |
| IV | Cytochrome oxidase‖ | 426,000 | 609,000 |
| Total | | 1,384,000 | 1,976,000 |

\* Unpublished data of J. Merola.
‡ Data of Ziegler and Doeg (81).
§ Data of Rieske, Zaugg, and Wharton (61).
‖ Data of Criddle, Bock, Green, and Tisdale (13); Ambe and Venketaraman (1).

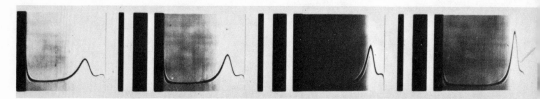

FIGURE 16   Sedimentation diagram of an elementary particle preparation. The particles were suspended in 90 per cent D$_2$O which was 0.02 M in Tris chloride and 0.001 M in EDTA. Protein concentration, 11 mg per ml. Rotor speed, 50,700 RPM; rotor temperature, 6°. Time interval between photographs, 4 minutes. The apparent sedimentation constant at 6° is 13.6 $S_{20,w}$ = 52. The particles were solubilized with phosphotungstate as described in the text. The slow minor peak in the diagram is that of phosphotungstate. The sedimentation diagrams read from right to left.

is 4.2 mμmoles/mg of protein. On the basis of 6 molecules of cytochrome $a$ per molecule of elementary particle (41), the minimal molecular weight of the particle would be $\frac{6 \times 10^6}{4.2}$ = 1.4 × 10$^6$ on a protein basis. Cytochrome $a$ is selected for this computation since its concentration is more accurately determined than any other component of the chain.

The minimal molecular weight is not necessarily the actual molecular weight. In a unit of minimal molecular weight, 1.4 × 10$^6$, it is assumed that there would be one molecule each of cytochrome $c_1$, succinic dehydrogenase ($f_S$), and DPNH dehydrogenase ($f_D$). The actual unit of electron transfer could contain more than one molecule of these components.

MOLECULAR WEIGHT OF THE ELEMENTARY PARTICLE FROM THE DATA OF RECONSTITUTION EXPERIMENTS: The elementary particle has been reconstituted by recombination of the four component complexes under specified conditions (30, 44, 45). In the companion paper by Blair *et al.* (5), we have discussed the evidence that the four complexes combine in 1:1:1:1 molecular stoichiometry. Table III contains the minimal molecular weights of each of the four complexes as determined by chemical analysis. The four complexes used in the reconstitution studies were at the stage of purity indicated in Table III. As we shall discuss later, complex I at the purity level used in these experiments is still highly impure, but the other three complexes are probably close to the limit of purification. The sum of the minimal molecular weights of the four complexes comes to 1.38 × 10$^6$ on a protein basis—a value which is in good agreement with the minimal molecular weight calculated on the basis of the composition of the isolated elementary particle.

Since the four complexes may combine in 1:1:1:1 molecular stoichiometry, it is necessary to

**238**

establish for only one of them that the minimal and actual molecular weights are the same in order to extrapolate to the actual molecular weight of the reconstituted unit. The molecular weight of the QH$_2$-cytochrome $c$ reductase (complex III) was determined by sedimentation analysis (J. Rieske and P. Yang, unpublished data) and found to conform to the minimal molecular weight listed in Table III. Takemori *et al.* (73) estimated the molecular weight of cytochrome oxidase (com-

plex IV) to be about 500,000—a value in good agreement with that for the minimal molecular weight of the complex (615,000 for the lipoprotein complex). Singer, Kearney, and Massey (66) have isolated a form of succinic dehydrogenase almost identical in composition with that of complex II. The molecular weight which they determined by sedimentation analysis of their preparation came to about 250,000—in good agreement with the value for the minimal molecular weight of com-

TABLE IV

*Inhibition of Electron Transfer Activities by Sodium Phosphotungstate*

| Activity measured | Particle type | Concentration of sodium phospho-tungstate | Inhibition |
|---|---|---|---|
| | | | *per cent* |
| 1. Oxidation of DPNH by O$_2$ | Mitochondria (heavy) | $5 \times 10^{-7}$ | 10 |
| | | $4 \times 10^{-6}$ | 50 |
| | | $8 \times 10^{-6}$ | 75 |
| | Mitochondria (washed with 0.9% KCl) | $4 \times 10^{-5}$ | 10 |
| | | $5.5 \times 10^{-5}$ | 50 |
| | | $6.5 \times 10^{-4}$ | 75 |
| | ETP$_H$ | $2.0 \times 10^{-5}$ | 10 |
| | | $6.0 \times 10^{-5}$ | 50 |
| | | $1.2 \times 10^{-4}$ | 75 |
| | EP | $5.0 \times 10^{-6}$ | 10 |
| | | $3.0 \times 10^{-5}$ | 50 |
| | | $5.5 \times 10^{-5}$ | 75 |
| 2. Oxidation of suc-cinate by O$_2$ | Mitochondria (heavy) | $5.0 \times 10^{-7}$ | 10 |
| | | $4.0 \times 10^{-6}$ | 50 |
| | | $7.0 \times 10^{-6}$ | 75 |
| | Mitochondria (washed with 0.9% KCl) | $2.0 \times 10^{-6}$ | 10 |
| | | $5.0 \times 10^{-6}$ | 50 |
| | | $8.5 \times 10^{-6}$ | 75 |
| | ETP$_H$ | $5.0 \times 10^{-7}$ | 10 |
| | | $2.0 \times 10^{-6}$ | 50 |
| | | $4.0 \times 10^{-6}$ | 75 |
| | EP | $1.0 \times 10^{-5}$ | 10 |
| | | $3.5 \times 10^{-5}$ | 50 |
| | | $5.5 \times 10^{-5}$ | 75 |

The above experiments were all carried out at a particle protein concentration of 50 $\mu$g per assay. When the protein concentration is increased to 5000 $\mu$g per assay, the concentration of sodium phosphotungstate required to achieve the same degree of inhibition as at the 50 $\mu$g protein level is 3 to 5 times higher.

When specimens are prepared for negative staining, the usual concentration range of sodium phosphotungstate concentrations is 0.1 to 1%, which corresponds in molar terms to $3.3 \times 10^{-5}$ M $- 3.3 \times 10^{-4}$ M.

Mitochondria or submitochondrial particles which have been exposed to phosphotungstate at inhibitory concentrations can be washed free of the reagent; the electron transfer activity after washing is the same as the original, uninhibited activity.

plex II. The available evidence supports the view that the minimal molecular weight calculated from analytical data is, in fact, the actual molecular weight of the elementary particle.

SEDIMENTATION ANALYSIS OF THE ELEMENTARY PARTICLE: The isolated elementary particle shows a strong tendency to aggregate despite the presence of residual deoxycholate which is not removed by exhaustive washing in 0.25 sucrose. Prolonged sonication partially disperses the suspension, but neither permanently nor completely, to the stage of the monomeric species. This tendency of the particles to aggregate has effectively blocked our attempts to establish the homogeneity of the preparation and to determine its molecular weight by sedimentation analysis.

The ultracentrifugal analysis of suspensions of the elementary particle following dispersion by sonic irradiation shows a broad distribution of particle sizes. We have sorted out the particles from the most aggregated to the least aggregated in successive fractions collected in the trunnion head of the Spinco ultracentrifuge and have determined the composition of each of these fractions. No measurable differences were found in the chemical composition of the different fractions. Thus, it is clear that the heterogeneity of particles is an expression of differences in degree of physical aggregation, but not in chemical composition.

The elementary particles can be brought into true solution by interaction with phosphotungstate. The optimal level for "solubilization" is a 1:1 ratio by weight of elementary particle (as protein) and phosphotungstate. The solution of the elementary particle-phosphotungstate complex is centrifuged at 50,000 RPM for 15 minutes. The precipitate consists of two layers—a hard packed sediment which is discarded and a fluffy layer which is mixed with 0.01 M Tris buffer of pH 7.5. Sedimentation analysis, by Dr. Pauline Yang, of

this phosphotungstate complex of the elementary particle showed a major component with a weight average sedimentation coefficient of $52 \times 10^{-13}$ sec. after extrapolation to zero concentration (cf. Fig. 16). Chemical analysis of the complex showed that 1 gm of elementary particle protein was combined with 0.9 gm of lipid and 1 gm of phosphotungstate. The minimal molecular weight of this complex should, therefore, be $2.9 \times 1.6 \times 10^6 = 4.6 \times 10^6$ (the minimal molecular weight of this particular preparation of EP was $1.6 \times 10^6$ on a protein basis). The observed molecular weight determined by the modified Archibald approach to sedimentation equilibrium was $5.8 \times 10^6$, in fair agreement with the minimal molecular weight calculated from analytical data. The difference could be accounted for by water of hydration.

From the experimentally determined values for the partial specific volume ($0.727$ cm$^3$/gm) and the sedimentation coefficient ($52 \times 10^{-13}$ sec.), the frictional coefficient of the elementary particle-phosphotungstate complex can be calculated by the Svedberg equation:

$$f = \frac{M(1 - \bar{v}\rho)}{NS}$$

where $f$ is the frictional coefficient of the elementary particle complex; $M$, the molecular weight of the complex ($5.8 \times 10^6$ gm/mole); $\bar{v}$, the partial specific volume; $\rho$, the density of the solvent ($1:00$ gm/cm$^3$); $S$, the sedimentation coefficient; and $N$, Avogadro's number. When the values indicated are substituted in the equation, the value for $f$ comes to $5.06 \times 10^{-7}$ (C.G.S. units). The frictional coefficient of a spherical molecule of the same molecular weight was calculated by the following equation:

$$f_o = 6\Pi\eta \left(\frac{3M\bar{v}}{4\Pi N}\right)^{1/3}$$

FIGURE 17  Electron micrograph of isolated elementary particles negatively stained with 1 per cent potassium phosphotungstate by microdroplet cross-spray technique. Isolation of elementary particles as described in text; electron transfer activity of particles fully preserved. In this typical field, discrete and conglomerated particles are seen in different orientations; ferritin molecules (dense core, diameter 120 A) added as a marker. × 420,000.

FIGURE 18  Preparation of isolated elementary particles embedded in thin film of phosphotungstate, selected from another specimen series. Note: asymmetry of particles; relative uniformity of particle size (120 × 160 A); minimal aggregation in this particular specimen. × 330,000.

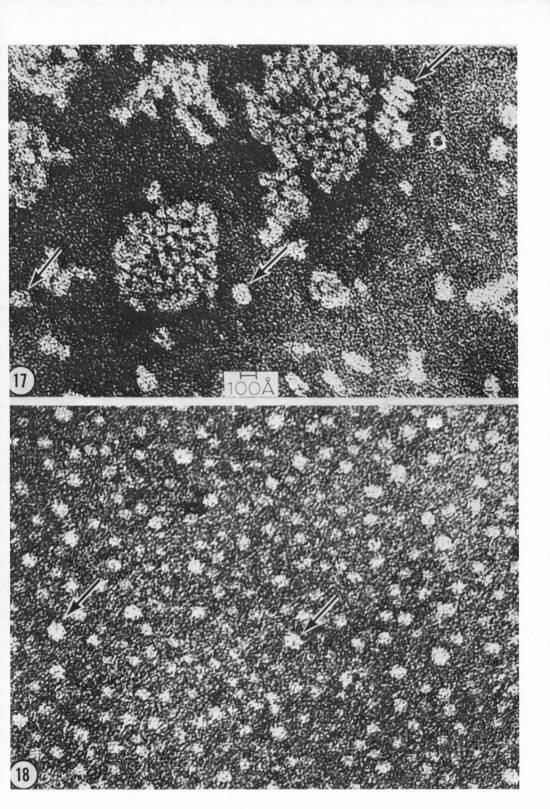

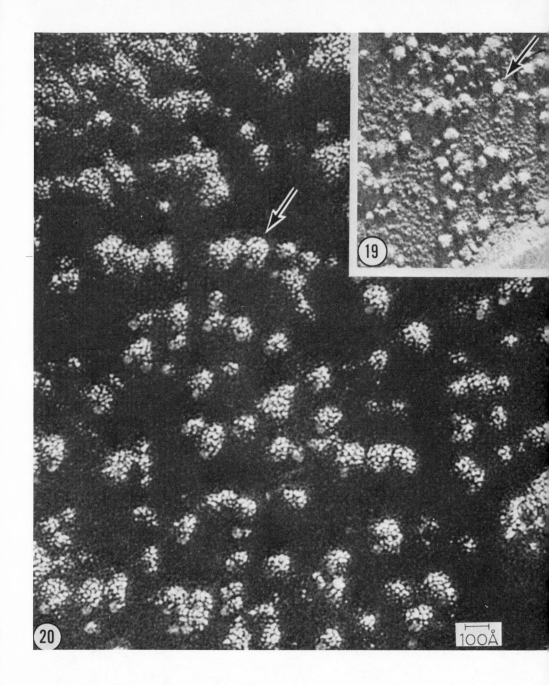

FIGURE 19  Isolated elementary particles examined by the shadow-casting technique. Details of preparation as in legend for Fig. 17. Individual particles of variable size and polyhedral shape clearly visible. × 300,000.

FIGURE 20  Microdroplet of isolated elementary particles, preparation positively stained with uranyl acetate and shadowed with platinum-carbon at very low grazing angle; the resulting "surface decoration" patterns indicate possible underlying subunit structure of individual elementary particles. × 600,000.

where $\eta$ is the viscosity of the solvent ($1.47 \times 10^{-2}$ poise) and the other symbols have been defined above. The value for $f_o$ comes to $3.28 \times 10^{-7}$ when the indicated substitutions are made. Therefore,

$$\frac{f}{f_o} = \frac{5.06 \times 10^{-7}}{3.28 \times 10^{-7}} = 1.54$$

The value for the ratio of $f$ to $f_o$ clearly indicates that the elementary particle-phosphotungstate complex is asymmetric, but the degree of asymmetry cannot be evaluated in terms of axial ratio until the hydration of the complex can be specified with precision.

EFFECT OF PHOSPHOTUNGSTATE ON ENZYMIC ACTIVITY: Phosphotungstate, at the levels used for the preparation of samples to be examined in the electron microscope, is a relatively mild reagent in its effects on enzymatic activity of mitochondria and submitochondrial particles (*cf.* Table IV). Even when enzymatic activity was almost completely blocked, the effects were found to be reversible. Thus, after exposure to inhibitory levels of phosphotungstate, the particles regained full activity when washed free of the reagent. These experiments clearly indicate that treatment with phosphotungstate under the described conditions does not lead to irreversible structural and functional modifications. Any such effects would be inconsistent with the partial inhibitory action of phosphotungstate at concentration levels that are used in electron microscopy and with the reversibility of whatever inhibition is observed at these levels.

X-RAY SCATTERING DATA: Drs. J. A. Anderegg and N. Chonacky have examined preparations of the elementary particle and of the phosphotungstate complex for low angle x-ray scattering. The Guinier plot (the log of the intensity of scattering versus the square of the scattering angle) was not linear—an indication that aggregation of particles took place during the period of the measurements. The available data clearly indicate that the smallest particles in the preparation have a radius of gyration of 60 A which corresponds to a diameter of 160 A. A spherical molecule, 160 A in diameter (density 1.2), corresponds to a molecular weight of $1.55 \times 10^6$. The preparations of the elementary particles submitted for examination would have a molecular weight in the range of 3 to $4 \times 10^6$ (after allowance was made for lipid and phosphotungstate). The discrepancy between the observed and calculated molecular weights provided independent confirmation of the asymmetric character of the isolated elementary particle and of its soluble phosphotungstate complex.

ELECTRON MICROSCOPY OF ISOLATED ELEMENTARY PARTICLES: The preparations of isolated EP present inherent difficulties as to an examination by electron microscopy. Although special precautions were taken to examine the specimens as soon as possible (within a few hours of isolation), marked color changes, increasing opalescence, and other visible changes were noted as the preparation stood. The phase contrast microscope showed the appearance of minute particles (0.1 to 0.2 $\mu$) a few hours after preparation, even when the specimen was kept at $0°C$. The aggregation was markedly enhanced by agitation. In view of this remarkable lability, and of the unavoidable contamination with bile salts, it has been difficult to obtain unequivocal electron microscopic evidence of a homogeneous, uniform size of the isolated elementary particles.

As seen in the best preparations (negative staining), the isolated EP's are polyhedral; the shape resembles that of a prolate ellipsoid. Depending on their orientation within the phosphotungstate film, the dimensions of the smaller diameter of the particles is 100 to 120 A whereas the dimension of the long axis is 140 to 180 A (Figs. 17, 18). All of these preparations, however, show characteristic electron opaque components in the core such as can be seen in the *in situ* particle. A number of preparations were examined by shadow casting in combination with positive staining (Figs. 19, 20). In these preaparations the individual particles stand out more clearly, although there is still a variation in size from about 120 to 180 A. Indications of subunit structure of approximately 20 to 30 A can be detected in shadowed specimens (Fig. 19) and in positively stained particles which are subsequently "decorated" by shadowing with platinum-carbon at an extremely low angle (Fig. 20).

On the basis of electron microscopy, it is, therefore, possible to establish the fact that the unit of electron transfer has a particulate character with a marked asymmetric configuration, the short and long dimensions being about 120 and 180 A, respectively. However, further improvements in preparative techniques will be needed to obtain elementary particles of uniform size and shape comparable to that of other isolated multienzyme complexes (for example, the pyruvate dehydrogenase complex examined by H. Fernández-Morán in collaboration with Lester Reed, 28, 58).

ELECTRON MICROSCOPY OF THE RECONSTITUTED ELEMENTARY PARTICLE: In principle, the specimens of reconstituted EP are subject to the same inherent limitations as are the isolated EP's. However, the variability in size was less (predominance of 120 to 140 A units). Moreover, in preparations of reconstituted EP there was a marked tendency for aggregation of the particles into a regular arrangement, resembling paracrystalline arrays (Figs. 21, 22). In some negatively stained preparations the phosphotungstate seems to exert a marked dissociating effect so that the reconstituted EP breaks down into smaller units. Nevertheless, these preparations afforded the opportunity of comparing by electron microscopy the dimensions and configurations of the reconstituted EP with those of the purified individual complexes.

ELECTRON MICROSCOPY OF INDIVIDUAL COMPLEXES: Although most of the complexes were available in purified form, the presence of bile salts in the respective preparations of these complexes interfered with the interaction with phosphotungstate. The best preparations were attained by microdroplet cross-spraying involving very small volumes (microdroplets of the order of 1 $\mu$ or less) and very short interaction times with phosphotungstate or with uranyl acetate.

An additional difficulty was encountered in trying to establish the precise delimitation of the zone of each individual complex. The most reproducible and clear-cut preparations were obtained with the largest of the four complexes, namely, cytochrome oxidase. As shown in Figs. 23 $a$, $b$, the cytochrome oxidase preparations appear as a mosaic of well defined units, approximately 60 to 80 A in diameter with an electron-opaque core of approximately 20 to 30 A. As described earlier (23, 25), the electron-opaque components (heme, Cu) often feature a characteristic tetrad arrangement with a diameter of the order of 15 to 20 A units. This is surrounded by a "halo" to give a total diameter of about 60 to 80 A. Preparations of the other complexes (I, II, and III) were not so well defined as preparations of cytochrome oxidase. However, complex I (DPNH–coenzyme Q reductase) was characterized by the presence of discrete, particulate units approximately 40 to 50 A in diameter (Fig. 26). Complex II (succinic coenzyme Q–reductase) showed a marked tendency to aggregate. The average uniform particles were approximately 50 to 60 A in diameter (Fig. 25) and resembled those of complex I in appearance. Complex III (QH$_2$–cytochrome $c$ reductase) appeared as an electron opaque series of particles approximating 40 to 50 A in diameter (Fig. 24). Based on this preliminary data, it is possible to assume that the four individual complexes, as seen by electron microscopy, could be fitted into the isolated elementary particle. This is an important point which, however, requires further investigation. The availability of more highly purified complexes, and further improvements in high resolution electron microscopy of the individual complexes, and of the elementary particles, should eventually permit unequivocal determination of the actual dimensions.

DISCUSSION

## Validity of Structures Revealed by Negative Staining

Although the elementary particles can best be seen in negatively stained preparations of mitochondria without prior fixation (either *in situ* or after isolation), particles of essentially the same characteristics can be observed in electron micro-

FIGURE 21 Preparation of reconstituted elementary particles negatively stained with phosphotungstate; elementary particles reconstituted as described in the text. Specimen prepared as in legend for Fig. 17. Note: discrete asymmetric particles and aggregates of individual particles. Ferritin molecules (dense core, diameter 118 to 120 A) added as calibration markers. $\times$ 420,000.

FIGURE 22 Reconstituted elementary particles negatively stained and prepared as in legend for Fig. 21. Note: discrete particles (120 to 140 A) and tendency to form extended linear aggregates resembling arrays of elementary particles as seen in ETP. $\times$ 330,000.

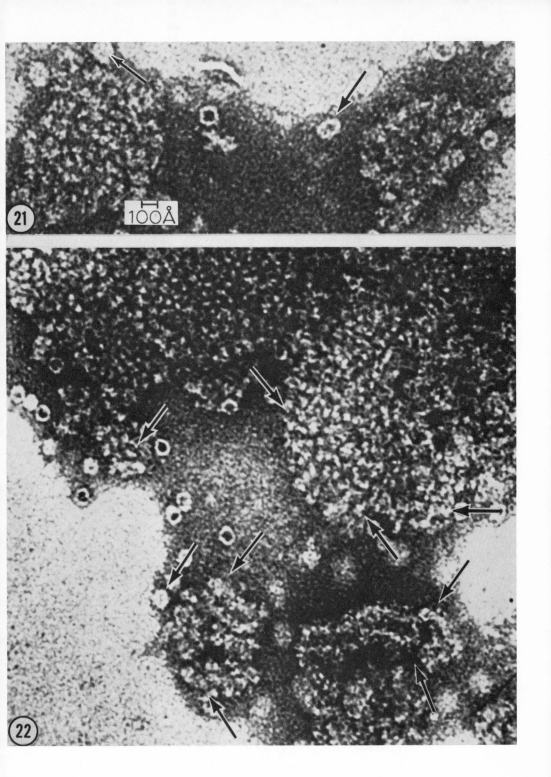

graphs of mitochondria treated with fixatives and reagents other than phosphotungstate (23, 27). In the section on Results, mention is made of the wide variety of supplementary techniques that have been used for visualization of the elementary particle and the wide range of experimental conditions under which visualization can be achieved. The same type of structures have been reported in negatively stained preparations of mitochondria from several sources by Parsons (55, 56), Smith (70, 71), and Stoeckenius (72). The presence of a well defined particulate component directly associated with mitochondrial membranes in negatively stained preparations now seems to be established beyond dispute.

The negative staining technique (7) has already disclosed the substructure of viruses, and proved to be extremely useful by yielding results that can profitably be compared with x-ray data and biochemical information to deduce the actual arrangement of the protein subunits in certain spherical virus particles (8). Although specimens embedded in a thin film of phosphotungstate are protected from artifacts due to surface tension forces, other artifact possibilities must also be considered. In particular, exposure of the unfixed labile lipoprotein systems of mitochondrial membrane to the phosphotungstate solution could conceivably lead to disruption, rearrangements, and other modifications of the original structure. It is, therefore, important that essentially the same type of structures can be observed in mitochondrial membranes which have been previously fixed with formalin, glutaraldehyde, osmium, and other reagents (27, 70, 71), provided that the necessary precautions are taken.

## The Biochemical Inertness of Phosphotung-state

From the data presented in the section on Results (cf. Table IV), phosphotungstate at pH 7.0 does not markedly inhibit electron transfer activity (DPNH oxidase and succinic oxidase activities) at concentrations that are sufficiently high to prepare specimens for examination in the electron microscope. In fact, it has proved to be practically impossible to abolish completely enzymic activity even at the highest concentration of phosphotungstate normally used in the preparation of negatively stained specimens. Moreover, the inhibitory effect of phosphotungstate on isolated mitochondria is reversible since activity can be restored by washing the treated mitochondria by centrifugation and resuspension in a medium free of the reagent.

The inference that phosphotungstate at concentration levels relevant to negative staining for electron microscopy has only a small, reversible effect on enzymic activity is highly significant; it would be difficult to invoke any major structural modification in the electron transfer chain at relevant concentration levels. The criterion of enzymic activity is even more stringent than is any physical measurement. Thus, the biochemical evidence is decisive in ruling out phosphotungstate as a reagent likely to induce chemical modifications in the structure of the mitochondrion. Phosphotungstate stands in contrast to osmium and other heavy metal reagents which at the concentration levels usually used in electron microscopy completely abolish enzymic activity and undoubtedly induce profound chemical and physical changes in mitochondria and other membranous systems. It should also be pointed out in this connection that negative staining with phosphotungstate and drying does not impair appreciably the viability of infectious polio virus and of certain other virus particles.

Phosphotungstate is, in fact, being used as a reagent for depolymerizing aggregates of the elementary particle into the soluble monomeric species. For this purpose, it appears to be superior to any of the bile salts.

FIGURE 23  Electron micrographs of isolated cytochrome oxidase (complex IV) negatively stained with phosphotungstate; details as in legend for Fig. 21. Note: mosaic of repeating substructures of annular shape (diameter of 60 to 80 A) with electron-opaque core of 20 to 30 A. FIGURE 23 a, × 500,000; FIGURE 23 b, × 700,000.

FIGURES 24 to 26  Electron micrographs of microdroplet preparations of individual complexes III, II, and I, respectively; stained with 1 per cent uranyl acetate by cross spray technique. Note: repeating substructures, about 30 to 60 A in diameter, with tendency to assume spherical or annular appearance. Figs. 24 and 26, × 500,000; Fig. 25, × 450,000.

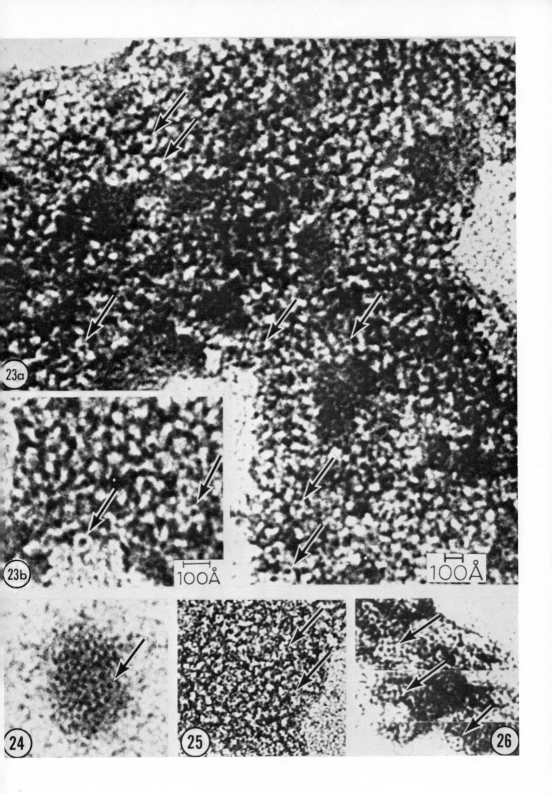

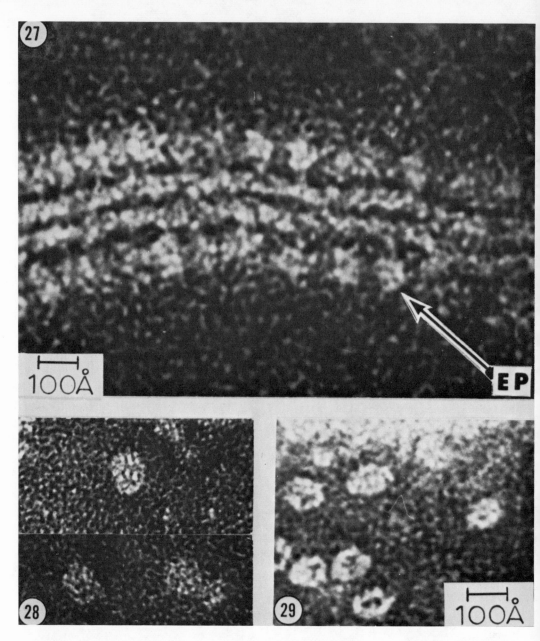

FIGURES 27 to 29   Comparison of the elementary particle as seen in electron micrographs of: native EP (Fig. 27); isolated EP (Fig. 28); reconstituted EP (Fig. 29). Details as in legend for Fig. 17. × 900,000.

## Dimensions of the Elementary Particle in Situ

We are defining the elementary particle as a composite of three parts: (1) the roughly spherical head piece (80 to 100 A in diameter); (2) the cylindrical stalk (30 × 50 A); and (3) the base piece (40 × 112 A). There appears to be a precise

relation between the segmentation of the limiting membrane layer of the crista and the periodicity of the head piece. That is to say, each head piece is linked by the stalk to a corresponding base piece. The base piece accounts for the segmentation of the outer layer of the membrane of the crista. It is difficult to specify where one base piece nds and the next begins. We shall make the simple assumption that the base piece can be no wider than the distance between two particles *i.e.*, *ca.* 110 A) and that the dense layer of the membrane of the crista (diameter 40 A) is made up entirely of nesting base pieces.

According to this interpretation, the crista is bounded by a structured, electron-opaque layer, 0 A in diameter, made up of fused base pieces to which the head pieces are joined by stalks. Within

mentary particle (head piece plus stalk plus base piece) should be sufficient to accommodate one complete electron transfer chain. This volume may be computed by assuming the head piece to be a sphere of diameter 90 A; the stalk a rectangular cylinder ($50 \times 32 \times 114$ A); and the base piece a cylinder ($114 \times 114 \times 45$ A). If we assume that there is an underestimation factor of about 12 per cent (observed size versus theoretical size) and correct each of the measured dimensions by a 12

TABLE V

*Theoretical Molecular Weight of the Electron Transfer Chain Based on the Stoichiometry and Minimal Molecular Weights of the Protein Components*

| Protein component | Molecular weight | Reference | Molecules/ Chain | Contribution to molecular weight of the chain |
|---|---|---|---|---|
| Succinic dehydrogenase ($f_S$) | 80,000* | (81) | 1 (5) | 80,000 |
| DPNH dehydrogenase ($f_D$) | 37,500‡ | (52) | 1 (5) | 37,500 |
| Cytochrome *a* (*a*) | 70,000 | (1) | 6 (5) | 420,000 |
| Cytochrome *b* (*b*) | 28,000 | (31) | 3 (5) | 84,000 |
| Cytochrome $c_1$ ($c_1$) | 37,000 | (6) | 1 (5) | 37,000 |
| Cytochrome *c* (*c*) | 13,000 | (74) | 2 (5) | 26,000 |
| Non-heme iron ($Fe_{NH}$) | 12,500/Fe§ | (60) | 18 (5) | 225,000 |
| Total | | | | 909,500 |

* Molecular weight of succinic–coenzyme Q reductase (81) corrected for 8 atoms of non-heme iron and one molecule of cytochrome *b*; 12,500 gm of protein per gram atom of non-heme iron and 28,000 gm of protein per mole of cytochrome *b* are assumed.

‡ Molecular weight of DPNH flavoprotein (52) corrected for 7 atoms of non-heme iron, if 12,500 gm of protein per gram atom of iron are assumed.

§ The assumption is being made that all the non-heme iron proteins have on the average the same molecular weight as the one isolated from complex III by Rieske *et al.* (60).

his boundary layer (*i.e.* within the interior of the crista) are more irregular structures that are less electron opaque. The structural protein-lipid network is probably localized in these interior structures. The width of each crista is highly variable— o much so that it appears that the material in the interior may be capable of extrusion. In some segments of a crista the two outer layers are in apposition, whereas in other segments the two outer layers are separated by distances of 200 to 1,000 A. n such distended tubules, the interior is filled with a matrix-like material that is readily distinguishable from the electron-opaque outer membrane layer.

The total volume occupied by a single ele-

per cent increment, the molecular weight contributions of head piece, stalk, and base piece (computed from the volumes with the assumption of 1.25 as the value for the density) are respectively 497,000, 193,000, and 607,000. The total computed molecular weight then comes to a value of $1.3 \times 10^6$. A sphere of density 1.25 with a molecular weight of $1.3 \times 10^6$ would have a diameter of 148 A.

## Dimensions of the Isolated Elementary Particle

In the companion paper, Blair *et al.* (5) described the preparation of the unit of electron transfer having a minimal molecular weight of

1.4 × 10⁶ on a protein basis. We shall, for the moment, make no correction for the lipid content of the isolated particle. The minimal molecular weight is computed on the basis of the composition of the particle; the assumption is made that one molecule of succinic flavoprotein or of DPNH flavoprotein is present per molecular weight unit of the electron transfer chain. The ultracentrifugal data given in the section on Results indicate that the minimal calculated molecular weight and the actual determined molecular weight are sufficiently close to permit the assumption of identity. Following the initial studies of Blair *et al.*, further progress has been made in the isolation procedure,

particle as isolated by the improved procedure c Tisdale, Tzagoloff, and Green (75).

The isolated unit no longer shows the thre distinct parts characteristic of the *in situ* ele mentary particle. We presume that, when th elementary particle is detached from the mitc chondrial membranes, the three component part round up to form a compact unit in which th individual parts are no longer recognizable. Th exact shape of the isolated particle is, therefore not necessarily relevant to the question of th shape of the particle *in situ*. In any event, th isolated particle must be "solubilized" by cor version into its phosphotungstate complex befor

TABLE VI

*Theoretical Molecular Weights of the Complexes of the Electron Transfer Chain
Based on the Composition of the Complexes and the Stoichiometry of the
Protein Components*

| Complex | Composition* | Reference | Computed molecular weight | |
| | | | (Protein basis) | (Normalized for 30 ‰ lipid) |
|---------|-------------|-----------|-----------------|--------------------------|
| I | $f_D$; $(Fe_{NH})_8$ | (46, 52) | 137,500 | 196,500 |
| II | $f_S$; $(Fe_{NH})_8$; $b$ | (81, 60) | 208,000 | 297,000 |
| III | $(b)_2$; $(Fe_{NH})_2$; $c_1$ | (46, 60) | 118,000 | 168,000 |
| IV | $(a)_6$ | (1, 13) | 420,000 | 600,000 |
| Total | | | 883,500 | 1,262,000 |

* See Table V for abbreviations of the components.

and a unit of molecular weight 1 × 10⁶ on a protein basis has been approached (75). If the molecular weight is normalized for the presence of lipid (the mass ratio of protein to lipid is 7:3), the corrected molecular weight of the isolated unit of highest purity comes to 1.4 × 10⁶—in fair agreement with the value of 1.3 × 10⁶ computed for the molecular weight of the elementary particle *in situ*.

It is possible to calculate the theoretical molecular weight of the electron transfer chain from the known molecular weights of each of the component oxidation-reduction proteins and from the molecular proportions of these proteins. Such a calculation is summarized in Table V. Implicit in this calculation is the assumption that the electron transfer chain does not contain any structural protein. The computed molecular weight comes to a value of 0.9 × 10⁶ on a protein basis and corresponds closely with that for the elementary

it can be examined in the ultracentrifuge, an the asymmetry and shape of this derived unit ar not necessarily indicative of the shape either unit in situ before extraction from the mitochon drial membranes.

The fact that the elementary particle is at onc external to, and part of, the outer membrar of the crista probably explains why simple sonica tion does not provide an effective means for sepa rating the elementary particle from the structura protein-lipid network.

*Identification of the Isolated Elementar
Particle with That Seen in Situ*

Evidence that the isolated elementary partic. is of the appropriate dimensions to correspon with the particle seen *in situ* merely eliminates th problem of size as a barrier to the identificatio but is not necessarily direct proof for the identi ation. We have, in fact, no direct proof for this identification if direct proof is possible; however, there is a wealth of circumstantial evidence which collectively makes the identification highly probable. The unit carrying the electron transfer chain can be purified some fivefold relative to the mitochondrion. Therefore, any structure presumed to be associated with electron transfer activity should not account for more than 20 per cent of the total dry weight of the mitochondrion. The particle visualized *in situ* would certainly fulfill this requirement. The isolated electron transfer unit, as well as the purified complexes, contains characteristic electron opaque substructures. Under favorable conditions similar substructures can also be seen in the head piece of the particle *in situ*. The mitochondrion contains a variety of particles that are concerned in implementing citric cycle oxidations, fatty acid oxidation, fatty acid synthesis, etc. When mitochondria are irradiated with sonic oscillations, the particles concerned with these auxiliary mitochondrial functions can, in large measure, be separated from the particles implicated in the electron transfer function. After such a separation, the presence of the characteristic elementary particles in the fraction retaining electron transfer activity is demonstrable. At least in heart muscle there is no evidence that integrated electron transfer activity can be observed in fractions (prepared by sonic irradiation) that are devoid of the characteristic particles. When bile salts are used in the isolation of the particles with electron transfer activity, there is a major change in the size and shape of the resulting particles. The characteristic appearance of the elementary particle can then no longer be used as a guide for identification. The more active a mitochondrion (per mg of protein), the more numerous are the cristae per mitochondrion and the greater is the number of the particles in question. Thus, there is a close correspondence between electron transfer activity and the number of native elementary particles. All lines of available evidence point to the identification of the isolated particles with those seen *in situ*, but in absence of direct evidence the identification must remain provisional.

## Interpretation of the Arrangement of Parts in the Native Particle

The electron transfer chain is made up of four interdigitating enzymic complexes which can re-assemble spontaneously to form the original electron transfer chain in 1:1:1:1 molecular proportions (44, 45, 47). How can this interrelationship of the four segments of the chain be rationalized in terms of the structural arrangement of the parts of the native elementary particle? The head piece could be assigned as the locale of complex IV (the cytochrome oxidase); the stalk as the locale of complex III (the $QH_2$ cytochrome $c$ reductase); and the base piece as the locale of complexes I (DPNH–coenzyme Q reductase) and II (succinic–coenzyme Q reductase). This tentative assignment of the four complexes is based on biochemical considerations. Complexes I and II must interact with DPNH and succinate, respectively, both of which are localized in the interior of the crista, whereas complex IV must interact with molecular oxygen which would be more readily available in the solution outside the crista rather than in its interior. The cytochrome oxidase appears to be the largest of the four complexes (*cf.* Table VI). The molecular weight of the cytochrome oxidase complex of highest purity is 420,000 on a protein basis. Normalized for 30 per cent lipid, that would come to a molecular weight of 600,000. A sphere of density 1.25 with a molecular weight of 600,000 would have a diameter of about 115 A. The dimensions of the head piece of the particle *in situ* (108 A after 12 per cent correction for underestimation) would not be incompatible with the assignment of the cytochrome oxidase to the head piece. Electron micrographs of isolated and purified cytochrome oxidase show an annular repeating unit about 80 A in diameter made up of structured subunits in the periphery and electron opaque material in the core. More remains to be done, but a case can be made for the provisional identification of cytochrome oxidase with the head piece of the native particle. Perhaps the best basis for comparison would be the experimentally determined diameters for the head piece (80 to 100 A) and the corresponding range for cytochrome oxidase (70 to 90 A). Cytochrome oxidase is a polymeric complex. The exact dimensions of the polymer unit may be affected by a variety of factors.

Complexes I, II, and III have molecular weight of 300,000 or less. The electron microscopic examination of these particular complexes has not been carried very far. None of them shows the marked regularity of the repeating units of the cytochrome oxidase. The available data suggest that the repeating units of complexes I, II, and III are considerably smaller than those of the cytochrome oxidase (diameters in the 40 to 60 A range). The measurements of size, tentative though they may be, are not incompatible with the assignment of complexes I and II to the base piece and of complex III to the stalk.

## Demonstration of Elementary Particles in other Laboratories

Since our preliminary announcement in 1961 of the presence of repeating particles of 80 to 100 A in diameter in the mitochondrial membranes (25, 34), there has been confirmation from several laboratories of our major findings. Parsons (55, 56) has done particularly fine work in devising new methods for negative staining of mitochondria and tissue preparations with phosphotungstate. The uniformity of the elementary particles in his mitochondrial preparations, and the clear visualization of the stalks, are indeed remarkable. Parsons has also concerned himself with the particles of the external envelope. He has postulated a new kind of unit peculiar to the external layer of the envelope (56). The elegant studies of Smith (70, 71) on the sarcosomes of insect flight muscle are of particular importance because these specialized mitochondria can be isolated from the fresh muscle fibers with a minimum of preparative manipulation. The presence of particles in the sarcosomes of the flight muscle (after staining with phosphotungstate) which were similar to those we have described was fully confirmed by Smith. Stoeckenius (72) has also presented extensive electron microscopic evidence of the repeating particles and their stalks in mitochondrial preparations.

## Collateral Evidence of Subunit Organization of Mitochondrial Membranes

Suggestions of regular repeating structures in the planes of unit membranes after various preparatory techniques have been obtained by others. Pease (57) has recently found a very regular pattern of dense beads repeating at a period of about 160 A along two closely apposed outer mitochondrial membranes in a spherule of cat retina.

Very recently Robertson (62) has demonstrated by electron microscopy that the synaptic discs in transverse section show a central beading repeating at a period of about 85 A associated with scalloping of the cytoplasmic surfaces. In front views, an hexagonal array of close-packed polygonal facets is seen. These repeat in a period of about 95 A. Each has a central dense spot about 25 A in diameter. Similar subunits are seen in the unit membranes of synaptic vesicles. Suggestions of a similar hexagonal pattern have also been found in mitochondrial membranes by Robertson (62). Whether or not his "geodesic" pattern represents a macromolecular pattern in intact native membranes remains to be determined. Further interpretations must await evidence from other technical approaches, notably x-ray diffraction studies of membranes.

Important collateral morphological evidence in support of the existence of a subunit structure of the membranes is afforded by the comprehensive studies of the transformations of mitochondria during spermatogenesis (2). As André (2) has clearly demonstrated in extensive electron microscopic studies in nearly 50 widely varied species, mitochondria exhibiting normal ultrastructure at the beginning of spermatogenesis undergo progressive modifications to derivative structures of unusual pattern. These transformations are particularly striking in *Testacella*. In this gastropod a true metamorphosis occurs during which membranes, matrix, pseudomatrix, and dense granules disappear, while orderly domains appear. These orderly domains expand and finally form two concentric muffs of paracrystalline structure. The constituent elements of this paracrystalline network are "hollow rodlets measuring 90 A in diameter." André suggests that these paracrystalline structures "represent a particular state of the respiratory proteins" (2) and points out that the dimensions of the units of this paracrystalline structure approach the dimensions of the EP described in our studies. Similar modifications of transformations of mitochondrial membranes in the course of physiological changes in various types of mitochondria have also been reported by Favard and Carasso (15), Fernández-Morán (21, 22), and others.

## The Oxysome Concept

Chance, Estabrook, and Lee (10) have recently interpreted the electron micrograph finds of Fernández-Morán and Parsons and the biochemical findings of our group in terms of the "oxysome" hypothesis. They consider that the particle which we have isolated may be an artifact rising from the fusion of the individual oxidation-reduction protein components of the electron transfer chain with each other as with the primary dehydrogenases and the coupling factors. According to Chance et al. (10), the native particles correspond to the component proteins of the electron transfer chain and to those of associated processes. Thus, one such particle might be cytochrome $b$, one cytochrome $c_1$, etc. The smallest molecular unit of the electron transfer chain contains one molecule each of cytochrome $c_1$, succinic dehydrogenase, and DPNH dehydrogenase, three molecules of cytochrome $b$, six molecules of cytochrome $a$, and some 18 molecules of non-heme iron protein. At least 15 more proteins would have to be involved to include the primary dehydrogenase systems and the coupling factors. One oxysome would have to encompass over 50 separate particles. There are three major objections to this interpretation. First, there is not a single protein component of the electron transfer chain large enough to account for the size of the particle visualized in situ. A molecule of cytochrome $b$ has a molecular weight of 28,000 according to Goldberger, Bomstein, and Tisdale (31). For an assumed spherical particle, the maximal diameter of cytochrome $b$ would be about 40 A. The corresponding value for cytochrome $c_1$ (molecular weight 38,000 according to Bomstein et al., 6) would be about 45 A; and for the non-heme iron protein, 40 A (molecular weight 25,000 according to J. Rieske et al., 60).

Second, the oxysome hypothesis involves the concept of molecular collisions between individual protein molecules of the chain—a concept that is incompatible with a vast amount of biochemical knowledge, in particular that concerning the arrangement of the complexes of the electron transfer chain, each a mosaic or fusion of four or more proteins. Within the solid state matrix of these complexes, there is no evidence of anything resembling molecular collision between adjacent proteins. Third, the dimensions of the individual proteins of the chain are too far removed from the dimensions of the particles seen in situ to justify serious consideration of the individual protein hypothesis.

## The Respiratory Assembly of Lehninger

Lehninger (50) has for some years visualized the respiratory assembly as a set of oxidation-reduction proteins and proteins concerned with the coupling function that are incorporated into the fabric of the mitochondrial membrane. Like Chance, Lehninger conceives of the electron transfer chain as a linear array of cytochromes and other oxidation-reduction proteins interacting one with the other by molecular collision. His estimate of the dimensions of the respiratory assembly comes to a molecular weight of 1.5 million, and he assumes that the respiratory chain accounts for 20 per cent of the total membrane (50, 51). Lehninger has never intended his respiratory assembly hypothesis to do more than serve as a model, since it is not based on direct experimental evidence. But implicit in the hypothesis is the notion that the respiratory assembly would not be separable from the mitochondrial membrane. The isolation of the elementary particle some five-fold more concentrated in oxidation-reduction components than the original mitochondrion establishes this separability.

## Universality of the Concept of the Elementary Particle

Elsewhere we have developed the thesis that all membrane systems of living cells contain particles analogous to the elementary particles of the mitochondrion (18, 25, 35). Sauer and Calvin (63) have isolated the quantasome from the chloroplast, which is similar in dimensions to the elementary particle of the mitochondrion. Hultin et al. (48) have demonstrated the intimate association of the glycolytic complex of enzymes with the membrane of the red blood cell. The particles which carry these activities may correspond to the particles seen in situ in the membrane of the red blood corpuscles when stained with phosphotungstate (Fernández-Morán, unpublished studies). The microsomal membrane contains a particulate unit having a complete electron transfer chain (DPNH flavoprotein, cytochrome $b$, high lipid content, etc.). These developments suggest that the mitochondrion is not unique; particles and complexes with comparable functions are present in other membranes, and thus the elementary particle (considered in its broadest sense) may be one of the universals of all membrane systems.

Regardless of alternative possibilities, the major conclusion to be derived from these correlative studies is that a repeating unit of mitochondrial structure, first disclosed by electron microscopy, has led to the isolation of a compact multi-enzyme entity which is similar in many respects to the native subunit. The combined approach, linking ultrastructure with biochemistry at the same level of resolution, for the first time invested a lamellar system (the mitochondrial membrane) with specific enzymic detail.

What remains to be done may be summarized under five headings: (1) the direct identification of the isolated and native elementary particles; (2) the identification of the three parts of the native elementary particle with the four complexes of the electron transfer chain; (3) the delineation of the gross molecular structure of the individual complexes; (4) the characterization of the particles associated with the outer membrane of the external envelope as functionally and structurally different from the elementary particles associated with the inner membrane and the cristae; (5) the isolation and characterization of elementary particles from other membrane systems. These are all problems that could not even be formulated before the discovery of the elementary particle. The combination of the biochemical and electron microscopic approaches has been decisive in opening the door to the molecular domain where structure and function merge. We would like to think that the first few lines of an exciting new chapter have been contributed in the present communication.

We are greatly indebted to Professors John Anderegg, William Beeman, and Robert Bock for their many suggestions, to Dr. Pauline Yang for carrying ou the ultracentrifuge runs, to Donald Silver for h technical assistance, and to Oscar Meyer & Com pany of Madison, Wisconsin, for kindly providin fresh beef hearts.

Sincere thanks are also due to Frederick B. Mer and Charles Hough for expert technical assistance and to Sandra J. Riddle and Janice Foss for thei help in preparing the manuscript.

The authors gratefully acknowledge stimulatin discussions with Professors Francis O. Schmitt Neurosciences Research Program, George Palad of The Rockefeller Institute, William H. Sweet c Massachusetts General Hospital, and Willian Bloom of the University of Chicago.

The substance of this communication was reporte in joint papers at the Annual Meeting, Nationa Academy of Sciences, April, 1963, and the abstract of which have been published in Science, 1963, **140** 381 and 382.

The work at the Institute for Enzyme Researcl was supported in part by the Division of Genera Medical Sciences, graduate training grant 2G-88 the National Heart Institute, research grant HE 00458, United States Public Health Service; th National Science Foundation, grant G-3227; an the Atomic Energy Commission, contract No. A' (11-1)-1151.

The work at the Mixter Laboratories and Th Department of Biophysics was supported by Unite States Atomic Energy Commission contract AT(3C 1)-2278; by grants B-2460, C-3174, and NB-0426 from the National Institutes of Health.

*Received for publication, November 1, 1963.*

## REFERENCES

1. AMBE, K., and VENKETARAMAN, A., *Biochem. and Biophys. Research Commun.*, 1959, **1**, 133.

2. ANDRÉ, J., *J. Ultrastruct. Research*, suppl., 1962, **3**, 1.

3. BANGHAM, A. D., and HORNE, R. W., *Nature*, 1962, **196**, 952.

4. BARRNETT, R. J., and PALADE, G. E., *J. Biophysic. and Biochem. Cytol.*, 1957, **3**, 577.

5. BLAIR, P. V., ODA, T., GREEN, D. E., and FERNÁNDEZ-MORÁN, H., *Biochemistry*, 1963, **2**, 766.

6. BOMSTEIN, R., GOLDBERGER, R., and TISDALE, H., *Biochim. et Biophysica Acta*, 1960, **50**, 527.

7. BRENNER, S., and HORNE, R. W., *Biochim. et Biophysica Acta*, 1959, **34**, 103.

8. CASPAR, D. L. D., and KLUG, A., *Cold Spring Harbor Symp. Quant. Biol.*, 1962, **27**, 1.

9. CHANCE, B., and WILLIAMS, G. R., *Advances Enzymol.*, 1956, **17**, 65.

10. CHANCE, B., ESTABROOK, R. W., and LEE, C. P Science, 1963, **194**, 379.

11. CRANE, F. L., GLENN, J. L., and GREEN, D. E *Biochim. et Biophysica Acta*, 1956, **22**, 475.

12. CRIDDLE, R. S., BOCK, R. M., GREEN, D. E and TISDALE, H., *Biochem. and Biophys. Re search Commun.*, 1961, **5**, 75.

13. CRIDDLE, R. S., BOCK, R. M., GREEN, D. E and TISDALE, H., *Biochemistry*, 1962, **1**, 82?

14. DASS, C., RIS, H., ZIEGLER, D. M., LINNAN A. W., and GREEN, D. E., *Biochim. et Bic physica Acta*, 1958, **28**, 524.

15. FAVARD, P., and CARASSO, N., *Arch. Ana micr. et morphol. Exp.*, 1958, **47**, 221.

16. FERNÁNDEZ-MORÁN, H., *Ark. Zool. K. Svensk Vetenskapsakademien*, 1948, **40A**, 1.

17. FERNÁNDEZ-MORÁN, H., *Exp. Cell Research*, 195? **3**, 282.

8. Fernández-Morán, H., *Rev. Modern Phys.*, 1959, **31**, 319.

9. Fernández-Morán, H., *Ann. New York Acad. Sc.*, 1960, **85**, 689.

0. Fernández-Morán, H., *J. Appl. Phys.*, 1960, **31**, 1840.

1. Fernández-Morán, H., *in* Macromolecular Complexes, (M. V. Edds, editor), New York, The Ronald Press Co., 1961, 113.

2. Fernández-Morán, H., *in* The Structure of the Eye, (G. K. Smelser, editor), New York, Academic Press, Inc., 1961, 521.

3. Fernández-Morán, H., *Research Publ. Assn. Nerv. and Ment. Dis.*, 1962, **40**, 235.

4. Fernández-Morán, H., *in* The Interpretation of Ultrastructure, (R. Harris, editor), Academic Press, Inc., New York and London, 1962, 411.

5. Fernández-Morán, H., *Circulation*, 1962, **26**, 1039.

6. Fernández-Morán, H., *in* Macromolecular Specificity and Biological Memory, (F. O. Schmitt, editor), Cambridge, Massachusetts Institute of Technology Press, 1962, 39.

7. Fernández-Morán, H., *Science*, 1963, **140**, 381.

8. Fernández-Morán, H., *in* Tercentenary of the Microscope in Living Biology, Royal Microscopical Society Journal, 1964, **83**, 183.

9. Fernández-Morán, H., and Finean, J. B., *J. Biophysic. and Biochem. Cytol.*, 1957, **3**, 725.

9a. Fernández-Morán, H., and Schramm, G., *Z. Naturforsch.*, 1958, **13b**, 68.

9b. Fleischer, S., Klouwen, H., and Brierley, G., *J. Biol. Chem.*, 1961, **236**, 2936.

0. Fowler, L., and Richardson, S. J., *J. Biol. Chem.*, 1963, **238**, 456.

1. Goldberger, R., Bomstein, R., and Tisdale, H., *J. Biol. Chem.*, 1961, **236**, 2788.

2. Green, D. E., *in* Harvey Lectures (Series 52, 1956–57), New York, Academic Press, Inc., 1958, 177.

3. Green, D. E., *Radiation Research*, suppl., 1960, **2**, 504.

4. Green, D. E., Plenary Lecture, Sixth International Congress of Biochemistry, Moscow, 1961, Preprint No. 176.

5. Green, D. E. *Scient. American*, *1964*, **210**, 63.

5. Green, D. E., Loomis, W. F., and Auerbach, V. H., *J. Biol. Chem.*, 1948, **172**, 389.

7. Green, D. E., and Hatefi, Y., *Science*, 1961, **133**, 13.

3. Green, D. E., and Oda, T. J., *J. Biochem.*, 1961, **49**, 743.

9. Green, D. E., Tisdale, H., Criddle, R. S., and Bock, R. M., *Biochem. and Biophys. Research Commun.*, 1961, **5**, 81.

0. Green, D. E., and Fleischer, S., *in* Horizons in Biochemistry, (M. Kasha and B. Pullman, editors), New York and London, Academic Press, Inc., 1962, 381.

41. Green, D. E., and Wharton, D., *Biochem. Z.*, **338**, 1963.

42. Griffiths, D. E., and Wharton, D., *J. Biol. Chem.*, 1961, **236**, 1850.

43. Hagihara, B., 12th Symposium on Enzyme Chemistry, Japan, 1960, 140.

44. Hatefi, Y., Haavik, A. G., and Griffiths, D. E., *Biochem. and Biophys. Research Commun.*, 1961, **4**, 441, 447.

45. Hatefi, Y., Haavik, A. G., Fowler, L. R., and Griffiths, D. E., *J. Biol. Chem.*, 1962, **237**, 2661.

46. Hatefi, Y., Haavik, A. G., and Griffiths, D. E., *J. Biol. Chem.*, 1962, **237**, 1676.

47. Hatefi, Y., Haavik, A. G., Jurtshuk, P., and Griffiths, D. E., *J. Biol. Chem.*, 1962, **237**, 1676.

48. Hultin, H., Richardson, S., Salmon, B., Murer, E., Brierley, G., and Green, D. E., in preparation.

49. Lehninger, A. L., and Kennedy, E. P., *J. Biol. Chem.*, 1949, **179**, 957.

50. Lehninger, A. L., *Rev. Modern Phys.*, 1959, **31**, 136.

51. Lehninger, A. L., *Physiol. Rev.*, 1962, **42**, 467.

52. Merola, J., and Coleman, R., in preparation.

53. Palade, G. E., *Anat. Rec.*, 1952, **114**, 427.

54. Palade, G. E., *J. Histochem. and Cytochem.*, 1953, **1**, 188.

55. Parsons, D. F., Proceedings 5th International Congress Electron Microscopy, (S. S. Breese, editor), New York, Academic Press, Inc., 1962, **2**, abstract X-1.

56. Parsons, D. F., *Science*, 1963, **140**, 985.

57. Pease, D. C., *J. Cell Biol.*, 1962, **15**, 385.

58. Reed, L. S., Chemistry and function of lipoic acid, *in* Comprehensive Biochemistry, 1963, Elsevier Publ. Co., Amsterdam, **3**.

59. Revel, J. P., Fawcett, D. W., and Philpott, C. W., *J. Cell Biol.*, 1963, **16**, 187.

60. Rieske, J., McLennan, D., Coleman, R., and Yang, P., in preparation.

61. Rieske, J., Zaugg, W., and Wharton, D., in preparation.

62. Robertson, J. D., *J. Cell Biol.*, 1963, **19**, 201.

63. Sauer, K., and Calvin, M., *J. Mol. Biol.*, 1962, **4**, 451.

64. Schmitt, F. O., *Develop. Biol.*, 1963, **7**, 546.

65. Siekevitz, P., and Watson, M. L., *J. Biophysic. and Biochem. Cytol.*, 1956, **2**, 653.

66. Singer, T. P., Kearney, E. D., and Massey, V., *in* Enzymes: Units of Biological Structure and Function, (O. H. Gaebler, editor),

New York, Academic Press. Inc., 1956, **185,** 215.

67. SJÖSTRAND, F. S., *Nature*, 1953, **171,** 303.

68. SJÖSTRAND, F. S., *Radiation Research*, suppl., 1960, **2,** 349.

69. SMITH, A., and HANSEN, M., *Biochim. et Biophysica Acta*, 1963.

70. SMITH, D. S., *J. Cell Biol.*, 1963, **19,** 115.

71. SMITH, D. S., personal communication.

72. STOECKENIUS, W., *J. Cell Biol.*, 1963, **16,** 483.

73. TAKEMORI, S., SEKUZU, I., and OKUNUKI, K., *Nature*, 1960, **188,** 593.

74. THEORELL, H., and AKESON, A., *J. Am. Chem. Soc.*, 1941, **63,** 1804.

75. TISDALE, H., TZAGALOFF, A., and GREEN, D. E., in preparation.

75a. TISDALE, H., WHARTON, D., and GREEN, D. E *Arch. Biochem. and Biophys.*, 1963.

76. WATSON, M. L., and SIEKEVITZ, P., *J. Biophysic and Biochem. Cytol.*, 1956, **2,** 639.

77. WHARTON, D., and TZAGOLOFF, A., *Biochem and Biophys. Research Commun.*, 1963, **13,** 121

78. WOLKEN, J. J., *J. Opt. Soc. America*, 1963, **53,**

79. ZIEGLER, D. M., LINNANE, A. W., GREEN, D. E DASS, C. M. S., and RIS, H., *Biochim. e Biophysica Acta*, 1958, **28,** 524.

80. ZIEGLER, D. M., and LINNANE, A. W. *Biochim et Biophysica Acta*, 1958, **30,** 53.

81. ZIEGLER, D. M., and DOEG, K. A., *Arch. Biochem and Biophys.*, 1962, **97,** 41.

**256**

# Correlation of Structure with Function in *Spinacea oleracea* Chloroplasts†

RODERIC B. PARK AND NING G. PON

*Lawrence Radiation Laboratory and Department of Chemistry, University of California, Berkeley, California, U.S.A.*

(*Received 16 July 1960*)

Spinach chloroplasts, isolated in isotonic sucrose medium, were sonically ruptured and separated by differential centrifugation into three main fractions: a green precipitate, a colourless supernatant and a yellow, low density lipid-containing layer. These fractions were analyzed for their physical, chemical and biochemical properties.

Comparison of a thin section of an isolated osmium-stained chloroplast with a thin section of osmium-stained green precipitate, by electron microscopy, shows that the particles in the green precipitate correspond both in thickness and lateral dimensions to the lamellar structure of the isolated chloroplast. Heavy metal shadowing of both air-dried and lyophilized green precipitate demonstrates the presence of lamellar structures from 10,000 to 20,000 Å in diameter. The lamellar structure, totaling 160 Å in thickness, is composed of two layers; each layer is made up of granular subunits 100 Å thick. Chlorophyll to nitrogen weight ratios are fairly constant for green lamellar structures from 800 to 20,000 Å in diameter, indicating that chlorophyll is uniformly distributed throughout the lamellar structure of the chloroplast. The similarity of relative photosynthetic pigment concentrations over the visible region, of the Hill reaction activity and of the carbon dioxide fixation capacities for the various sized particles in the green precipitate suggests that the smallest lamellar fragments used in these experiments are large in comparison with the smallest fragment which converts electromagnetic to chemical energy. A model for chloroplast lamellar structure is proposed on the basis of the results obtained.

The supernatant, by electron microscopy, is seen to consist principally of oblately spherical particles, 100 Å thick and 200 Å in diameter. These particles are indistinguishable from the main water-soluble protein of the chloroplast with sedimentation coefficient 16 (Fraction I protein). About 90% of the total carboxydismutase activity is associated with the supernatant proteins. In addition, these proteins are able to convert fructose-6-phosphate into other photosynthetic carbon cycle intermediates. This supernatant must be added to the green precipitate in order to obtain maximum carbon dioxide fixation rates.

Electron micrographs of unfractionated osmium-fixed chloroplast sonicate show large osmium-stained spherical objects corresponding in size and staining properties to the osmiophyllic granules observed in thin sections of osmium-stained chloroplast in the intact leaf. Similar granules, 500 to 1500 Å in diameter, were obtained when the yellow, low density lipid layer was fixed with osmium and then shadowed.

## 1. Introduction

Green plant photosynthesis is generally considered to consist of two component processes, light reactions and dark reactions. The light reactions convert electromagnetic energy into chemical potential necessary for oxygen production, reduction

†The work described in this paper was sponsored by the United States Atomic Energy Commission.

of $CO_2$ and formation of adenosine triphosphate (ATP). The dark reactions fix $CO_2$ and regenerate $CO_2$ acceptor from the first products of photosynthesis. Studies on isolated chloroplasts have shown that both the light and dark reactions of photosynthesis in higher plants are associated with this cytoplasmic plastid (Arnon, Whatley & Allen, 1954). Trebst, Tsujimoto & Arnon (1958) first showed that it was possible to fractionate isolated chloroplasts in such a way that the light and dark reactions of photosynthesis became physically separated. Trebst found that the colourless supernatant obtained by centrifuging osmotically swollen spinach chloroplasts carried out the dark reactions of photosynthesis, $CO_2$ fixation and regeneration of $CO_2$ acceptor from photosynthetic products. The green precipitate obtained from the centrifugation carried out the light reactions of photosynthesis, production of oxygen, reducing power and ATP. The physical separation of the two major series of photosynthetic reactions obtained by Trebst suggests the possibility of correlating the chemical, physical and enzymatic properties of the separated particles with structures observed by electron microscopy of an intact chloroplast.

*Spinacea oleracea* leaves were washed with cold tap water and allowed to drain as completely as possible. All operations were carried out at, or near, 0°C. Leaves (125 g) were homogenized in 250 ml. of 0·5 M-sucrose, 0·1 M-potassium phosphate buffer, pH 7·4, and 0·01 M-versenol titrated to pH 7·4, in a blender operated at full speed for 30 sec. The green homogenate was filtered through 8 layers of cheesecloth.

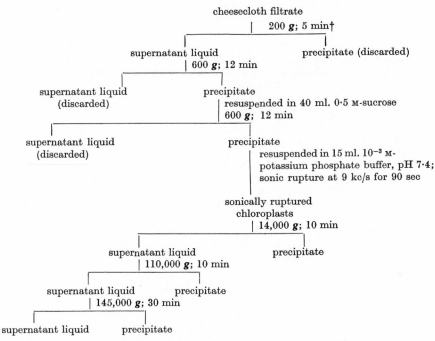

FIG. 1. Typical flow sheet for the preparation of chloroplast fragments.
†The accelerations due to gravity (*g*) are maximum values.

Such a correlation study would require a wide size spectrum of chloroplast particles from very simple units to the more complex structure. Recent work in this laboratory showed that sonic rupture of isolated spinach chloroplasts produces a photosynthetic system in which $^{14}CO_2$ fixation rates are comparable to the $CO_2$ fixation rates for intact chloroplasts on a unit chlorophyll basis (Park, Pon, Louwrier & Calvin, 1960). A wide spectrum of particle sizes is present in this sonically ruptured system. By observing the chemical, enzymatic, centrifugal and electron microscopic properties of the various types of particles separated from a sonically ruptured suspension of spinach chloroplasts, we are now able to attribute specific functions and chemical properties to some of the structures seen in an electron micrograph of a thin section of spinach chloroplasts.

## 2. Experimental

### (a) *Preparation of chloroplasts and chloroplast fragments*

Chloroplasts were isolated from *Spinacea oleracea* leaves using a method similar to that of Holm-Hansen, Pon, Nichida, Moses & Calvin (1959). The precipitated whole chloroplasts obtained by this procedure were resuspended in $10^{-3}$ M-potassium phosphate buffer pH 7·4. This suspension was sonically ruptured for 90 sec in a 9 kc/s Raytheon 100 watt magnetostriction oscillator operated at full voltage. Following sonication the fragmented chloroplasts were subjected to fractional centrifugation. This general scheme is outlined in Fig. 1.

### (b) *Enzyme assays*

The organic cofactors and metal cofactors used in the photosynthetic reactions were prepared separately from one another and titrated to pH 7·4 (see Table 1). The photo

TABLE 1

*Reaction mixture used for studying $^{14}CO_2$ fixation by chloroplast fragments*

| Compound | $\mu$M | Compound | $\mu$M |
|---|---|---|---|
| MgSO$_4$ | 4·0 | Thiamine pyrophosphate | 1·4 |
| MnCl$_2$ | 1·6 | Ascorbate | 2·5 |
| Adenosine diphosphate | 1·0 | NaH$^{14}$CO$_3$ | 4·0 (100 $\mu$C) |
| Triphosphopyridine nucleotide | 0·02 | Glutathione | 1·3 |
| Diphosphopyridine nucleotide | 0·2 | Phosphate (pH 7·4) | 1·0 |

Each flask contained 1 mg of chlorophyll as chloroplast material in 1·2 ml. total volume. Incubation time: 30 min at 24°C.

synthetic reactions were run at 24°C at a light intensity of 1000 ft candles in airtight 35 ml. flasks. The total reaction mixture volume was about 1·2 ml. and contained about 1 mg of chlorophyll. After 30 min incubation, the enzymatic reaction was stopped by adding 4 ml. ethanol to the reaction mixture. The precipitate was then extracted with 20% ethanol, 100% ethanol and water. The extracts were pooled. A small portion was acidified and placed on an aluminum planchet for assay of the total radioactivity in the reaction mixture. Another portion was applied to the origin of a paper chromatogram. Two-dimensional chromatography of the photosynthetic products and counting of the radioactive areas on the chromatograms was carried out according to the methods described by Bassham & Calvin (1957).

The carboxydismutase assay used in these experiments is described by Park *et al.* (1960).

### (c) Ultracentrifugal analysis

The sedimentation rates of Fraction I protein were studied in a Spinco ultracentrifuge model E (serial number 1). The Fraction I protein was dissolved in pH 7·25 potassium maleate buffer, ionic strength 0·2, at a concentration of 10 mg/ml. Centrifugation was performed at 49,330 rev/min at an average temperature of 17·4°C. In the Fraction I run, the calculation of $S_{20,w}$ (the sedimentation coefficient in water at 20°C) from $S_{obs}$ (the observed sedimentation coefficient) was made by using the specific viscosity of sodium succinate and density of potassium tartrate, respectively.

### (d) Nitrogen analysis

Nitrogen was determined according to the usual Kjeldahl method except that $SeOCl_2$ was used as a catalyst instead of $HgSO_4$. The reproducibility of the method was tested on plant tissues by digesting the algae, Chlorella pyrenoidosa and Scenedesmus obliquus, under a variety of conditions, e.g. varying amounts of digestion mixture and varying digestion times. The results of this test showed that the method was reproducible to within $\pm$ 0·3%.

### (e) Chlorophyll analysis

Chlorophyll concentrations were determined spectrophotometrically in 80% acetone according to the method of Arnon (1949).

### (f) Electron microscopy

The electron microscopic observations were performed with an RCA EMU-2 instrument. The sectioned material was fixed and embedded according to the methods outlined by Farquhar (1950). Shadowing for particle work was done with a gold, palladium and platinum alloy, or nichrome wire from a tungsten filament at a pressure of less than 0·1 $\mu$. The frozen dried specimens were prepared following the procedure of Williams (1953).

## 3. Results and Discussion

Leyon (1954), Steinmann & Sjostrand (1955), von Wettstein (1958), Hodge (1959) and others have used electron microscopic observations to describe the principal features of higher plant chloroplast structure. Electron microscopic observations of osmium-stained chloroplast-containing material have shown that the plastid is surrounded by an outer membrane. Within the chloroplast membrane there is a series of lamellar structures. Thickened areas on the lamellae are called grana, while the structures surrounding the grana are called stroma. Heavily stained spherical objects 500 Å to 1500 Å in diameter are also seen in thin sections of chloroplast material. These structures have been termed "osmiophyllic granules" in the literature (Leyon (1954)).

The principal features of chloroplast structure described above are seen in the electron micrographs of spinach chloroplasts shown in Plates III and IV. The tissues in Plates III and IV were fixed at 0°C for 30 min in buffered 2% osmium tetroxide and 0·5% potassium permanganate respectively. It is seen that the dimensions of the structures within chloroplasts as viewed in the electron microscope are quite dependent on the fixation method used. The dimensions used in this paper are taken primarily from the permanganate-fixed material since this tissue is relatively less disrupted than that fixed in osmium.

Our experiments were designed to obtain direct evidence for the functions and chemistry of the chloroplast structures described above and shown in Plates III and IV.

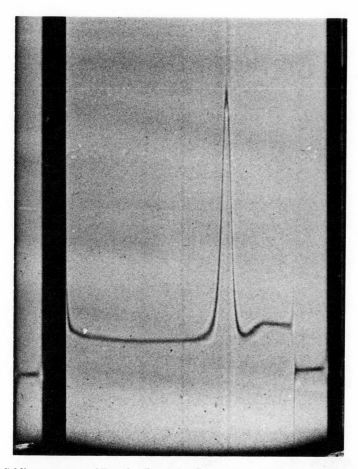

PLATE I. Schlieren pattern of Fraction I protein ($S_{20,w} = 16$) in Spinco model E ultracentrifuge. Sedimentation is from right to left.

[ *To face page* 4

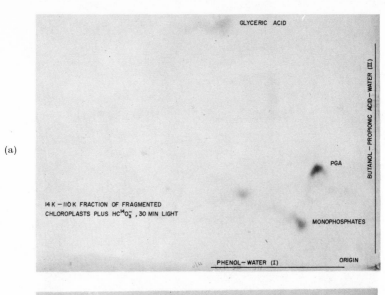

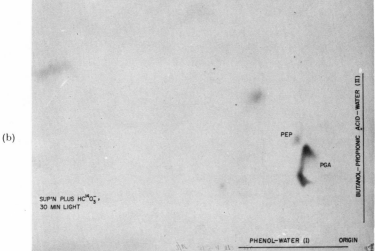

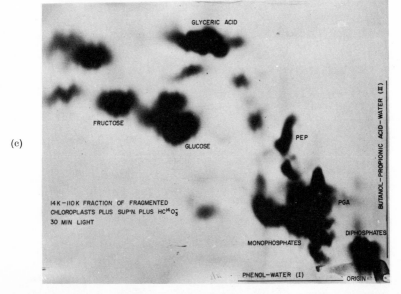

PLATE II. Comparison among the products of $^{14}CO_2$ fixation by green precipitate, supernatant and green precipitate plus supernatant in light.

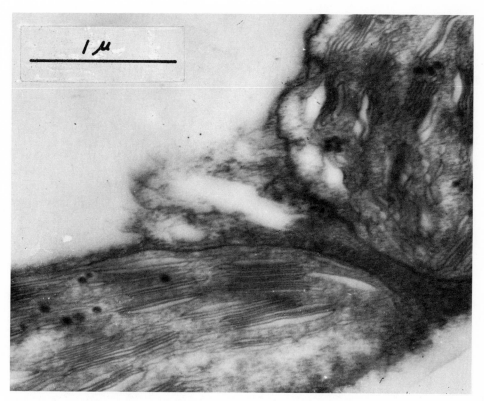

PLATE III. Thin section of spinach leaf showing chloroplasts. Fixed in buffered 2% OsO₄.

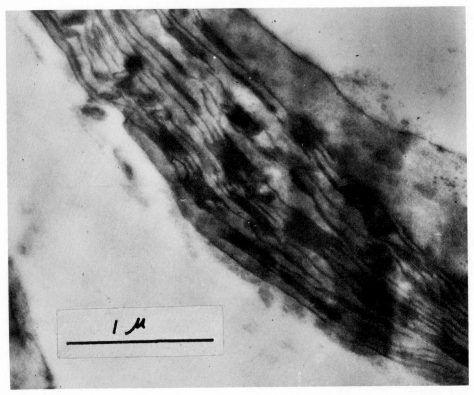

PLATE IV. Thin section of spinach leaf showing chloroplasts. Fixed in 0·5% KMnO$_4$.

PLATE V. Comparison between thin sections of buffered 2% osmium fixed (a) chloroplasts, and (b) 20,000 to 40,000 $g$ precipitate of chloroplast sonicate.

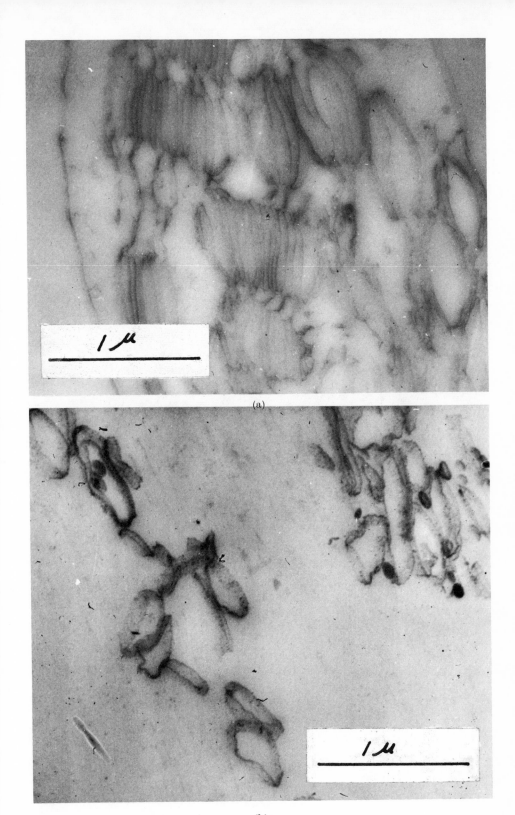

(a)

(b)

Plate V. (*see facing page*)

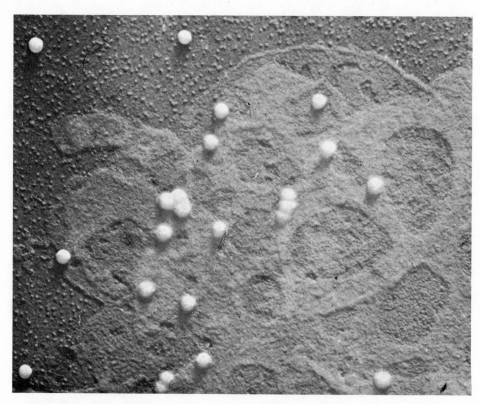

PLATE VI. 5,000 to 10,000 **g** precipitate of spinach chloroplast sonicate. 880 Å diameter poly-
styrene latex (PSL) marker molecules.

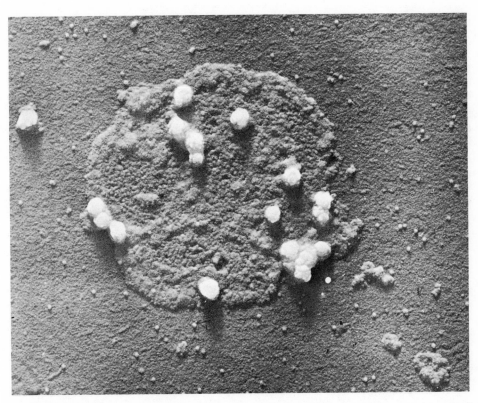

PLATE VII. 5,000 to 10,000 **g** precipitate of frozen dried spinach chloroplast sonicate. 880 Å diameter PSL marker molecules.

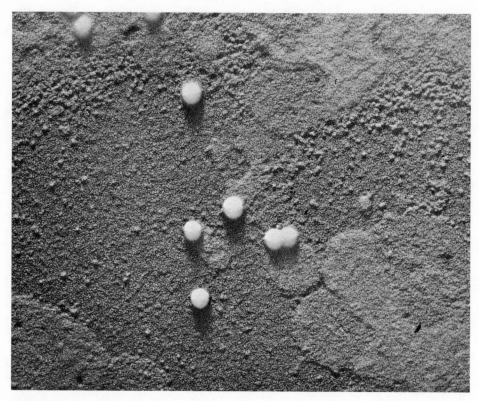

PLATE VIII. 5,000 to 10,000 *g* precipitate of spinach chloroplast sonicate. 880 Å diameter PSL marker molecules.

Chloroplasts were isolated from spinach leaf tissue following the scheme in Fig. 1. The isolated chloroplasts were placed in dilute buffer, and sonically ruptured. The sonically ruptured chloroplast preparation was then fractionated by centrifugation. High speed centrifugation of a chloroplast sonicate in dilute buffer yields three principal fractions: a green precipitate, a colourless supernatant and a layer of lipid-containing material which rises to the surface of the tube during centrifugation. The electron microscopic, chemical and enzymatic properties of these three separate fractions are considered below. The enzymology of the recombined fractions is also described and a correlation is made between the isolated fractions and structures observed in a whole chloroplast.

## Green precipitate

Plate V is a comparison between a thin section of an isolated chloroplast stained with osmium in isotonic sucrose and a thin section of osmium stained 20,000 to 40,000 $g$ green precipitate. The green precipitate corresponds both in thickness and lateral dimension to the lamellar structures of the isolated chloroplast. The lamellar structures in the green precipitate contain a number of closely spaced osmium-staining particles in the outer surface which are not evident in the isolated chloroplasts. The two preparations have comparable enzymatic activities. Whether the particles are a result of the sonic treatment, excessive swelling of the lamellar structure or are an artifact is not known. A comparison between Plates V(a) and III shows that either the chloroplast is considerably disrupted during the isolation procedure or it becomes less resistant to distortion during fixation in the isolated state.

If the 5,000 to 10,000 $g$ green precipitate is metal shadowed rather than sectioned, micrographs such as those shown in Plates VI and VII are obtained. Plate VI is an electron micrograph of green material precipitated between 5,000 and 10,000 $g$ which was air-dried and shadowed with gold, palladium and platinum alloy. Plate VII is an electron micrograph of the same fraction, but frozen dried and shadowed with chromium. Both figures show a lamellar structure from 10,000 to 20,000 Å in diameter. The complete lamella is about 160 Å in thickness. The 200 Å diameter particles seen on the background in Plates VI and VII are contaminating supernatant proteins which are described in the next section. In Plate VI two layers are evident within the lamellar structure: an upper smooth layer and a lower granular layer which can be seen through the depressions on the lamellar structure. This suggests that at least two layers are present in the lamellar structure. The frozen dried preparation in Plate VII also indicates that at least two layers are present. A number of thickness measurements have shown that the lamellar structures seen in Plates VI and VII are made of two layers of equal thickness (100 Å). The total thickness of the lamellar structure is about 160 Å, or less than twice the thickness of the two individual layers from which it is made. Apparently the granular surfaces are packed in such a way as to allow a reduction of overall thickness. The inner surfaces of the two layers appear more granular than the outer surfaces when observed in the electron microscope. That the layers of the granular subunits run throughout the lamellar structure is indicated in Plate VIII. Here apparently solid structures are seen breaking down into particles along their length. This has never been observed in the frozen dried preparations, suggesting that the forces of surface tension are responsible for releasing the subunits from the layers.

Chlorophyll-to-nitrogen weight ratios (Table 2) for green lamellar structures from 20,000 Å to 800 Å in diameter are fairly constant though precipitation of colourless supernatant protein at high $g$ values reduces the ratio slightly. The large lamellar structures such as those seen in Plate VI appear to be stripped of grana. These structures have chlorophyll-to-nitrogen ratios similar to the precipitates obtained at higher $g$ values which contain grana. This fact can be interpreted to mean that chlorophyll is uniformly distributed throughout the lamellar structure of the chloro-

TABLE 2

*Chlorophyll-to-nitrogen weight ratios of spinach leaves, chloroplasts, and chloroplast fragments*

| Fraction | $\dfrac{\text{Chlorophyll (mg)}}{\text{Nitrogen (mg)}}$ | Particle size ($\mu$) |
| --- | --- | --- |
| Leaves | 0·32 | |
| Whole chloroplasts | 1·06 | 4 |
| 600 to 5,000 $g$ precipitate | 1·91 | |
| 5,000 to 10,000 $g$ precipitate | 1·80 | |
| 10,000 to 20,000 $g$ precipitate | 2·07 | 1 to 2 |
| 20,000 to 40,000 $g$ precipitate | 1·99 | |
| 40,000 to 145,000 $g$ precipitate | 1·82 | |
| 145,000 $g$ precipitate (30 min) | 1·37 | < 0·1 |
| 145,000 $g$ supernatant | 0·52 | |

plast. Chlorophyll may be more evident in the grana regions of a chloroplast when observed by a light or fluorescence microscope primarily because of the increased amount of chlorophyll-containing lamellar structure present in the grana areas. That grana are not essential to photosynthesis is indicated by electron micrographs of algal chloroplasts. Grana are absent from algal chloroplasts, though the lamellar structures are still present.

Spectrophotometric examination of 80% acetone extracts of different sizes of lamellar fragments has shown that relative photosynthetic pigment concentrations within the fragments are similar over the range 400 to 700 m$\mu$. The Hill reaction rates of the various green precipitates, assayed manometrically with Fe $(CN)_6^{3-}$ as the oxidant, were uniform over the particle size range studied. The $^{14}CO_2$ fixation capacities of these particles are also similar (Table 4). These results all indicate that the smallest lamellar structures we have used (800 Å in diameter) are large in comparison to the smallest lamellar fragment which will convert electromagnetic energy to chemical potential.

The model for chloroplast lamellar structure presented in Fig. 2 is in accord with our results. The model for a lamella consists of two layers of 100 Å maximum thickness with an overall thickness of 160 Å. The outer surfaces of the layers represent the osmium-staining material of the lamellar structure seen in Plates III, IV and V. The layers are made of subunits 100 Å in thickness and 200 Å in diameter which are osmiophyllic over the outer surface. The rounder inner side of such subunits are evident in Plate VII. The granular layers in the depressions in the lamellar structure of

Plates VI and VII would represent the inner surface of the lower layer in this model, while the smooth upper layer would represent the outside surface of the upper layer. This model combines features previously proposed by Frey-Wyssling & Steinmann (1953) and Steinmann & Sjostrand (1955).

The model predicts that the top or bottom layer of a stack of grana should consist of a single 30 Å thick osmium-staining layer. This prediction is verified in a number of instances in Plate III. The swelling of the lamellar structures in Plate V indicates that the bond between the two lamellar layers is fairly weak. The weakness of this bond compared with the bond between the osmium-staining layers could explain the

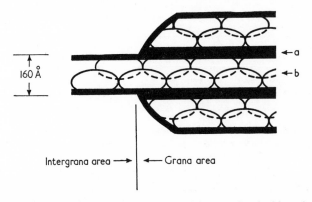

FIG. 2. Model for the lamellar structure within a spinach chloroplast

(a) Osmium-staining layer of the lamellar structure. Thickness 30 Å in the intergrana regions and 60 Å in the grana regions.

(b) Particles forming the granular inner surface of the two layers making up the lamellar structure. The packing of oblate spheres would not be as simple as illustrated in the figure since the central axis of both layers would not be in the same vertical plane shown here.

depressions in the lamellar surface in Plate VI if these areas had been the site of grana which had been sheared away from the large lamellar structure during sonication. The subunits 100 Å in height and 200 Å in diameter correspond in size to Fraction I molecules described in the next section. Smith & Kupke (1956) report that extracted protochlorophyll holochrome has a sedimentation coefficient typical of Fraction I protein. It will be interesting to find whether Smith & Kupke's extracted holochrome corresponds to the lamellar subunit in an early stage of development.

### *Supernatant*

Plate IX is an electron micrograph of frozen dried supernatant from a 145,000 **g** centrifuge run for one hour's duration. This material is nearly colourless and therefore differs from the subunits described above. The supernatant in Plate IX is seen to consist principally of oblately spherical proteins about 200 Å in diameter and 100 Å in height. An ultracentrifugal analysis of this preparation shows that about half of the protein has an $S_{20,w}$ of 16. The remaining components are slower moving. The similarity between this sedimentation coefficient and that of Fraction I protein (Eggman, Singer & Wildman, 1953), as prepared by Lyttleton & Ts'o (1958) suggested that the 200 Å protein particles seen in Plate IX are actually Fraction I protein. To test this hypothesis Fraction I protein was prepared from spinach chloroplasts according to the method of Lyttleton & Ts'o. This preparation having an $S_{20,w}$ of 16 (see

Plate I), when observed under the electron microscope (Plate X), was indistinguish-able from the 200 Å particles shown in Plate IX. The oblately spherical 200 Å super-natant proteins seen in Plate IX are apparently Fraction I protein.

Our analysis of the distribution of carboxydismutase activity in various centri-fugal fractions from sonically ruptured chloroplasts is given in Table 3. About 90%

TABLE 3

*Distribution of the carboxydismutase activity in various chloroplast fractions*

| Fraction | Activity in % of total |
| --- | --- |
| 0 to 20,000 **g** supernatant | 100† |
| 20,000 to 40,000 **g** precipitate | 3 |
| 40,000 to 145,000 **g** precipitate | 6 |
| 40,000 to 145,000 **g** supernatant | 90 |

†In another experiment 96% of the total carboxydismutase activity was present in this fraction. The remaining 4% was in the 0 to 20,000 **g** precipitate. Carboxydismutase activity was determined by mixing together in the order listed, in $\mu$M: $NaH^{14}CO_3$, 1·34 (20 $\mu$c); RuDP *ca.* 0·1; tris 15 (pH 8·3); $MgCl_2$, 2; and enzyme fraction 24 to 31 $\mu$g. Water was added to make 200 $\mu$l. final volume. Incubation was for 10 min at 25 °C. Reaction was stopped by adding 50 $\mu$l. of 6 N-acetic acid. One-tenth of this mixture was plated and counted.

of the total carboxydismutase activity is associated with the colourless supernatant protein from the centrifugation. Incubation of $^{14}$C-labeled fructose-6-phosphate with the supernatant protein yielded a number of radioactive photosynthetic carbon cycle intermediates (Turner, private communication) which also confirms Trebst's observation (Trebst *et al.*, 1958) that the dark reactions of photosynthesis are associ-ated with the colorless supernatant from a centrifuged chloroplast preparation. Our observation that this preparation is largely Fraction I protein could be interpreted to mean that Fraction I protein contains a number of enzymatic sites of the photo-synthetic cycle. The possibility of adsorption of small enzymes to the surface of this large (200 Å) protein cannot, however, be excluded by these experiments.

### $^{14}CO_2$ fixation in green precipitate and supernatant

The difference between $^{14}CO_2$ fixation by precipitated green fragments resuspended in 1 ml. $10^{-3}$ M-phosphate (pH 7·4) and those resuspended in 1 ml. of supernatant from the 145,000 **g** centrifugation is presented in Table 4. The cofactors (Table 1) and $H^{14}CO_3^-$ were added to the system which was then incubated for 30 min in the light or dark at 24 °C. Apparently, supernatant must be added to the chloroplast fragments to obtain high $^{14}CO_2$ fixation rates. The green fragments in the 145,000 **g** precipitate average 800 Å in diameter and were as active in $CO_2$ fixation on a unit chlorophyll basis as the largest fragments. Actually the calculated size for a photosynthetic unit of 600 chlorophyll molecules is considerably smaller than the 800 Å particles used in these experiments. Diminution of fixation rate owing to the preparation of incomplete photosynthetic units would not be expected until the green particles were reduced to a size of 200 Å (Thomas, Blaauw & Duysens, 1953). The relatively high light fixation rates of the 110,000 to 145,000 **g** precipitate resuspended in $10^{-3}$ M-phosphate is appar-

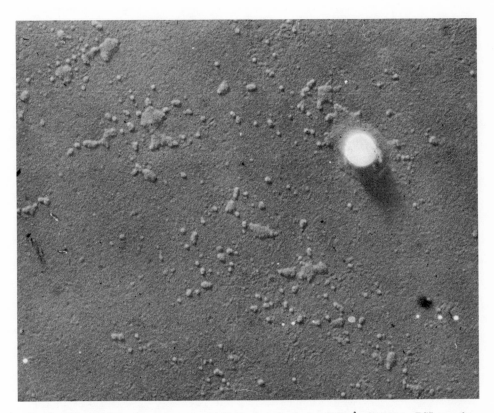

PLATE IX. 145,000 **g** supernatant of chloroplast sonicate. 1880 Å diameter PSL marker molecules.

[*To face page* 8

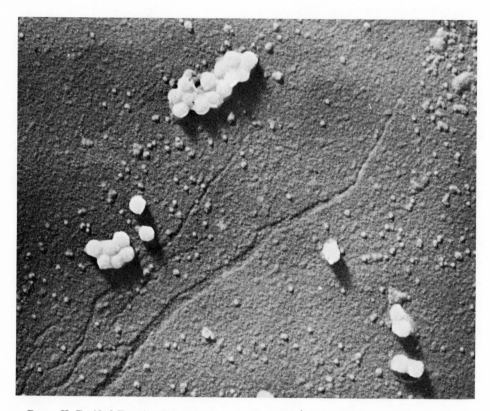

PLATE X. Purified Fraction I protein. Frozen dried. 880 Å diameter PSL marker molecules.

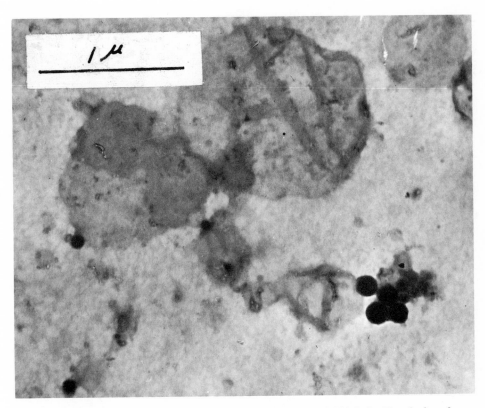

PLATE XI. Spinach chloroplast sonicate. Fixed in buffered 2% $OsO_4$. Not shadowed.

PLATE XII. Isolated osmiophyllic granules. Fixed in buffered 2% OsO₄. No PSL present.

ently due to the precipitation of some of the supernatant protein along with the green particles at this high *g* value. Chromatograms of ethanol extracts from the 14,000 to 110,000 *g* precipitate, 145,000 *g* supernatant and 14,000 to 110,000 *g* precipitate plus 145,000 *g* supernatant after incubation with $^{14}CO_2$ are given in Plate II. Although a small amount of reduction is carried out by the green fragments alone, it is evident that this effect is enormously enhanced by addition of supernatant protein, which contains the photosynthetic carbon cycle enzymes, to the reaction mixture.

TABLE 4

*Fixation of $^{14}CO_2$ by various fractions from sonically fragmented chloroplasts*

| Fraction | Counts/min/mg of chlorophyll | |
|---|---|---|
| | Light | Dark |
| Total sonicate | 2,100,000 | 40,000 |
| 0 to 14,000 *g* precipitate | 76,000 | 9,000 |
| 0 to 14,000 *g* plus supernatant | 3,300,000 | 28,000 |
| 14,000 to 110,000 *g* precipitate | 18,000 | 4,200 |
| 14,000 to 110,000 *g* plus supernatant | 3,000,000 | 22,000 |
| 110,000 to 145,000 *g* precipitate | 210,000 | — |
| 110,000 to 145,000 *g* plus supernatant | 2,500,000 | 22,000 |
| Supernatant alone, 1 ml. | 30,000 | 53,000 |

Details of the preparation of these fractions are given in Fig. 1. Supernatant refers to the supernatant liquid obtained from 145,000 *g* centrifugation in Fig. 1. A fixation rate of $3 \times 10^6$ counts/min/mg chlorophyll/30 min is equivalent to 1 micromole of $CO_2$ fixed/mg chlorophyll/hr.

## Lipid layer

Plate XI is an electron micrograph of unfractionated osmium-fixed chloroplast sonicate which has undergone no further treatment. The large osmium-stained spherical objects in this micrograph correspond in size and osmium staining properties to the osmiophyllic granules seen in Plate III. These osmiophyllic granules are not evident in the preparation unless osmium staining is carried out (Hayes, Murchio, Lindgren & Nichols, 1959). If the lipid layer obtained upon centrifugation is osmium-fixed and shadowed, a picture such as Plate XII is obtained. It is seen that some of the lipid materials are very similar in dimensions to the osmiophyllic granules of Plates III and XI, and are very probably identical with them. These large lipid granules do not acquire $^{14}C$-label rapidly during photosynthesis by the chloroplast sonicate. For example during a 30-minute incubation, less than 1% of the fixed carbon is associated with the lipid granules. This, of course, may not be the case in the intact leaf. That these granules might be reservoirs for some interesting lipids associated with photosynthesis, such as diglycerol phosphate (Benson, Wintermans & Wiser, 1959), is an interesting possibility.

## 4. Conclusions

From the electron microscopic, ultracentrifugal, enzymological and chemical data presented in the preceding sections we can correlate certain structures and functions in spinach chloroplasts. The light reactions of photosynthesis are associated with the pigment-containing lamellar structures within the chloroplast. The lamellae are made of two layers of subunits. The layers are osmiophyllic on the outer surface. On the inner surface the granular appearance of the subunits is evident. Chlorophyll-to-nitrogen ratio studies on the lamellar structures may be interpreted to mean that the localization of chlorophyll in the grana of spinach plants is due to the greater number of chlorophyll-containing lamellar structures in this area of the spinach chloroplast rather than to localization of chlorophyll exclusively in the grana area. Small fragments of the lamellar structures are capable of Hill reaction though not capable of rapid light-dependent $CO_2$ fixation without addition of stroma protein. The stroma proteins within which the lamellar structures lie contain the enzymes associated with the dark reaction of photosynthesis and are largely Fraction I protein. The dimensions of Fraction I protein were determined from frozen dried preparations. Fraction I protein appeared as oblate spheres 100 Å in height and 200 Å in diameter.

Osmiophyllic granules ranging in size from 500 to 1500 Å in diameter have been isolated from the chloroplasts by nature of their low density. Presumably these structures are lipid in character.

The authors wish to thank Dr. Thomas Hayes of the University of California Donner Laboratory, both for the use of his electron microscope and for his many helpful suggestions during the course of this work.

## REFERENCES

Arnon, D. I. (1949). *Plant Physiol.* **24**, 1.
Arnon, D. I., Whatley, F. R. & Allen, M. B. (1954). *J. Amer. Chem. Soc.* **76**, 6324.
Bassham, J. A. & Calvin, M. (1957). *The Path of Carbon in Photosynthesis.* Englewood Cliffs, New Jersey: Prentice-Hall, Inc.
Benson, A. A., Wintermans, J. F. G. M. & Wiser, R. (1959). *Plant Physiol.* **34**, 315.
Eggman, L., Singer, S. J. & Wildman, S. A. (1953). *J. Biol. Chem.* **205**, 969.
Farquhar, M. G. (1950). *Lab. Investigation,* **5**, 317.
Frey-Wyssling, A. & Steinmann, E. (1953). *Vjschr. Naturf. Ges., Zurich,* **98**, 20.
Hayes, T. L., Murchio, J. C., Lindgren, F. T. & Nichols, A. V. (1959). *J. Mol. Biol.* **1**, 297.
Hodge, A. J. (1959). *Rev. Mod. Phys.* **31**, 331.
Holm-Hansen, O., Pon, N. G., Nishida, K., Moses, V. & Calvin, M. (1959). *Physiol. Plant.* **12**, 475.
Leyon, H. (1954). *Exp. Cell Res.* **7**, 265.
Lyttleton, J. W. & Ts'o, P. O. P. (1958). *Arch. Biochem. Biophys.* **73**, 120.
Park, R. B., Pon, N. G., Louwrier, K. P. & Calvin, M. (1960). *Biochim. biophys. Acta,* **42**, 27.
Smith, J. H. C. & Kupke, D. W. (1956). *Nature,* **178**, 751.
Steinmann, E. & Sjostrand, F. S. (1955). *Exp. Cell. Res.* **8**, 15.
Thomas, J. B., Blaauw, O. H. & Duysens, L. N. M. (1953). *Biochim. biophys. Acta,* **10**, 230.
Trebst, A. V., Tsujimoto, H. Y. & Arnon, D. I. (1958). *Nature,* **182**, 351.
von Wettstein, D. (1958). *Brookhaven Symp. Biol.* **11**, 138.
Williams, R. C. (1953). *Exp. Cell. Res.* **4**, 188.

# FRACTURE FACES OF FROZEN MEMBRANES*

### By Daniel Branton

DEPARTMENT OF BOTANY, UNIVERSITY OF CALIFORNIA, BERKELEY

Communicated by Melvin Calvin, March 11, 1966

The biological membrane, according to one widely accepted concept, has as its framework a bimolecular leaflet which under appropriate conditions can be seen in the electron microscope as two dark 20-Å-thick layers separated by a lighter 35-Å-thick layer.[1] Well-known theories and evidence[2-9] suggest that this structure is composed of a bimolecular leaflet of oriented lipid molecules sandwiched between two layers of protein. Though Robertson[10] has formalized these ideas as the basis of his generalized unit membrane concept, new chemical[11-13] and structural[10, 12, 14-16] evidence requires that other molecular arrangements also be considered. This has been the case in several recently proposed membrane models. Though some of these models take as their starting point the general notion of a bimolecular leaflet[17, 18] and others take as a starting point a repeating particulate subunit,[11, 14, 16] they all emphasize the possibility of dynamic interrelations between the several membrane components and explicitly deny the notion of a biological membrane which is spatially and temporally uniform.

The structural implications of these recent models are difficult to study, as there are few high-resolution techniques which can be used to examine rapidly changing forms.   However, the recently improved freeze-etching technique[19, 20] should provide a direct view of membrane structure.   Since this method does not involve the use of chemical fixatives or stains and the freeze-fixation employed need not kill the cells,[21] one can study membranes as they respond to a given physiological environment, rather than as they respond to a fixative environment.   Furthermore, surfaces exposed in freeze-etching are three-dimensional fractures in which spatially extended areas of membranes can be examined.

Initial experiments with freeze-etching have demonstrated its applicability to a wide variety of biological specimens.[21-25]   This report presents a more detailed interpretation of the fractured membrane faces exposed by this technique.   Preliminary observations of freeze-etched root tip cells[24] revealed membrane faces whose morphological features could not be equated with the known features of membrane surfaces.   The investigations reported here have explained this by demonstrating that what is usually considered as the true membrane surface (the interface between a membrane and any contiguous protoplasm, cell wall, or vacuolar material) is rarely seen in freeze-etched preparations.   Instead, the fracture process splits the membrane and exposes an internal membrane face.

*Materials and Methods.*—Adventitious roots of onion sets (*Allium cepa* L., var. White Globe) were used for most of the experiments.   They were grown in 20% glycerol.[24]   Other experiments involved *Porphyridium cruentum* (Ag.) Naeg. or *Saccharomyces* sp.   The unicellular red alga *P. cruentum* (Indiana University culture collection) was grown as described elsewhere.[26]   *Saccharomyces* sp. cells (Fleischmann's yeast cakes) were separated by centrifugation from the starch used as a binder in the cakes and suspended in fresh tap water for 2 hr.

In preparation for freeze-etching, onion roots were cut in half lengthwise.   A 1–2-mm piece of the half tip was placed in a thin syrup of gum arabic dissolved in 20% glycerol, transferred to a 3-mm copper disk, and then rapidly frozen in liquid Freon 22 (chlorodifluoromethane).   Gum arabic helped to cement the frozen root tip to the copper disk but had no observable effect on cell ultrastructure.   The *Porphyridium* and *Saccharomyces* cells were collected by centrifugation.   Small droplets of the cell pellet were placed on copper disks and frozen in Freon 22.

The frozen specimens were freeze-etched (Fig. 1) as described by Moore *et al.*[20, 22]   In some experiments the amount of etching applied to the fractured surface was varied by manipulating either the etching time or the etching temperature, or both.   "Normal etching" was accomplished by leaving the freshly fractured specimens *in vacuo* (less than $2 \times 10^{-6}$ torr) for 1–5 min at $-100°C$.   "No etching" was accomplished by keeping the temperature of freshly fractured surfaces below $-165°C$ and by replicating the surfaces as rapidly as possible (less than 10 sec) after they were fractured.   "Deep etching" was accomplished by leaving the freshly fractured surfaces *in vacuo* for 10 min at $-95°C$.

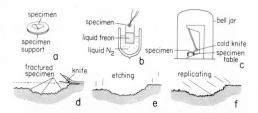

FIG. 1.—Freeze-etching.   (*a*) The fresh specimen was placed on a Cu disk, (*b*) rapidly frozen in liquid Freon 22, and (*c*) placed in the precooled freeze-etching vacuum chamber.   (*d*) The frozen specimen was fractured with a microtome knife at $-185°C$, and in some cases (*e*) the freshly fractured surface was etched.   (*f*) The surface was shadowed and replicated with Pt and C.

All micrographs have been printed so that shadows appear as light areas and have been mounted for publication with shadows extending from bottom to top.

*Results.*—Basic observations:   A consistent feature in all freeze-etched preparations is the presence of a small ridge (Figs. 2–4) at the base of most exposed mem-

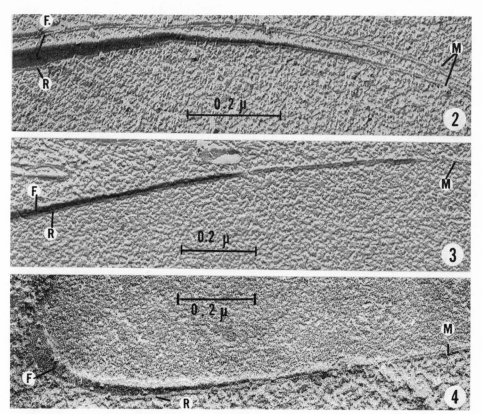

Figs. 2–4.—Fig. 2.: Endoplasmic reticulum in onion root tip. Fig. 3: Vacuolar membrane face in onion root tip; view from inside the vacuole. Fig. 4: Vacuolar membrane face in onion root tip; view from outside the vacuole. In Figs. 2, 3, and 4, the fractures are tangent to the membrane surfaces on the left and almost perpendicular to the membrane surfaces on the right. The small ridge (R) at the base of an exposed membrane face (F) on the left is continuous with one of two ridges which forms the typical freeze-etch image of a single membrane (M) on the right.

brane faces. After careful scrutiny of a large number of photomicrographs, it became apparent that the small ridge was in fact continuous with and identical to one of the ridges that had previously been assumed to represent part of a unit membrane.[22, 24] This same type of fracture was observed in freeze-etched preparations of the plasma, nuclear, vacuolar, and dictyosomal membranes. Figure 5 is an interpretative diagram of what can be seen in the micrographs of Figures 2–4. It implies that during fracturing, membranes are split to expose either one or the other

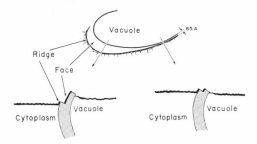

Fig. 5.—*Top*, a representation of Fig. 4. *Bottom*, diagrams of imaginary sections perpendicular to the plane of the page through the fractured tissue along the *dashed arrows*. These diagrams assume arrival of shadow-replica material from upper left, and show why fracture of an inclined *ca.* 75-Å-wide single membrane frequently produces the freeze-etch image seen in Figs. 2–4.

**281**

of two nonetchable inner faces.    Since the diagram is intended as a generalized scheme, it also implies that freeze-etching will show neither the true membrane surfaces nor the surfaces of any materials contiguous to membranes.    These implications have been verified by the experiments and observations described below.

*Etching variations:*   Two sets of onion root tips were freeze-etched.    In order to control the amount of water sublimed from the fractured surface, one set received no etching, whereas the other set received normal etching.    Figure 6 shows cells which received no etching, and Figure 7 shows cells which received normal etching. Comparison reveals a striking similarity in the over-all appearance of the membrane faces in spite of clear differences in the textural appearance of the rest of the protoplasm.    Whereas etching had little apparent effect on the membrane faces, it gave the protoplasmic matrix a distinct pebbled appearance.    In other words, water was sublimed from the fractured cytoplasmic matrix, karyoplasm, and vacuole, but not from any of the faces along which the fractures followed membrane contours.    This suggested the prediction, diagrammed in Figure 8, that deep etching would reveal more of the true membrane surface than had normal etching.    Since etching removes primarily water and not other cell constituents, the effects of deep etching could best be seen in yeast cells which had been suspended in plain tap water for 2 hr.    Figure 9 is the result of such an experiment and shows that with deep etching a greater portion of the true membrane surface is exposed.    As anticipated, this is particularly noticeable at the edge of vacuoles, because of the high water content, and consequent etchability, of vacuolar fluid.

*Surface features:*   If freeze-etching splits membranes so as to reveal inner faces rather than the true surface, structural features known to exist on membrane surfaces should not be visible on membrane faces exposed in freeze-etching.    Ribosomal particles, frequently associated with the surface of the endoplasmic reticulum in chemically fixed preparations, cannot be seen on the endoplasmic reticulum faces revealed in freeze-etching.    Small particles, averaging *ca.* 85 Å in diameter, are

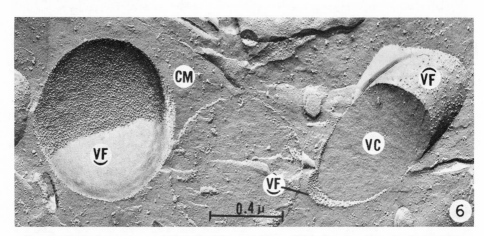

Fig. 6.—Part of an onion root tip cell with no etching.   With the exception of a few small protuberances, the surface of the cytoplasmic matrix (*CM*) and vacuolar contents (*VC*) is relatively smooth.   Both concave faces (*VF*) and convex faces (*VF̂*) of vacuolar membranes have been exposed.   The vacuole in the upper right has been partially fractured and shows that the concave and convex vacuolar membrane faces had been apposed before fracturing. See Fig. 7.

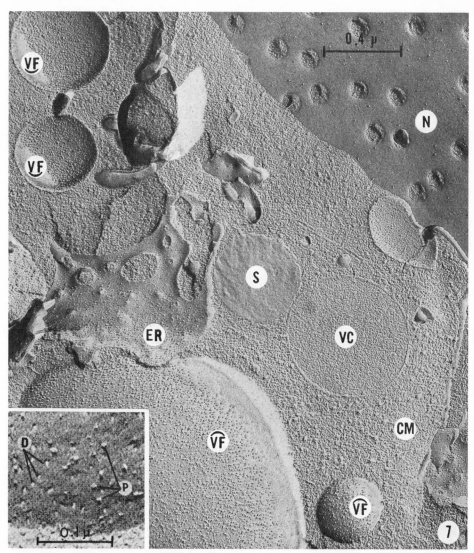

Fig. 7.—Part of an onion root tip cell with normal etching. Surfaces of the cytoplasmic matrix (*CM*) and vacuolar contents (*VC*) are pebbled as the result of etching, but vacuolar membrane faces (*VF*) are similar to those in Fig. 6, indicating that they are nonetchable. Note the smooth, non-etchable appearance of lipoidal material in the spherosomes (*S*) and compare with the smooth portions of membrane faces, including nuclear membrane (*N*) and endoplasmic reticulum (*ER*). Compare with Fig. 6. *Inset* shows a typical vacuolar membrane face and associated small particles (*P*), as well as depressions (*D*) where some of these particles were pulled off during the fracture process.

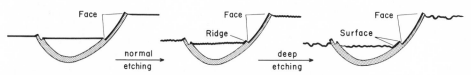

Fig. 8.—Interpretation of the etching procedure.

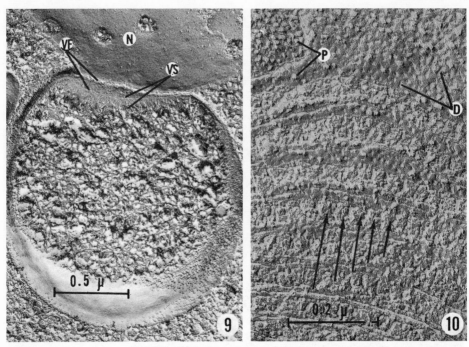

FIG. 9.—Deep etching in a yeast cell.   Nuclear (*N*) and vacuolar membrane faces (*VF*) are similar to those seen in normally etched preparations (Fig. 7), but, as predicted in Fig. 8, a portion of the true vacuolar membrane surface (*VS*) has been exposed by the deep etching.   Cf. with Fig. 3.
   FIG. 10.—Freeze-etched *P. cruentum*, normal etching.   Note the regular array of large particles (*arrows*) between the chloroplast membranes, but the absence of these particles on exposed membrane faces.   Only smaller particles (*P*) and depressions (*D*) are on the exposed faces.

seen in varying numbers on all of the membrane faces in onion root tip cells (Fig. 7).   Similar particles have been reported in other freeze-etch studies.[21-24]   As previously suggested,[24] these small particles cannot be equated with ribosomes because they are too small and are found on membranes (including Golgi membranes) which are known from fixed and sectioned preparations to be devoid of ribosomes.[27]

   Photomicrographs of *Porphyridium cruentum*[26] show that in these cells 320-Å particles are attached in extremely orderly arrays on the outer surfaces of the chloroplast membranes.   Our own sections of chemically fixed *P. cruentum* confirmed these findings.   The extraordinary regularity and large size of these particles suggested their use as markers of the outer membrane surface.   Figure 10 illustrates the appearance of the plastid membranes in freeze-etched *P. cruentum*.   Although the 320-Å particles are seen between the chloroplast membranes, neither these particles nor any depressions out of which they might have been fractured are evident on the tangentially fractured membranes; only smaller, randomly distributed particles and depressions similar to those found in other plant chloroplasts[28] are visible on these fractured faces.   These observations confirm the proposition that freeze-etching does not normally expose the true outer membrane surface and indicate that freeze-etching does expose a hitherto unseen inner membrane face.

   *Discussion.*—Three lines of evidence suggest that during freeze-etching, membranes are split in half, revealing either of two internal membrane faces.   The first evidence for this type of fracture was encountered when it became possible to follow the contours of a single membrane which had been fractured almost normally in one part and tangentially in another part. In such preparations (Figs. 2–4) it became clear that the *ca.* 85-Å-thick rim representing a normally fractured membrane was an image formed by the confluence of two ridges, one bordering the base, the other forming the top, of the tangentially fractured portion. It appears unlikely that either of these ridges alone can be considered the entire membrane, as this would reduce the thickness of the biological membrane to less than 40 Å. For similar reasons these confluent ridges cannot be mere eutectic mixtures or organized, but nonmembrane, cytoplasmic components, as this would reduce the dimension of the biological membrane to that of a Euclidean plane.

A second line of evidence arises from the fact that in vitrified cells all of the fracture planes which follow membrane surfaces are nonetchable. Figure 6 shows convex faces over the top of vacuoles and concave faces out of which vacuoles have been removed. Comparison of these faces with analogous faces in Figure 7 shows that all exposed membrane faces appear to be identical whether or not they are etched. Such a result indicates that the fracture process in freeze-etching exposes two nonetchable membrane faces. If the fracture did not split the membrane but separated it from contiguous vacuolar or cytoplasmic material, only one of the exposed faces would be that of the membrane while the other would be that of some cell material such as protoplasmic matrix or vacuolar fluid. If this were the situation, at most one of the two exposed faces—that of the membrane—would be nonetchable. The other face would be that of protoplasmic matrix, vacuolar fluid, etc., and therefore would be etchable (cf. Fig. 6 with Fig. 7).

The third line of evidence rests on the observation that freeze-etched membrane faces do not show the structural features associated with the true membrane surfaces. The absence of the 320-Å particles on freeze-etched *P. cruentum* chloroplast membrane faces, in spite of the demonstrable presence of these particles in chemically fixed and in freeze-etched material, is graphic evidence that the membrane faces exposed after normal freeze-etching are not true membrane surfaces. A completely analogous situation has been observed in attempts to view the outer cell wall surface of yeast and bacterial cells. The outer wall surface of these unicells is rarely exposed by the fracture process but it can be exposed by deep etching.

Though at first it may appear surprising that membranes should split in two, consideration of the same types of evidence which led Danielli and Harvey[4] to postulate the presence of proteins on membrane surfaces leads to the prediction that fractures in vitrified cells might not occur along the true membrane surface. Danielli and Harvey postulated the existence of protein layers on membrane surfaces to account for the lower interfacial tension observed at surfaces of living cells. Though recent evidence[11, 12] suggests that in some membrane systems lipids with highly polar groups may assume the emulsifying roles which Danielli attributed to proteins, any adsorbed emulsifier would not only reduce interfacial tension, but would also provide the membrane interface with mechanical stability.[29] A macromolecular interface such as the surface of a membrane can interact with the surrounding aqueous phase by various types of polar bonds, and must be encased in a thin layer of bound water molecules whose properties merge, gradually, with those of the bulk phase.[18] As a result, it appears unlikely that the surface of a membrane with low interfacial tension vis-à-vis any contiguous protoplasmic material would present a sharp discontinuity of the sort which would make it uniquely liable to mechanical rupture while in the vitrified state.

Small particles, averaging *ca.* 85 Å in diameter, are seen on many freeze-etch membrane faces (see figures here and in refs. 21–25). One important difficulty presently under study, and one which should serve to emphasize the tentative nature of all freeze-etch interpretations so far proposed, is the absence of an adequate number of depressions (Figs. 7 and 11) into which these particles can be fitted. Although the nature of these small particles is currently being investigated, the tentative hypothesis adopted is that these substructures represent units within which membrane components have assumed globular or micellar configurations (Fig. 11). Such particles may represent lipoprotein associations analogous, perhaps, to those which have been reported in mitochondria,[11, 15] plastids,[12, 16] and other membranes.[14] According to this interpretation, the smooth regions between the 85-Å particles would represent regions in which the membrane components exist as an extended bilayer. The appearance and nonetchability of these smooth faces is similar to that of lipid material seen in spherosomes (Fig. 7). Thus, these smooth regions appear to be free of water and may be lipid faces.

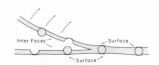

FIG. 11.—Interpretation of the fracture process. The inner membrane faces are seen in normal freeze-etching. Either particles, or depressions out of which the particles have been fractured, are seen (see *inset*, Fig. 7).

Comparative studies show that the number and manner in which the small particles are associated within a given membrane is a function of the type of cell organelle examined.[22, 24] For example, the freeze-etch results shown here indicate that the nuclear membrane in onion root tips (Fig. 7) appears to exist primarily as an extended bilayer, whereas similar freeze-etching studies of chloroplast membranes[28] show that they are composed almost entirely of the globular substructures. The function of these particles in different membranes as well as the environmental factors which modify their configuration is under study.

*Summary.*—Fracture planes within frozen cell membranes have been examined by freeze-etching. The frozen membrane is fractured so as to expose inner membrane faces. Examination of these faces suggests that the biological membrane is organized in part as an extended bilayer and in part as globular subunits. The relative proportion of the membrane which exists in either of these organizational modes varies among the different cell organelles.

The author gratefully acknowledges the expert assistance of Miss Susan Whytock.

* Research supported by National Science Foundation grant GB 2365.

[1] Elbers, P. F., *Recent Progr. Surface Sci.*, **2**, 443 (1964).
[2] Overton, E., *Jahrb. Wiss. Bot.*, **34**, 669 (1900).
[3] Gorter, E., and F. Grendel, *J. Exptl. Med.*, **41**, 439 (1925).
[4] Danielli, J. F., and E. N. Harvey, *J. Cellular Comp. Physiol.*, **5**, 483 (1935).
[5] Danielli, J. F., and H. Davson, *J. Cellular Comp. Physiol.*, **5**, 495 (1935).
[6] Schmitt, F. O., R. S. Bear, and G. L. Clark, *Radiology*, **25**, 131 (1935).
[7] Schmidt, W. J., *Z. Zellforsch. Mikroskop. Anat.*, **23**, 657 (1936).
[8] Fernández-Morán, H., and J. B. Finean, *J. Biophys. Biochem. Cytol.*, **3**, 725 (1957).
[9] Robertson, J. D., *Biochem. Soc. Symp.*, **16**, 3 (1959).
[10] Robertson, J. D., *Symp. Soc. Study of Development and Growth*, **22**, 1 (1964).

[11] Green, D. E., and S. Fleischer, *Biochim. Biophys. Acta*, **70**, 554 (1963).

[12] Park, R. B., *J. Cell Biol.*, **27**, 151 (1965).

[13] Maddy, A. H., and B. R. Malcolm, *Science*, **150**, 1616 (1965).

[14] Sjøstrand, F. S., *J. Ultrastruct. Res.*, **9**, 340 (1963).

[15] Fernández-Morán, H., T. Oda, P. V. Blair, and D. E. Green, *J. Cell Biol.*, **22**, 63 (1964).

[16] Weir, T. E., A. H. P. Engelbrecht, A. Harrison, E. B. Risley, *J. Ultrastruct. Res.*, **13**, 92 (1965).

[17] Hechter, O., *Bull. Neurosci. Res. Progr.*, **2**, 36 (1964).

[18] Kavanau, J. L., *Structure and Function in Biological Membranes* (San Francisco: Holden-Day, Inc., 1965).

[19] Steere, R. L., *J. Biophys. Biochem. Cytol.*, **7**, 167 (1957).

[20] Moor, H., K. Muhlethaler, H. Waldner, and A. Frey-Wyssling, *J. Biophys. Biochem. Cytol.*, **10**, 1 (1961).

[21] Moor, H., *Z. Zellforsch. Mikroskop. Anat.*, **62**, 546 (1964).

[22] Moor, H., and K. Muhlethaler, *J. Cell Biol.*, **17**, 609 (1963).

[23] Moor, H., C. Ruska, and H. Ruska, *Z. Zellforsch. Mikroskop. Anat.*, **62**, 581 (1964).

[24] Branton, D., and H. Moor, *J. Ultrastruct. Res.*, **11**, 401 (1965).

[25] Jost, M., *Arch. Mikrobiol.*, **50**, 211 (1965).

[26] Gantt, E., and S. F. Conti, *J. Cell Biol.*, **26**, 365 (1965).

[27] Whaley, W. G., H. H. Mollenhauer, and J. H. Leech, *Am. J. Bot.*, **47**, 401 (1960).

[28] Branton, D., and R. B. Park, in preparation.

[29] Adam, N. K., *Physics and Chemistry of Surfaces* (London: Oxford University Press, 1941).

# Membrane structure and function

J. LEE KAVANAU

*Department of Zoology, University of California, Los Angeles, California*

Pʀᴏʙʟᴇᴍs ᴏғ ᴍᴇᴍʙʀᴀɴᴇ ᴛʀᴀɴsᴘᴏʀᴛ inevitably lead to the problem of membrane structure. Insofar as structure and function doubtless are closely interrelated, it behooves us also to consider other membrane functions briefly, to place the problem of membrane transport in proper perspective. This may be particularly appropriate in this case for the active transport mechanism may utilize much of the same machinery and actions that are involved in facilitated diffusion, impulse conduction, and many other membrane functions.

Concepts of biological membrane structure have been influenced greatly by the model proposed in 1935 by Danielli, Davson, and Harvey (7, 8). This consisted of a liquid-lipid phase of unspecified composition and thickness with the molecules at the outer faces oriented with their polar head groups at the surface and their lipophilic regions extending inward. Proteins were postulated to be adsorbed to the outer lipid layers. Many workers now regard the lipid phase to consist of a bimolecular leaflet, with the polar head groups facing outward and the lipophilic chains in the interior. Proteins are believed to be adsorbed to the leaflet at both faces in extended conformations. Sjöstrand (28, 29) suggests that globular proteins are adsorbed at the cytoplasmic interface; Robertson (25, 26) and Finean (10, 11) suggest that carbohydrates wholly or partly compose the envelope of the membrane which is exposed to the extracellular milieu. While isolated cell membranes contain carbohydrates (37–39), these probably are components of the extracellular coat rather than of the plasma membrane itself. Recently it has been proposed that the lipid phase exists in the form of globular micelles that either are embedded in a protein matrix (30) or sandwiched between layers of protein (19, 20).

I have taken the view that the biological membrane is a far more complex entity than is suggested by, and embodied in, these primarily static structures (16). The departure from the static models and concepts results from considering the entire spectrum of known and probable functions and actions of membranes together with the physical and colloid chemistry of their constituent mole-cules. Some of the membrane actions and functions for which we have to find both mechanisms and regulating systems are:

1) Facilitated diffusion, active transport, and impulse conduction.
2) Coalescence and fragmentation.
3) Growth and degrowth.
4) Contraction and expansion.
5) Translational and rotational movements of membrane-bounded organelles.
6) Impelling and conveyance of cytoplasmic and luminal matrix.
7) Reversible geometrical transformations between spherical, tubular, and lamellar forms.
8) Transformations from elastic to highly rigid forms.
9) Differentiation and dedifferentiation.
10) Facilitation and inhibition of enzyme action.

The measure of a theory of membrane structure should be the success which it achieves in helping to elucidate all membrane functions, not just the one or two functions with which the investigator happens to be concerned. When examined from this point of view, the simple picture of a static bimolecular or globular-sub-unit lipid leaflet embedded in or with proteins adsorbed at its two faces seems quite inadequate. I have proposed, instead, a dynamic picture of membrane structure and function (16) which is consistent with the old observational data and derives considerable support from the most recent electron-optical findings. According to these views, the biological membrane is an exceedingly complex structure which transforms between several different configurations in the course of different membrane functions. The configuration which is most familiar to us from electron-optical studies—two dense lines enclosing a less dense line—is proposed to be but the desiccated remnant of the most stable of these configurations, to which the membrane transforms automatically in the course of dehydration and exposure to multivalent cations during the initial preparative treatments.

The starting point for my analyses of membrane struc-

Reprinted by permission of the author and the Federation of American Societies for Experimental Biology from *Federation Proceedings*, **25**, 1096–1107 (1966).

ture and transformations was the central problem of how the cell transforms chemical energy into kinetic energy. The mechanism embodied in the muscle fiber is a well known, if incompletely understood, one. But I believe that the muscle fiber mechanism is an evolutionary specialization of the more primitive contractile mechanism of biological membranes, in which the function of contraction has been elaborated at the expense of the deemphasis and loss of virtually all other functions. According to this postulate, the basic contractile mechanism of the unspecialized membrane involves the lipid components, the contractile actions of proteins being ancillary. The contracting and expanding membrane system simultaneously performs many other functions, whereas in the specialized muscle fiber system contraction and relaxation are the principal functions.

Initially, I considered the classical bimolecular lipid leaflet sandwiched between two protein layers. However, it was quite clear that this structure had severe limitations so I turned next to the consideration of composite structures, first those involving a lipid leaflet of roughly spherical globules, then those involving the natural extensions of spheres—oblate and prolate spherocylinders. Structures containing a subdivided lipid leaflet permitted a certain amount of progress to be made in understanding certain membrane functions and properties, but these structures too eventually led to a dead end, dynamically speaking. Such membranes appear to be relatively passive structures with little or no biologically significant capacity for doing work. But once oblate and prolate spherocylinders had been considered, the next, and what turned out to be the crucial step, was more or less obvious. This was that the micellar subunits making up the lipid phase be capable of reversible structural and phase transformations between two forms of complementary geometrical asymmetry— broad, flat, primarily liquid-condensed discs roughly 55 A thick and 150 A in diameter, and tall, narrow, primarily liquid, circular cylinders or pillars roughly 200 A tall and 60–80 A in diameter, as shown in Fig. 1. These dimensions are for a generalized membrane; there is every reason to expect that a more or less continuous spectrum of sizes of the discs and pillars exists in different differentiated membranes and in different species. This type of transformation of lipid micelles may be the principal chemical to kinetic energy-transforming mechanism of biological membranes. It is evident that chemically induced cycles of collapse of the pillars into discs and opening out of the discs into pillars provide broad potentialities for doing work.

The proposed molecular and phase structure of these micelles has been given in detail elsewhere (16), so it will be treated only superficially here. The structure of the disc form (Fig. 1, upper) comes closest to the classical bimolecular picture.

*1*) Extending inward from the surface are the lipophilic segments of phospholipids and of other long-chain ionogenic and highly polar lipids. These molecules are compacted into the liquid-condensed state in the region e by several different actions, one of which is the presence

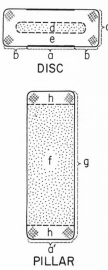

FIG. 1. Schematic cross-sectional diagram of the proposed disc and pillar forms of the subunit lipid micelles of biological membranes. Stippled regions, d and f, are in the liquid state. Clear regions, e and h, are primarily in the liquid-condensed state but they gradually grade into the liquid condition as the regions d and f are approached. Pillar-base regions are a and a', b denotes the outer ringlike region, and c and g denote the cylindrical walls of the disc and pillar, respectively. Hatching shows the regions in which severe deformations would be expected (due to crowding of lipophilic chains) unless compensating changes in the composition of the amphiphiles and in the spacing of their head groups were to occur. (Reproduced by courtesy of Holden-Day from (16).)

of weakly polar nonionogenic lipids, such as cholesterol and triglycerides, between their lipophilic segments, and another of which is the cross-linking of the phosphoryl head groups by divalent cations. Since the lipophilic chains are of different lengths and contain polar and polarizable substituents, such as double bonds and —OH groups, the liquid-condensed condition cannot be maintained all along the length of the chains. Instead, the phase state gradually transforms to the fully liquid condition in the region d, where the chains can bend over and dovetail with one another. The transverse structure of the disc departs from the bimolecular condition chiefly in that small amounts of weakly polar lipids are dissolved in the liquid region d.

*2*) The orientation of the terminal polar residues such as choline, cholamine, and serine is proposed to differ considerably in the regions a, b, and c; these residues primarily extending outward at a and c and primarily bending back into the weakly polar regions of the ester bonds of the phospholipids and between the phosphate groups at b.

*3*) The lipophilic regions near the edges of the discs, shown in cross section by the hatching, are regions where oriented-wedge crowding would tend to be severe. Accordingly, lipids with the most highly ionogenic head groups and the least bulky and least polar and polarizable lipophilic segments would tend to accumulate in these regions. The action of oriented-wedge crowding is illustrated by the sketch of spherical micelles in Fig. 2. Note in the micelle at a that in order for there to be sufficient room in the interior of the micelle for the hydrocarbon segments, the polar head groups must be widely separated from one another. Any action which brings the head groups closer together or which increases the bulkiness of the lipophilic segments would render the spherical packing configuration unstable and the micelles

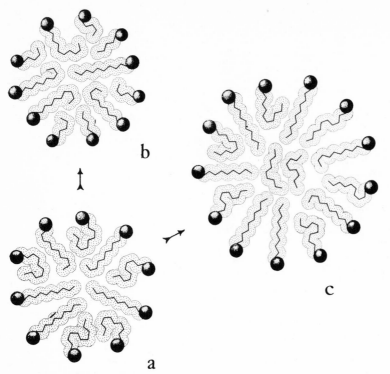

FIG. 2. Schematic scale (van der Waals radii) representation of spherical micelles, depicting changes that occur upon amphiphile (*n*-pentanol) solubilization (*b*) and nonpolar (nonane) solubilization (*c*) by spherical micelles of a pure *n*-decane-salt soap (*a*). The hydrogen atoms are omitted. A two-dimensional representation such as this is oversimplified and does not give an accurate picture of the packing geometry (for example, no overlap of the chains is shown). The presence of gauche kinks in the chains leads to nonplanar paraffin-chain conformations. (Reproduced by courtesy of Holden-Day from (16).

would tend to transform into prolate or oblate spherocylinders, depending primarily upon such factors as the severity of the crowding and the electrical free energy of the double layer. Conversely, any action which spaces the head groups apart or decreases the volume of the chains tends to stabilize spherical micelles.

*4*) Cholesterol is concentrated and serves its compacting function at *regions b*, whereas cholesteryl esters and triglycerides are concentrated and serve this function primarily at the pillar-base *regions a*.

Considering now the cylindrical micelles or pillars, the molecular and phase structure is modified but slightly in the pillar-base regions because of the relatively great stability of the lipid-protein interactions there. All other regions are modified greatly.

*1*) The lipophilic segments extending laterally from the walls into the interior are in the fully liquid condition. The compacting, weakly polar molecules, such as cholesterol, have slipped out from between these segments and become associated with one another, dissolved in the interior region. It is the presence of such large amounts of solubilized material in the interior that is responsible for the 15–20 A increase over a roughly bimolecular thickness.

*2*) The terminal polar residues extend outward laterally into the matrix and bend back at various angles

toward, into the plane of, and between the phosphoryl groups. The phosphoryl groups are spaced far apart by this means and by mutual repulsion and the penetration of monovalent counterions and water between them.

*3*) In the hatched regions near the pillar rim, oriented-wedge crowding tends to be even more severe than at the disc rims, so that similar considerations apply to both regions.

Figure 3 shows how the discs and pillars are integrated with the protein envelopes into the proposed structure of two membrane configurations and how the membrane might transform between these two configurations concomitantly with pillar-disc transformations.

Figure *3a* shows a membrane in the open configuration. The pillars are arrayed hexagonally between the protein envelopes at a center-to-center spacing of about 150 A. Figure *3e* shows the closed configuration. The discs are closely packed in a hexagonal array and sandwiched between the two protein envelopes. The protein envelopes are shown schematically as zig-zag lines. I believe their structure to be quite complex, both as regards composition and conformation, that it changes characteristically with different phases of function, and that it differs in different configurations. The basic framework of the envelopes consists of proteins with their backbones in extended conformations in most regions but i

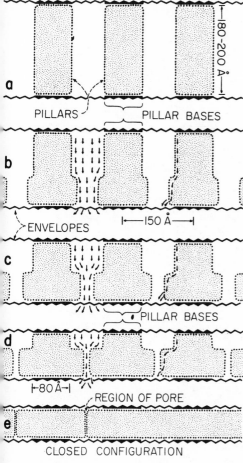

OPEN CONFIGURATION

**a**

PILLARS  PILLAR BASES

180-200 Å

**b**

ENVELOPES  |←150 Å→|

**c**

PILLAR BASES

**d**

|←80 Å→|  REGION OF PORE

**e**

CLOSED CONFIGURATION

FIG. 3. A highly diagrammatic cross-sectional representation of the postulated gross geometrical changes of micellar form that occur in the transformation from the open to the closed configuration of a region of a biological membrane. Dots show roughly the regions of the lipid phosphoryl groups, zig-zag lines the positions of the protein envelopes, and solid zig-zag regions the positions of the pillar bases. Shaded areas show regions containing weakly polar and nonionogenic lipids and the lipophilic chains of strongly polar lipids. Arrows at the left show the movements of matrix that is "pumped" from between the cylindrical micelles and force filtered through the lower envelope (which might be either luminal or cytoplasmic) as the cylinders collapse into "bimolecular" discs. Arrows at the right show the direction of flow of the lipid head groups of the collapsing cylindrical micelles. The moving polar head groups carry the adjacent matrix molecules with them; the more distant matrix is impelled by the adjacent matrix as a result of viscous traction. A close abutment of the "bimolecular" discs giving rise to pores is shown at the left in *e*; the coalescence into a continuous lamella is shown at the right in *e*. Molecular components are not to scale. (Reproduced by courtesy of Macmillan and Co., Ltd. from *Nature*.)

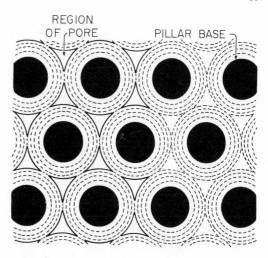

REGION OF PORE  PILLAR BASE

FIG. 4. A surface view of a region of the membranous element that is shown in Fig. 3. Solid circular regions show the positions of the pillars and pillar bases. Dashed circles show the corresponding successive positions of the rims of the "bimolecular" discs. Area to the left shows the outlines of pore regions before compressional and dilational deformations occur. Area to the right shows an absence of pore regions on the assumption of coalescence of the abutting "bimolecular" discs. (Reproduced by courtesy of Macmillan and Co., Ltd. from *Nature*.)

coiled and globular conformations in others. The point of balance between the two conformations shifts toward the globular in the open configuration and toward the extended in the closed configuration. Other proteins are adsorbed to the envelopes, mostly at the pillar bases, in the primarily globular conformation.

The solid regions of the zig-zag lines in Fig. 3 are the pillar-base regions. Here the lipid-protein interaction is relatively strong, being quadruply stabilized by polar binding, hydrogen bonding, hydrophobic bonding, and site binding. But in the regions between the pillar bases, the lipid-protein interaction is much weaker, consisting primarily of polar bonds and hydrogen bonds. Figure 3 illustrates one of several means by which the pillar-disc transformation could convert chemical energy to kinetic energy, namely by imparting momentum to the inter-envelope matrix. Thus, as the pillars collapse, the flowing lipid head groups carry adjacent molecules of the inter-envelope matrix with them by adhesive drag and these influence other matrix molecules by viscous traction, with the result that all of the matrix between the pillars is impelled between the rims of the forming discs and force filtered through the protein envelope into the lumen or exterior of the membranous element. It is proposed that this type of transformation is involved in many types of protoplasmic streaming (see ref. (16)).

Figure 4 gives a surface view of the membrane showing the positions of the pillar bases in both configurations, the successive positions of the rims of the forming discs,

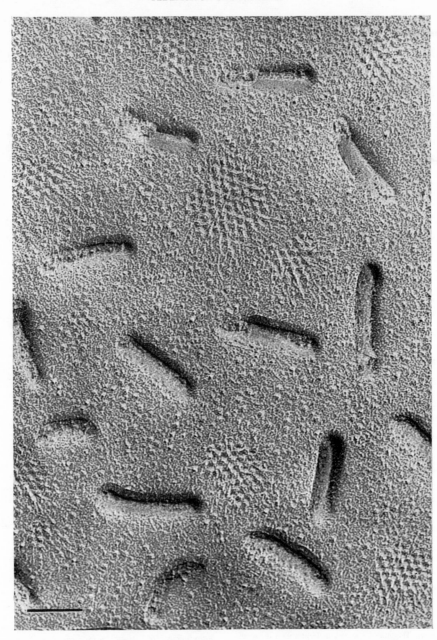

FIG. 5. A platinum-carbon replica of the frozen-etched surface of the plasma membrane of *Saccharomyces cerevisiae* showing the hexagonal substructure and the invaginated grooves which increase the total surface area of the membrane by about 50%. It should be emphasized that the preparative treatment used to obtain this electron micrograph and that of Fig. 6 does not involve the use of metal-ion-containing fixatives nor stains. The scale markers in Figs. 5–8 show a distance of 1,000 A. (Reproduced by courtesy of Drs. Moor and Mühlethaler.)

FIG. 6. The transfer of the contents of vesicles in the onion root cap cell through the plasma membrane to the exterior by a method in which the contents remain encapsulated. In the upper half of the picture the plasma membrane is seen in surface view; in the lower half, a portion of the cross-fractured cytoplasm is visible. (Reproduced by courtesy of Drs. Branton and Moor, and Academic Press from (2).)

and the pore regions between the triads of discs, which are discussed below.

A large amount of electron-optical evidence has accumulated recently that is suggestive of this substructural organization of biological membranes. Only three illustrative examples are considered here. Figure 5 shows an extraordinary finding of Moor and Mühlethaler (21). When yeast cells are frozen by a technique which does not kill them, and then are section fractured, frozen etched, and platinum-carbon replicated—all at very low temperatures—clear indications of hexagonal substructural features are revealed in the replicas of the cell membrane. I believe that the dark regions (180 A center-to-center spacing) mark the locations of the pillar bases, and that the difference in the appearance of these regions in this and other electron-optical preparations depends upon local differences in the protein envelopes and the lipid-protein interactions.

Figure 6 shows an extremely interesting preparation made by the same techniques by Branton and Moor (2). Unlike the process of reverse phagocytosis, in onion root cap cells the contents of certain vesicles are transferred from within the cell to the exterior by a method in which the contents remain encapsulated. As the contents of the

vesicles become externalized interactions between the vesicle membrane and the plasma membrane take place, as a result of which substructural order is revealed in surface views of the membrane in the region of interaction. This order consists of arrays of apparent structural subunits spaced 145–175 A apart in concentric circles, as shown best in the penetrating vesicle at the upper center in Fig. 6 (arrow). Subunits of similar appearance at roughly the same spacing, but ordered more or less at random, can be seen in virtually all regions of the plasma membrane. It can be suggested that in the transfer process the overlying region of the plasma membrane becomes incorporated into each transferred vesicle while part of each vesicle membrane is contributed to the plasma membrane. Among other functions this exchange may be one of the methods by which the composition of the plasma membrane becomes modified. At the same time, of course, the vesicle membrane would acquire a large segment having the same specificity as the plasma membrane of its cell of origin.

Figure 7 shows cross sections through the membranes that limit the cell body of a species of foraminifers (14). A "conventional" cell membrane is not present but is replaced by a system of up to 10 layered honeycomblike

**293**

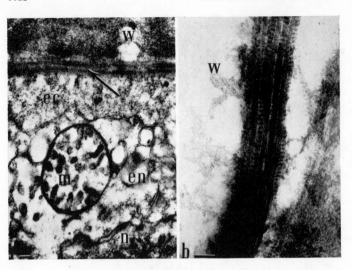

FIG. 7. *A:* the peripheral region of the cytoplasm and part of the cell wall (W) of *Gromia oviformis* showing the layers of honeycomblike membranes (arrow); ec, ectoplasm; en, endoplasm; m, mitochondrion; n, nucleus. *B:* enlarged section of the shell from an entire animal preparation showing a layer of 10 honeycomblike membranes in cross section. (Reproduced by courtesy of Drs. Hedley and Bertaud, and The Society of Protozoologists from (14).)

membranes lying between the shell and the cytoplasm. These membranes consist of cylindrical bodies about 200 A tall and 100 A in diameter which are spaced hexagonally at a center-to-center distance of 210 A. This substructure is shown better in an oblique section in Fig. 8. In this view (Fig. 8) it can be seen that the cylinders are connected by narrow septa. These seemingly specialized membranes may be fixed permanently in the open configuration by structural modifications. Accordingly, they may reveal the basic pattern of substructural organization (but not composition) of many membranes.

Let us turn now to the matter of the mechanism of the disc-pillar transformation cycles and the means by which chemical energy could be funneled into driving them. Expressed very briefly it is proposed that cationic displacements brought about by quantitative and qualitative alterations of the populations of counterions of the ionogenic lipid head groups lead to alterations of the spacings of these head groups and to concomitant alterations of the geometry and phase structure of the micelles. The latter alterations make it possible to accommodate the lipophilic segments to the conditions of packing of the head groups.

The pillar-to-disc transformation is taken as an example, emphasizing the major factor of oriented-wedge effects. When divalent countercations displace monovalent ones from the Stern layer of the pillar wall, the poorly screening monovalent cations leave their positions between and around the phosphoryl groups. The divalent cations bridge the phosphoryl and carboxyl groups together closely and screen their charges more effectively than do monovalent counterions. As a result of this divalent-cation-bridging and the decreased repulsion between the head groups, the phosphoryl groups become much more closely spaced to one another. The ensuing oriented-wedge crowding is such that there is insufficient room in the interior of the 70-A-diameter cylinders for the bulky liquid lipophilic segments. Consequently the

pillars collapse into the disclike micelles, which provide a far more favorable geometry for the accommodation of the bulky chains. This collapse begins near the envelope at which the divalent cations are released, where the oriented-wedge crowding first becomes severe.

It is proposed that the chief agency whereby chemical energy is utilized to trigger or drive disc-pillar and membrane transformation cycles is the increase in the activities of protons and divalent cations due to the release of these ions which accompanies ATP splitting, and the decrease in the activities of the same ions which accompanies ATP synthesis. The proposed cycle of cation displacements is shown schematically in Fig. 9. Considering the open-to-closed transformation, the splitting of ATP which provides the energy to drive membrane catalyzed reactions at one envelope of a membrane releases divalent cations and protons. It also provides some of the energy to drive the reverse transformation back to the open configuration. The released protons displace the divalent cations which bridge side-chain carboxyl groups to one another and to cytoplasmic anions. The displaced divalent cations, together with those displaced directly from the split ATP, in turn displace monovalent cations from the pillar walls beginning near the one envelope. These displacements lead to the collapse of the pillars and the other events of the open-to-closed transformation. The displaced monovalent cations, in turn, become the counterions at sites vacated by protons and divalent cations. Essentially the reverse sequence of displacement occurs during the reverse transformation.

The difference in the strength of the lipid-protein bonding at different regions of the discs of membranes in the closed configuration provides the basis for the different responses of these regions to proton and other ion activity changes. Thus, the quadruply stabilized region at the pillar bases cannot be disrupted by these changes whereas the lipid-protein interactions in the regions between the pillar bases, depending as they do almost

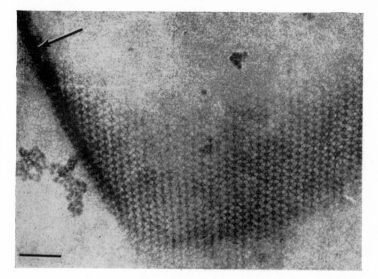

FIG. 8. A section of a folded honey-comblike membrane from a dissected shell of *Gromia oviformis* showing its appearance both in edgewise view and in a direction almost normal to the surface (arrow). (Reproduced by courtesy of Drs. Hedley and Bertaud, and The Society of Protozoologists from (14).)

entirely upon polar and hydrogen bonding, are extremely sensitive to ion activity changes.

Let us consider now the significance of the proposed membrane structure and transformations, and the roles of cationic displacements, for facilitated diffusion, active transport, and impulse conduction.

Facilitated diffusion is a highly specific passive mediation of movement which occurs at sites on the cell membrane that have a very limited extent, chiefly under the driving force of thermal agitation. It leads to the same equilibrium conditions as does ordinary diffusion but far more rapidly. The work of several investigators (5, 6, 12, 15, 18, 22, 23, 31, 32, 36) has led to the concept that facilitated diffusion occurs at small porelike regions of from 7 to 8½ A "equivalent pore diameter." These pores are postulated to be chiefly of a polar nature, so that the passage of small polar molecules is greatly accelerated. Danielli (5, 6) has suggested that they consist of aqueous channels lined by hydrogen-bonding groups which are extensions of the protein envelopes and which are capable of proton conduction by the Grotthuss mechanism. In the present model, the pores are identified with the regions between triads of closely packed lipid discs.

The most reasonable expectations for the structure of the discs in the neighborhood of pores are that:

*1)* At the rims of the discs (and in nearby regions) the polar head groups would be loosely packed and would tend to retain their associations with monovalent cations.

*2)* The lipophilic regions would be closely packed in the liquid-condensed condition. Some of the hydrocarbon chains would be bent back to allow their polar and polarizable regions to fill the spaces between the head groups, and at the same time to relieve the oriented-edge crowding in the interior.

*3)* Dilational deformations and the populating of the rim regions by short-chain and single-chain lipids with highly ionogenic head groups would occur. These expectations follow, of course, because the space in the lipophilic interior near the rims would be at a premium, so that arrangements that could bring about the maximum spacing of the head groups and the minimum lipophilic bulk would be favored strongly.

The close approach of the rim regions would make possible many interdisc interactions which could lead to a decrease in the interfacial free energy. The numerous cationic and anionic groups of phospholipid residues and the polar ring systems of cerebrosides and diphosphoglyceroinositides extending from adjacent rims would engage in many types of interactions. The interpenetration and interdigitation of the extending phospholipid terminal residues (such as cholamine and choline) would facilitate greatly the spacing apart of the phosphoryl groups, an action that amounts to the production of dilational deformations of the rim regions. Such interactions would be favored, for in this way more space would be made available in the interior for the bulky lipophilic chains.

If the rims of the discs were to abut closely where triads meet, so as to leave only small, tortuous, aqueous channels through cell membranes, a high degree of localized compressional and dilational deformations of the discs would have to be assumed to account for the small equivalent pore diameter found experimentally and for the fact that the total area of the pores for different cell membranes falls in the range of only 0.01–3.0 % (9, 23). On the assumption that no pore regions are obliterated, that the average equivalent pore diameter is 7½ A, and that the center-to-center spacing of hexagonally distributed pillar bases is 150 A, pores would account for less than 0.5 % of the total membrane area.

According to this picture, then, the pores that facilitate the passage of small polar substances through plasma membranes each consist of irregular tortuous channels in the regions where triads of deformed discs meet. In

## CATIONIC DISPLACEMENTS

### OPEN—TO—CLOSED TRANSFORMATION

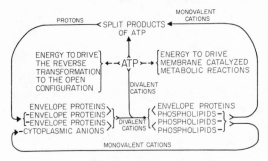

### CLOSED—TO—OPEN TRANSFORMATION

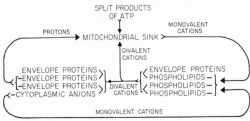

FIG. 9. Cationic displacement schemes for the open-to-closed and the closed-to-open transformations. Brackets in the lower parts of the diagrams enclose the specific sites to or from which cations are displaced. Angular connectors depict divalent-cation bridges. The "envelope proteins" that are shown to be divalent-cation bridged but that are unbracketed refer to those side-chain carboxyl groups that retain their bond to one of the divalent-cation valences but that alternate between being bridged by the other valence either to other side-chain carboxyl groups or to phospholipid phosphoryl groups, according to the transformation. The diagram for the closed-to-open transformation is for those cases in which the ATP resynthesis occurs exclusively in nearby mitochondria, rather than by means of glycolytic processes occurring upon the transforming membranes themselves. (Reproduced by courtesy of Holden-Day from (16).)

these regions, the terminal polar residues of the lipid molecules undergo extensive interactions—interlacing, adlineating, hydrogen bonding, salt linking, and divalent-cation bridging into a complex semirigid brushlike meshwork of high stereochemical specificity. The differences between the pores and the adjacent, more highly occluded regions of rim contact would be essentially quantitative, the terminal residues interlacing and interdigitating much more closely with one another in the latter regions than in the pores.

The passage of hydronium and hydroxyl ions through such pores might occur fairly readily by excess and defect proton exchanges, i.e., by the Grotthuss mechanism. The diffusion of other ions and small polar molecules of the same order of size as the interstices of the pores could occur by a series of thermally activated site-to-site steps. In these, the highly hydrated diffusing particles would tend to lose more loosely held water molecules upon

entering the pore regions, and would exchange disrupted water-binding interactions with the successively encountered polar groups and water of hydration in the pore channels. It seems likely, though, that the passage of bulk matrix would be hindered greatly because of the relatively high viscosity of the hydration crust that would line such pores.

The specificity of facilitated diffusion would depend both upon the constitution of the protein envelopes bounding the pores and upon the stereochemical properties of the pore channels. The types of terminal polar residues present at the rims and the length and bulkiness of their lipophilic segments would have direct and indirect effects upon the size, shape, structure, degree and type of hydration, zeta potential, etc. of the pore channels. For example, if cross-linking of many phosphoryl head groups by divalent-cation bridging could occur readily, the zeta potential of the pores would tend to be relatively low and negative, and the passage of cations would be favored. But if steric restraints were to prevent such bridging, the divalent cations would tend to have one valence free, in which case the sign of the zeta potential might be reversed, favoring the passage of anions—with the pores possibly behaving, in the limiting condition, as selectively permeable anion exchangers.

The size of the pores formed under the conditions I have described would not necessarily be fixed at a certain constant value. Most likely the pore size would be distributed about some mode, the precise value of the mode differing under different functional, environmental, and compositional conditions. This would help to account for the apparent presence of pores or "active patches" of more than one kind or size in plasma membranes.

It is important to emphasize that since the obstruction of the spaces between the discs depends upon the close abutment of the discs and upon interactions between the polar residues extending from their rims, one cannot exclude the possibility that facilitated diffusion of ions also occurs at sites other than the pore regions. The mere presence of adjacent sheets of polar residues at abutting disc rims implies possibilities for ion transport, even though the polar residues interlace and interact closely. Accordingly, one should bear in mind the possibility, even the likelihood, that ions can traverse regions between closely abutting discs at sites other than the pore regions. In this view all of the regions of abutting disc rims would be potential sites of facilitated diffusion.

The anticipated changes in the size and structure of the pore regions are in agreement with the classical effects of ions upon membranes. For example, with calcium ions present in low concentrations, divalent-cation cross-linking between the adjacent disc rims would be reduced, with a concomitant reduction in the dilational deformations. Accordingly, the pore regions would tend to enlarge, and the membrane would become "leaky," losing its selective permeability. High concentrations of calcium ions would lead to strong competition with sodium and potassium for certain fixed-charge sites. By both increasing the dilational deformations of the discs (with concomitant further occlusion of the pores) and

## MEMBRANE CONFIGURATIONS

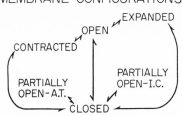

FIG. 10. Diagram of the postulated partial and complete transformations between the different configurations of biological membranes. Arrows indicate reversible transformation pathways. A.T.: active transport, I.C.: impulse conduction. (Reproduced by courtesy of Holden-Day from (16).)

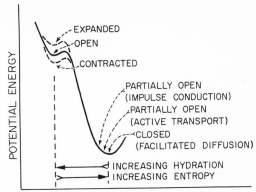

## TRANSITION STATE & CONFIGURATION

FIG. 11. Schematic potential energy diagram of the postulated biological membrane configurations and transition states. Facilitated diffusion occurs in the nontransforming membrane in the closed configuration (Fig. 3e). Active transport involves minute pulsatory partial transformation cycles between the closed configuration (Fig. 3e) and a transition state intermediate between stages d and e of Fig. 3. Impulse conduction involves a propagated partial transformation cycle of the plasma membrane from the closed configuration to a condition slightly more advanced toward stage d (Fig. 3) than is involved in active transport, and then back to the closed configuration. (Reproduced by courtesy of Holden-Day from (16).)

interfering directly with sodium and potassium permeation, the electrical resistance of the membrane would be increased and its excitability reduced.

This picture of membrane structure and transformations has fairly evident implications for active transport and impulse conduction. I have suggested that active transport involves a mechanical pumping mechanism, in which a selective forced filtration of cytoplasmic matrix and extracellular fluids plays an important role (16). The pumping may be brought about by transformation cycles that involve only very small departures from the closed configuration towards the open configuration, followed by the return to the closed configuration, i.e., by minute pulsations rather than by major transitions.

In terms of the diagram of Fig. 3 it is suggested that the transformation cycle involves a change in the configuration of the membrane that proceeds only fractionally from stage e to stage d and then back again to stage e. According to this scheme of active transport, during each partial transformation from the closed configuration toward the open configuration, tiny amounts of luminal matrix and extracellular medium are selectively force filtered into the pore regions, which simultaneously enlarge slightly. During the reverse partial transformation, as the pores contract to the size characteristic of the closed configuration, small molecules and ions within the slightly enlarged pore regions are selectively force filtered back through the protein envelopes into the matrix and medium. In effect, submicroscopic jets of matrix would be selectively force filtered into the expanding pores during one phase, and would be expelled and selectively force filtered from the contracting pores during the other phase. Accordingly, this membrane transformation cycle provides a basis for the supplementation of the "two force" theories based upon activity and potential gradients alone, by providing for a third driving force, namely water pressure gradients, such as have been proposed by Teorell (34, 35) in conjunction with his theory of "fixed charges."

Figure 10 gives a sketch of the proposed membrane transformation pathways. The expanded configuration is simply one in which the pillars are spaced farther apart than 150 A, while the contracted one is one in which the pillars are fairly closely packed. Impulse conduction may occur as the result of a plasma membrane transforming just slightly beyond the condition achieved in active transport, to the point that the partial transformation becomes self propagating—the immediate energy source for driving the transformation being the electrochemical potential gradient of sodium ions.

Figure 11 shows the potential energy relationships between the different configurations that I have adopted as a working hypothesis. According to this scheme, the open-to-closed transformation merely needs to be triggered by the proton activity changes accompanying ATP splitting. Once over the potential-energy hump the transformation proceeds spontaneously. On the other hand, all transformations from the relatively stable equilibrium well of the closed configuration must be driven by a free energy input (by the driving of endergonic cationic displacements and molecular rearrangements).

For the proposed mechanism to accomplish selective transfers of material, it would have to involve asymmetric exchanges. Asymmetries could be based upon: *1*) differences in the penetrability and catalytic activity of the two protein envelopes; *2*) differences in the penetrability of the pore channels that depend upon the direction of pumping of the matrix; and *3*) asymmetries of the transformation processes themselves. All three factors probably are important.

*1*) Differences in the composition of the protein envelopes are suggested by the known participation of enzymes in active transport. In this connection, the effects of insulin upon the permeability of muscle cells to certain sugars (6, 27) may depend upon interactions that occur between the insulin molecules and the external protein envelopes bounding the pore regions.

*2*) The impelling of water into and out of the pores as the result of minute pulsatory changes of pore dimensions could affect the passage of metabolites in at least two ways: *a*) momentum exchanges and adhesive drag with water molecules that were moving in a given direction would facilitate directly the movement of other substances in the same direction and hinder their movements in the opposite direction; and *b*) an indirect effect of water movement would result from the tendency for the water molecules to reorient the brushwork of polar lipid residues extending into the pore channels. There would be a tendency for those polar groups of the residues having the greatest work of adhesion for water to be pushed and pulled downstream. Thus, substances would encounter markedly different penetration barriers depending upon their direction of movement in the pore channels.

*3*) Asymmetries of the transformation processes are built-in features of them. Thus, the energy that drives the minute pulsations of active transport probably is applied through the agency of cationic displacements that are initiated at the inner interfaces of the plasma membrane. This being the case, the inner envelope would be the first to undergo transformation changes. In addition, fluid and solutes that enter the membrane during the opening transformation would be selectively force filtered through an envelope undergoing an expansion of the basic backbone and main-chain spacings and the establishment of a fine meshwork of side chains bridging between the backbones (16). On the other hand, fluid and solutes that leave the interenvelope spaces during the closure transformation would be selectively force filtered through an envelope in which the basic backbone and main-chain spacings were diminishing and the fine meshwork of the side-chain bridges was being disrupted (16).

The idea that protein monolayers could act as sieves goes back at least to Danielli and Davson in 1935 (7). The rate of penetration of water and hydronium and hydroxyl ions scarcely would be affected by a barrier consisting of a closely cross-linked protein monolayer— because of the small dimensions of the water molecule and the occurrence of proton and hydrogen bond exchanges. However, many molecules and large ions would be susceptible to a slowing of their movement or to an actual filtration, depending upon specific conditions within the monolayer. In this connection a protein monolayer can exert a marked effect upon the passage of molecules as small as carbon dioxide (13), whereas lipid monolayers have to be in a closely packed condition to offer an appreciable resistance to small polar molecules.

If active transport involves the mechanisms postulated, it shares some features in common with facilitated diffusion. The same pore regions would provide the route of passage of substances in both cases, albeit in slightly different states, and the same protein-envelope barriers would be involved, although under different conditions—possibly affecting both the direct passage and the catalysis-influenced passage of substances. In active transport, work would be performed by the membrane to transport and selectively force filter bulk material, whereas in facilitated diffusion, thermal agitation would provide the sole energy source for the selective passage of substances. This relationship accords well with the fact that both active transport and facilitated diffusion show about the same degree of specificity and are poisoned by the same types of substances (6, 33).

A mechanism of this general type was, in fact, suggested by Danielli in 1954 when he stated that "the active form of the membrane may be an expanded lattice structure which collapses into a more stable structure and requires energy for re-expansion" (5). The idea that changes in the lattice-work dimensions of a protein might be important in the selective passage of molecular species also was expressed by Danielli, while Bowyer (5) suggested that if the lattice expanded and collapsed asymmetrically, it would constitute a pump that would impart one-way transfer of those species that were able to enter the expanded lattice.

The phenomenon of plasma membrane shimmering is of great interest in connection with the preceding discussion. Vibratory movements of the cell membrane and in the cytoplasm have been noted in erythrocytes, erythroblasts, and bacterial protoplasts. The studies of Pulvertaft (24) and of Blowers, Clarkson, and Maizels (1) have established a close relationship between the shimmering phenomenon and active transport. In terms of the theories outlined above it can be suggested that the irregular pulsatory changes that have been observed in the cytoplasm and cell membrane are visible manifestations of the participation of the cell membrane in active transport processes. The proposed partial transformation cycles of the cell membrane may lead to small cyclic changes in the cell volume and internal pressure, causing the cytoplasmic effects, while changes in the membrane configuration may be responsible directly for some of the observed pulsatory movement of the cell membrane.

As mentioned above, the conduction of impulses by cell membranes may be accomplished by a propagated transformation from the closed to the partially open configuration. In the case of propagated pumping transformations of intracellular membranes, the membranes probably achieve the fully open condition during each cycle. In the case of impulse conduction in cell membranes this could not occur, for the equivalent static capacitance of conducting regions falls only 1 or 2 % at most in the squid axon (4) and about 15 % in *Nitella* (3). If the fully open configuration were to be achieved, the capacitance would be expected to fall off markedly (unless its value were due primarily to extraneous coats). Furthermore, the selective ion-permeability properties of the excited membrane render it unlikely that the change from the resting to the excited state involves more than a minute dilation of pore regions.

The substructural modifications of the axonal membrane which occur during impulse conduction may involve transition changes that modify the membrane a greater fraction of the way toward stage *d* (Fig. 3) than is achieved in the pulsatory partial transformation cycles of active transport. The facts that the capacitance of the membrane diminishes very little whereas the conductance increases many fold are not inconsistent, for relatively minor changes in the size, configuration, and dielectric properties of the pore channels could have incommensurately large effects upon ion permeability.

In the case of impulse conduction by the axonal membranes of nonmedullated nerve fibers, it can be postulated that the unexcited, fully recovered membrane is in the closed configuration. The event that initiates an impulse causes the membrane to begin transforming locally toward the open configuration. In the initial stages of this transformation the same events probably occur as those which take place in the corresponding phase of active transport, i.e., a selective forced filtration of tiny amounts of fluids into the opening membrane. However, in the case of impulse conduction the initiating event drives the opening transformation slightly beyond the limit that is attained in active transport—to the point where it becomes self-propagating.

In view of what is known about the superficial changes that occur during nerve impulse conduction, it is plausible to suggest that the basis of the propagation of the transformation to other regions is the opening of the membrane to the point where it becomes highly permeable to sodium ions. Once a critical level of depolarization has been passed (17), the permeability to sodium ions is known to rise in a regenerative manner. By partially displacing the divalent cations that stabilize the closed configuration, this sodium-ion flooding could cause adjacent closed regions also to begin the transformation toward the open configuration. Thus, a self-regenerative process would be established that could be the basis for the chain-reaction propagation of the nerve impulse.

The recovery process may consist of the lesser pulsatory, cyclic, partial transformations of active transport, during the course of which sodium ions are pumped out of the cell and potassium ions are pumped in. In this connection, active transport is known to be brought to a standstill by dinitrophenol, although the passage of the impulse is affected very little (15). This finding need not imply that the recovery processes are unrelated to the processes that occur during impulse conduction, as sometimes is assumed. Interpreted in accord with the views I have presented, the free energy of the active transport processes of the recovery phase is derived from the aqueous hydrolysis of ATP, and the funneling of this free energy into active transport is blocked by DNP. But most of the energy for the nerve impulse probably comes from the potential energy of the electrochemical potential gradients that are established by active transport. Accordingly, DNP, so to speak, prevents the storage of new fuel, but it does not prevent the utilization of the fuel that already is stored. In this view, active transport not only maintains the level of the potential energy reservoir that is drawn upon to drive impulse conduction, but it also keeps the impulse conduction machinery "tuned" for action. Just a slight push beyond the limiting partially open configuration attained during active transport starts the self-regenerative processes that accomplish impulse conduction.

## REFERENCES

1. BLOWERS, R., E. M. CLARKSON, AND M. MAIZELS. *J. Physiol., London* 113: 228, 1951.
2. BRANTON, D., AND H. MOOR. *J. Ultrastruct. Res.* 11: 401, 1964.
3. COLE, K. S., AND H. J. CURTIS. *J. Gen. Physiol.* 21: 37, 1938.
4. COLE, K. S., AND H. J. CURTIS. *J. Gen. Physiol.* 22: 649, 1939.
5. DANIELLI, J. F. *Symp. Soc. Exptl. Biol.* 8: 502, 1954.
6. DANIELLI, J. F. In: *Surface Phenomena in Chemistry and Biology*, edited by J. F. Danielli, K. G. Pankhurst, and A. C. Riddiford. New York: Pergamon, 1958, p. 246.
7. DANIELLI, J. F., AND H. DAVSON. *J. Cellular Comp. Physiol.* 5: 495, 1935.
8. DANIELLI, J. F., AND E. N. HARVEY. *J. Cellular Comp. Physiol.* 5: 483, 1935.
9. DAVSON, H., AND J. F. DANIELLI. *The Permeability of Natural Membranes*. New York: Macmillan, 1943.
10. FINEAN, J. B. *Brain Lipids and Lipoproteins and the Leucodystrophies*. Amsterdam: Elsevier, 1961, p. 57.
11. FINEAN, J. B. *Circulation* 26: 1151, 1962.
12. GOLDSTEIN, D. A., AND A. K. SOLOMON. *J. Gen. Physiol.* 44: 1, 1960.
13. HAWKE, J. G., AND A. E. ALEXANDER. In: *Retardation of Evaporation by Monolayers: Transport Processes*, edited by V. K. La Mer, New York: Academic, 1962, p. 67.
14. HEDLEY, R. H., AND W. S. BERTAUD. *J. Protozool.* 9: 79, 1962.
15. HODGKIN, A. L., AND R. D. KEYNES. *J. Physiol., London* 128: 28, 61, 1955.
16. KAVANAU, J. L. *Structure and Function in Biological Membranes*. San Francisco: Holden-Day, 1965.
17. KEYNES, R. D., AND R. H. ADRIAN. *Discussions Faraday Soc.* 21: 265, 1956.
18. KOEFOED-JOHNSEN, V., AND H. H. USSING. *Acta Physiol. Scand.* 28: 60, 1953.
19. LUCY, J. A. *J. Theoret. Biol.* 7: 360, 1964.
20. LUCY, J. A., AND A. M. GLAUERT. *J. Mol. Biol.* 8: 727, 1964.
21. MOOR, H., AND K. MÜHLETHALER. *J. Cell Biol.* 17: 609, 1963.
22. MULLINS, L. J. *J. Gen. Physiol.* 43: 105, 1960.
23. PAGANELLI, C. V., AND A. K. SOLOMON. *J. Gen. Physiol.* 41: 259, 1957.
24. PULVERTAFT, R. J. *J. Clin. Pathol.* 2: 281, 1949.
25. ROBERTSON, J. D. *Progr. Biophys. Biophys. Chem.* 10: 343, 1960.
26. ROBERTSON, J. D. *Ann. New York Acad. Sci.* 94: 339, 1961.
27. SACKS, J. *J. Gen. Physiol.* 43: 129, 1960.
28. SJÖSTRAND, F. S. In: *The Interpretation of Ultrastructure*, edited by R. J. Harris. New York: Academic, 1962, p. 47.
29. SJÖSTRAND, F. S. In: *Proc. Intern. Pharmacological Meeting*. New York: Pergamon, 1963, vol 4, p. 1.
30. SJÖSTRAND, F. S. *Nature* 199: 1262, 1963.
31. SOLOMON, A. K. *J. Gen. Physiol.* 43: 1, 1960.
32. SOLOMON, A. K. In: *Membrane Transport and Metabolism*, edited by A. Kleinzeller and A. Kotyk. New York: Academic, 1961.
33. STEIN, W. D., AND J. F. DANIELLI. *Discussions Faraday Soc.* 21: 238, 1956.
34. TEORELL, T. *Discussions Faraday Soc.* 21: 9, 1956.
35. TEORELL, T. *J. Gen. Physiol.* 42: 831, 1959.
36. USSING, H. H. In: *Metabolic Aspects of Transport Across Cell Membranes*, edited by Q. R. Murphy. Madison: University of Wisconsin Press, 1957, p. 39.
37. WALLACH, D. F., AND E. B. HAGER. *Nature* 196: 1004, 1962.
38. WALLACH, D. F., AND V. B. KAMAT. *Proc. Natl. Acad. Sci. U.S.* 52: 721, 1964.
39. WALLACH, D. F., AND D. ULREY. *Biochim. Biophys. Acta* 88: 620, 1964.

# Role of water structure in the molecular organization of cell membranes

OSCAR HECHTER[1]

*Worcester Foundation for Experimental Biology,*
*Shrewsbury, Massachusetts*

In ALL LIVING SYSTEMS, water is the bulk component comprising some 80% or so of the total mass. Elucidation of the state and structure of water in the living cell thus is a fundamental problem in biology, with implications for diverse fields, including cryobiology. Despite the importance of this subject, it seems fair to say that we have little or no definitive information about water structures inside the cell. That this should be the case is not really surprising, when we consider that our knowledge of the structure of water in very much simpler systems is incomplete and still subject to considerable debate. Other authors represented here, expert in physical chemistry, have discussed several theories of water structure in simple aqueous solutions; the nature of possible water structures at the surfaces of proteins and other macromolecules has also been considered. While all of the theories presented emphasize the existence of hydrogen-bonded networks of water molecules, it is apparent that considerable differences of opinion exist regarding specific structural details at the molecular level.

Any discussion of water in our present conceptual model of the cell must take into account principles of cellular organization derived from electron microscopic examination of diverse cell types (31). Electron microscopy has revealed that animal and plant cells (but not bacteria) generally exhibit a profusion of membrane systems in the cell interior as well as at the surface. The membrane at the cell surface often infolds tortuously into the cell interior; a greater or lesser part of the cytoplasm, depending upon cell type, is found to be filled with a paired membrane system designated as the endoplasmic reticulum. And all of the characteristic organelles of the cell, including the nucleus, mitochondria, Golgi apparatus, lysomes, various plastids, etc., are bounded by membranes. Biochemical studies of various cell fractions correlated with electron microscopic studies have established that the organelles are functionally specialized. It has become clear that a central principle of cellular organization involves the ample use of membranes to provide a solid framework for the precise

arrangement of active functional units and to separate the cell interior into dis crete cmpartments.

In terms of this picture, it is no longer possible to visualize intracellular water as a single "well stirred" aqueous compartment, as is the fashion in certain models used in permeability and transport theories. Instead, it is now evident that there are morphologically distinctive types of aqueous regions present in the cell, where water molecules find themselves in different environments and, accordingly, different types of water structures can be envisaged. It is most unlikely that water within the various membranes of the cell, or at the surface of a membrane, has the same structure as water in the hyaloplasm—the aqueous region between organelles and structural protein filaments. Water between paired membrane systems, as in mitochondria or in the cysternae of the endoplasmic reticulum, or within organelles (as in the interior matrix of mitochondria or in the nucleus) represents still other types of aqueous regions. The important point is that a sizable fraction of the water of the cell is intimately associated with membrane systems, whether at surface or within the membrane. Water thus associated with membranes and other fixed "immobile" macromolecular structures in the cell such as filaments of actomyosin in muscle or deoxyribonucleic acid (DNA) in strands in the nucleus of cells should therefore be differentiated from water in the hyaloplasm. Here the water is associated with mobile solutes, some of which are macromolecules (e.g., certain enzymes and ribonucleic acids (RNA's)), not "fixed" in the structure, which are translocated directionally from one site to another in the cell. The structure of most of the water in the hyaloplasm, unlike water associated with membranes, may resemble the structures which occur in aqueous solutions containing soluble globular proteins.

It has been estimated that in certain cell types, where the endoplasmic reticulum is well developed, the membrane systems of the cell plus attached components may account for perhaps as much as 80–90% of the total cell mass. The estimated value for membrane plus componentry in the case of the hepatic parenchymal cell is about 50–60%; in bacterial protoplasts, where

[1] Aided by a fellowship from the Commonwealth Fund and a grant from the Ittleson Family Foundation, New York, N. Y.

Reprinted by permission of the author and the Federation of American Societies for Experimental Biology from *Federation Proceedings*, **24**, 2:3: S91–S102 (1965).

subcellular organelles are not present, the cell membrane by itself accounts for about 10 % of the mass. These rough estimates give some idea of the variations in the proportions of hyaloplasm to "membrane" in different cell types. Various proportions of diverse water structures are therefore to be expected in different cell types, depending upon the specific organization of the membrane systems and structural proteins of the particular cell type.

Such a view may be important to cryobiology; the mechanisms whereby ice crystals produce cell damage and different cell types exhibit wide variations in resistance to freezing and thawing are incompletely understood. Although a multiplicity of factors may well be involved, one cannot help wondering whether the exceptional ability of bacteria to resist freezing and thawing, as compared with animal cells, may not be related to the facts that bacteria do not possess membrane-bound organelles characteristically found in the latter, and the single membrane system present—the cell membrane— is in intimate contact with a rigid, nonreactive cell wall material which serves as a support for the more fragile membrane structure. In bacteria, the DNA of the genome appears to be a system of fine fibrils in a central irregular zone of the protoplasm (41). Though capable of oxidative phosphorylation, bacteria do not possess recognizable mitochondria. The unit parts of the mitochondrial membrane system for adenosine triphosphate (ATP) synthesis appear to be present in impocketings of the bacterial cell membrane called mesomes (17, 31). Whether for replication (DNA → RNA → protein) or for bioenergetics (ATP synthesis), the unit parts of these functional systems in bacteria appear to be relatively resistant to damage produced by freezing and thawing. The bacterial cell has a cell volume about 500 times smaller than the animal, and this difference of course has an important influence on rates of freezing and thawing of cellular componentry. However, the question must be raised whether one of the important difficulties with animal cells in cryobiology is the vulnerability of intracellular membranes to ice crystals formed during freezing or thawing. Membrane fragmentation in animal cells would mean that the active functional units involved in replication and bioenergetics could not be segregated into organized, compartmentalized structures again after freezing and thawing. Careful restudy of the comparative survival rates of appropriate species of bacteria and fungi containing membrane-bounded organelles and rigid cell walls subjected to standardized freezing and thawing might permit experimental evaluation of the importance of the factor of intracellular membrane fragmentation as a mechanism of cell damage.

MEMBRANE STRUCTURE AND FUNCTION

It seems axiomatic that the structure of water, within or at the surface of membranes, depends upon the molecular organization of membrane systems. If precise information about the chemistry and spatial arrangement of the other component parts of the membrane were available, in principle this would serve to define the nature of the water structures involved.

Our concepts of membrane structure were initially derived from physiological studies which attempted to account for two fundamental properties of the cell that were ascribed to a semipermeable barrier, called the plasma membrane: a) permeability and active transport processes, and b) electrical phenomena, e.g., bioelectric potentials, with particular reference to excitability in nerve and muscle. Diverse disciplines and subdisciplines, each with their own concepts and technics concentrating on one aspect of membrane function or another, have contributed to our conceptual picture of cellular membranes in a voluminous literature, difficult to integrate and impossible to review here. Of the very large number of reviews and monographs dealing with various aspects of biological membranes, we cite three (20, 26, 49) to illustrate the range of problems and experimental approaches in this field. All of the diverse disciplines involved in study of membranes use their own special language and basic assumptions, some of which are unstated. All converge at the molecular level where a universal language can be employed. It is apparent that the goal of molecular membranology is to formulate a model of cell membranes in a unifying configuration equally satisfactory and meaningful to the biophysicist, physical chemist, biochemist, and physiologist.

Studies of a wide variety of cells led to the general conclusion that a relatively thin lipoprotein layer plays a dominant role in the translocation of solutes into and out of the cell. The plasma membrane permeability barrier was studied by a variety of indirect methods, and early speculations concerning its molecular structure were summarized by Davson and Danielli (7, 8) in their now classical pauci-molecular model of the cell membrane. This model postulated that the cell membrane consisted of one or more bimolecular leaflets of lipid, each polar surface of which had on it a monolayer of protein. This theory incorporated evidence from polarization microscopy and X-ray diffraction studies, which indicated that in several membrane systems the lipid molecules were arranged in bilayers, with the hydrocarbon chains orientated radially (16a, 43-47). Electron microscopy then revealed the characteristic features of a morphological structure at the cell surface, now attributed to a lipid-containing membrane of the type predicted from earlier studies. In potassium-permanganate-fixed preparations, two narrow dense lines were observed separated by a band of low density but of similar width, the thickness of the trilaminar unit being about 75 A (35). With further study it became evident that most, if not all, of the characteristic membrane systems of the cell exhibited the trilaminar feature; this morphological uniformity has found expression in the now widely accepted unit-membrane concept, vigorously promulgated by Robertson (36-38, 40). This concept holds that all biological membranes are built on a single fundamental design principle where the basic plan of structural organization consists of two lipid monolayers sandwiched between two fully spread monolayers of nonlipid components. There are similarities as well as differences between the present unit membrane concept and the Davson-Danielli model, which have been discussed by Robertson (40).

As noted previously, concurrent with the advent of electron microscopy, technics developed for cell fractionation permitted the isolation of certain characteristic organelles for biochemical studies. Used together, these two technics revealed that cellular membranes exhibited considerable functional diversity as expressed, for example, in profound differences in the types of enzymes bound to different membranes. The association of morphological uniformity with functional diversity in membrane systems can be ascribed in large part to the periodic arrangement of different types of specialized transducing units in a highly ordered lipoprotein matrix, fundamentally similar in all membrane systems (11–14). The transducing units are considered to be ordered macromolecular assemblies consisting of enzymes and other macromolecules, coupled both spatially and energetically, that are involved in the energized vectorial translocation of ions and other solutes, in contraction, and in other active membrane processes. Though we have some general ideas about the nature of the componentry required for these specialized energized membrane "units" (and an encouraging approach to this problem has been achieved in mitochondrial membranes where periodically arranged membrane subunits have been visualized (15)), neither the chemistry of the essential componentry nor its molecular arrangement in the matrix of the membrane is known with certainty. It is also appreciated that functional differences between membranes may reside in mucopolysaccharides or glycoproteins which may serve as extrinsic coatings of outer membrane layers (10). We shall accordingly not attempt to discuss the membrane as a "whole," but concentrate on the lipoprotein matrix which appears to have a structural organization common in most, if not all, cellular membranes.

Figure 1 is a representation of the unit membrane concept. The two nonlipid layers, generally thought to be protein, differ somehow in chemical structure to produce an asymmetrical membrane, and this difference is thought to be related to the presence of glycoprotein or mucopolysaccharides associated with the outer nonlipid layer. Though the thickness of the trilaminar unit membrane is about 75 A, it is recognized that different membranes in the cell may vary in thickness, some being 90–100 A. The lipids in the bimolecular leaflet are a set of phospholipids mixed with smaller amounts of triglyceride and cholesterol; variations in membrane thickness can be attributed to differences in lipid constituents, and their packing arrangements, to differences in the protein layers or to specialized transducing units without fundamental modification of the basic design principle.

A major development in membrane chemistry was made when Green and his associates succeeded in isolating a homogeneous colorless protein from beef heart

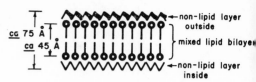

**Unit membrane concept**

FIG. 1. A representation of the unit-membrane concept. The asymmetrical nonlipid layers, presumably protein in nature but of unknown composition and structure are represented as continuous structures. The mixed lipid bilayer consists primarily of phospholipids; the hydrophilic portion of the lipid molecules are represented by the filled-in circles (●) and the extended hydrocarbon chains by the attached tails ( | ).

mitochondrial membrane preparations, which appears to be the protein component of the basic lipoprotein matrix of this membrane system (6, 17). Designated as structural protein, it comprises at least 50 % of the total protein of mitochondria; similar structural proteins have been isolated from other membrane systems (34) suggesting that mitochondrial structural protein may be a prototype of the structural protein of membrane systems generally. As isolated, mitochondrial structural protein is a water-insoluble polymer; after treatment with cationic detergents (or dilute alkali or strong acetic acid), a monomeric species (ca. 25,000 mol) is obtained which combines with three of the cytochromes ($a$, $b$, and $c_1$) of the mitochondrial electron-transfer chain or with mitochondrial lipids to form reproducible complexes. Mitochondrial structural protein has a higher than average content of non-polar, amino acid side chains, and the characteristic tendency of structural protein to polymerize has accordingly been attributed to extensive hydrophobic bonding between monomeric units. The formation of mixed complexes of structural protein, phospholipids, and the various cytochromes is likewise believed to be due to hydrophobic bonding predominantly, although other bonding modes are also involved.

SOME FUNCTIONAL QUESTIONS

Although some of the chemical details have been filled in, our modern picture of the unit membrane retains many of the fundamental gaps inherent in the original Davson-Danielli model, with respect to the physiological role of membranes. Consider, for example, the fact that membranes exhibit high selectivity both for ions and nonelectrolytes, some processes apparently involving selective pores or channels, and others involving energized transport pumps. We have agreed to consider the membrane as a heterogeneous structure, where energized membrane pumps or contractile units are macromolecular assemblies arranged in periodic fashion through a lipoprotein matrix. The question arises, however, whether the selective pores or channels required for passive transport of solutes are built-in properties of the lipoprotein matrix or whether specialized devices must be invoked here as well. Our present model of the lipo-protein matrix does not provide an explicit molecular basis for selective channels. We also know that biological membranes (but particularly the plasma membrane) exhibit profound changes in state in response to excitation, whether expressed in nerve depolarization after stimulation or as changes in membrane transport processes induced by certain hormones (e.g., insulin and vasopressin) in responsive cell types. If our present picture of the unit membrane represents one state of the membrane matrix, what is the other state? More particularly, what is the nature of the phase transitions which must occur in each layer as the membrane changes from one state to another? After excitation, whether in nerve stimulation or in hormone action, a local perturbation is somehow transmitted through the bulk phase of the membrane to influence sites at a distance. What is the molecular basis for the classical problem in physiology designated as "the propagation of a local disturbance?"

Kavenau (19) developed a new molecular theory of the membrane structure which provides answers to these and other questions about membrane function. Regarding the membrane as a dynamic and labile structure, Kavenau postulates that the membrane shifts between different substructural states with different phases of function. The primary differences in the various states are related to the arrangement of lipids in the membrane, the two extremes being equilibrium states designated as the open and closed configurations. In the open configuration, it is postulated that the lipids are arranged in cylindrical micelles (pillars) 180–200 A thick, attached at each end to the external protein monolayers 10–15 A thick, and the pillars, about 80 A in width, are separated and arranged hexagonally so that there are very large aqueous regions between them. The closed configuration results when the pillars collapse and the lipid micelles either coalesce or closely abut each other, obliterating the aqueous regions. If coalescence between micellar units is complete, it results in a continuous lamina of the familiar bimolecular lipid leaflet; if coalescence is incomplete, pores are formed as the lipid units closely abut. Intermediate states between the open and closed configurations are envisaged, and Kavenau on the basis of his model is able to account for a large body of evidence bearing on membrane function in terms of plausible molecular mechanisms.

Limitations of time and space do not permit adequate discussion of Kavenau's theory, which gives primary importance to shifts and transitions of the lipid phase of the membrane. This lipid phase of the membrane structure is what we know most about. Ordered arrangements of polar and non-polar lipids in bilayers have been produced and their properties are being studied (29, 30, 50). It is not difficult to envisage shifts between ordered lipid bilayers and various micellar arrangements as demonstrated by Stoeckenius (48) and Luzzatti and Husson (27) as a plausible basis for phase transition in the lipid

layer, when the membrane changes from one state to another as in the Kavenau theory.

If we are to have a complete picture of membrane structure, more information is needed about the non-lipid components of the membrane, particularly the structural protein of the membrane and the water structures present in the membrane matrix. These two problems are related. We know in principle that the aqueous environment is a major determinant of protein conformation, and that the conformation of protein likewise influences the structure of water at the macromolecular surface; changes in one are reflected and find expression in changes in the other. If we but knew the arrangement of water in the membrane, it would help us with our problem of structural protein conformation. Conversely, if the structure and conformation of the structural protein of the membrane matrix were known, they could help us define the state of membrane water.

WATER IN MEMBRANE SYSTEMS

Let us therefore direct our attention to the water structure in the membrane. It has long been appreciated that water is a bulk component of membrane systems, comprising 30–50% of the total system, and must therefore figure importantly in the molecular organization of the system (11–14, 16, 46). In an ordered lamellar system, it has seemed reasonable that the water in the membrane must somehow be highly ordered in relation to the ordered polar groups of both protein and phospholipids. Fernández-Morán (12, 13) in particular has emphasized the possibility that water in the membrane may be organized in icelike or crystal-hydrate lattices as an integral structural component of the membrane systems serving an essential role for various membrane processes. Localized reversible phase changes in ordered water structure might provide the basis for conformational changes in protein layers and concurrently modify the arrangement of the polar lipids from an ordered bimolecular leaflet to a less tightly packed micellar form. These phase transitions could spread through the membrane phase of the cell as water structure changes reversibly, and thus represent the molecular basis for propagation of a local perturbation. Selective permeability might be envisaged in terms of molecular sieves lined with ordered water; the marked permeability changes induced by excitation could be the consequence of the melting of water structures in special regions. By providing an interconnected hydrogen bonding medium, ordered water structures could participate in fast protonic charge transport mechanisms (9), or in electron transport, via hydrogen-free radical or hydride ion as suggested by Klotz (22).

The concept of Fernández-Morán that ordered water lattices are an integral structural component of membranes has great power in providing a conceptual basis for understanding a multiplicity of fundamental mechanisms associated with membrane function. The difficulty arises when one asks, what is the precise structure of the organized water? Is the ordered water arranged hexagonally as in ice, pentagonally as in clathrate cages, or in yet another form? How many layers of interconnected hydrogen-bonded water structures are there, over what distances are they present, and where should they be placed in Fig. 1 to fill in our model of the unit membrane? There are no definitive answers to these questions; in the absence of hard evidence it is possible to argue convincingly for either icelike or crystalline-hydrate types of water in the membrane.

Though nuclear magnetic spectroscopy offers the potential of a nondestructive method for evaluation of water structures (12), there are profound difficulties in interpreting changes in the proton resonance signal of water in systems of this order of complexity. It has not been possible, as yet, to experimentally approach the arrangement and structure of water in the membrane by looking at water structures directly. Can we solve this problem indirectly by considering the structural protein component of the membrane? Though we do not know the conformation or even the amino acid sequence of a single structural protein of a membrane, we may nevertheless ask whether there may be structural principles from protein chemistry that could give us insight into the possible conformation of the protein subunits of the membrane, and hence to the water structure.

### DESIGN PRINCIPLES IN CONSTRUCTION OF A PROTEIN COAT FOR MEMBRANES

Caspar and Klug (4) expanded the idea of Crick and Watson (5)—that small viruses are built up of identical protein subunits packed together to form a protective shell for the nucleic acid—into a general theory for the construction of ordered biological structures, be they virus coats or membranes. The essence of their far-reaching concept is that if one is given as building blocks a large number of identical protein molecules, then there are only a very limited number of efficient architectural designs for the construction of a biological container. The two basic designs are helical tubes and icosahedral shells. Drawing upon architectural principles inherent in the Buckminster Fuller geodesic dome, wherein steel rods are bonded together in quasi-equivalent triangles, grouped in arrays of hexagons and pentagons, Caspar and Klug pointed out how the protein shells of icosahedral viruses and membranes could be assembled from a single type of protein subunit by introducing a suitable ratio of pentamers to hexamers. If a single type of protein subunit is utilized to form the protein matrix of membranes—and this appears likely from the studies on mitochondrial structural protein—the geometrical and architectural principles of the Caspar-Klug theory would appear fundamental to the problem of the protein structure of the membrane.

The Caspar-Klug concept of a geodesic pattern has been considered as a possible explanation for certain electron microscopic findings obtained by Robertson (39, 40), who observed a typical honeycomblike pattern, involving hexagonal subunits plus a few pentagonal subunits in favorable frontal sections of synaptic discs and frog retinal rods (39). Robertson considered the possibility that the honeycomb pattern observed represented a derivative macromolecular pattern localized in the outer surface of unit membranes. From a review of the available literature, he concluded that while a geodesic pattern may eventually be recognized as a general feature of unit membrane systems, further correlative work was necessary and it seemed premature to accept any far-reaching conclusions.

Despite this cautionary note, let us accept the design principles of Caspar and Klug as a basis for further discussion, and proceed to consider the conformations of a protein subunit which could serve as the monomers of the hexamers and pentamers required to build a geodesic dome. Caspar and Klug have stated that there are two types of efficient designs: helical tubes and icosahedral shells. Does this imply the existence of two fundamental types of protein subunit conformation to serve as the building blocks for these different types of structures? If the $\alpha$-helical conformation for protein serves for protein structures exhibiting helical symmetry, is there a second conformation of protein utilized for icosahedral symmetry?

### CONFORMATIONS OF PROTEINS

On the subject of protein conformation, we think it fair to say that we have one major structural principle, the helix of Pauling. Once all biological polymers were random. After Pauling's helix, all biopolymers became helical. With increasing experience, it became apparent that only a few proteins were completely helical in structure; most proteins exhibited partial helical structure, the per cent helix varying from protein to protein. Today, we know that the concept of the $\alpha$-helix, powerful as it has been, does not account for the structure of all proteins (33).

Since some proteins do exist in nonhelical conformations, one must look to more fundamental unifying principles for protein structure. These fundamental principles underlying protein structure arise from energetics and thermodynamic considerations of the folding of peptide chains to achieve a minimal energy state (3), the folding being dependent on the character and sequence of the amino acid residues of the polypeptide chain and the nature of the solvent environment. In aqueous media, the non-polar groups of a polypeptide have such a high aversion to water molecules that a polypeptide or protein tends to fold so that a maximum number of hydrophobic bonds are shielded from the water by close-packing mutual interactions (primarily by van der Waal's forces), while the interactions of the polar side chains with solvent at the aqueous surface and with each other (as in intrachain hydrogen bonding) secondarily contribute to sta-

**304**

bility. Depending upon the character of the amino acid sequences involved, the minimal energy state of a protein can be achieved with a total or partial helical arrangement, but other modes of folding exist to achieve protein conformation of minimum energy. If there is a large preponderance of non-polar amino acid side chains, a minimal energy state can be achieved by polymerization as non-polar regions of the monomer react with each other.

We have already asked whether there may be a second basic structural principle in peptide and protein conformation, as general and as powerful as the $\alpha$-helix principle has been, which could be applied not to water soluble proteins but to a water-insoluble polymerized system built of hexamers plus a few pentamers. Dr. Donald Warner in a series of theoretical publications (51–53) developed a new approach to peptide and protein conformation, which we can call the hexagonal concept. This hexagonal conformation is of interest because it permits us to visualize how hexamers might be packed (with a few pentamers) to form the protein coats of membranes; additional principles, inherent in the hexagonal conformation, emerge with striking implications for membrane function as well as structure.

*Warner hexagonal conformation.* Warner undertook the study of molecular models of several peptide hormones and peptide antibiotics to determine whether it was possible to discover a unifying structural feature or arrangement of peptide bonds in biologically active compounds in the peptide series. Using molecular models, Warner found that the peptide bonds of various polypeptides studied could be arranged to form regular hexagonal patterns in which all of the carbonyl oxygens of the peptide

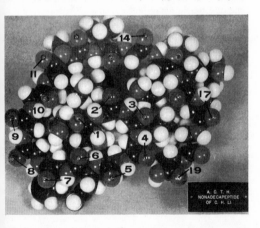

FIG. 2. Hexagonal pattern of carbonyl oxygens of the peptide bonds on the hydrophilic surface of the model are shown here. Oxygen atoms in the photograph (grey) contrast with hydrogen atoms (white) and carbon atoms or aromatic rings (black). The amino acids are numbered in sequence starting from the N-terminus, and numbers placed on the $\alpha$-hydrogen atom of the NH group are connected by a black line to identify the carbonyl oxygens corresponding to each amino acid.

bonds occupy positions on one planar surface, the oxygens being so arranged that they form the corners of a hexagonal unit; all the amino acid side chains project downward to form the second surface of the model. This type of hexagonal arrangement gives rise to a planar face (designated hydrophilic) containing the carbonyl oxygens of the peptide bonds separated by a 4.8 A distance (oxygen center to oxygen center), the second surface produced by the closely packed side chains, being designated as hydrophobic. It was found in the models of small peptides studied that the polar amino acid side chains of the hydrophobic face frequently were so placed that stabilizing hydrogen bonds between neighboring polar groups could be easily envisaged, and that hydrophobic interactions of the non-polar side chains were also probably contributing to conformational stability. Warner called attention to the fact that the 4.8 A distance in the carbonyl oxygen pattern of the hydrophilic face of these hexagonal peptides coincide with the second-neighbor oxygen pattern of water in a hexagonal arrangement, and visualized additional stabilization arising in consequence of hydrogen bonding between hexagonal water units and the hydrophilic surface of the peptide. Using these principles, Warner built a series of models of linear peptide hormones of increasing length: the N-terminal decapeptide of ACTH (10 amino acids), the N-terminal nonadecapeptide of ACTH (19 amino acids), and $\beta$-chain of insulin (30 amino acids). He then extended the hexagonal concept to the protein subunit of the tobacco mosaic virus (TMV) and considered how subunits might be arranged to construct a protein coat for the virus (53).

To illustrate the hexagonal principle, let us examine the Warner model of the *N*-terminal nonadecapeptide ACTH of Li (25). The hydrophilic face is shown in Fig. 2, the hydrophobic face in Fig. 3. In another paper to be published, I have considered the hexagonal conformation of hormonal peptides in relation to the recognition phenomenon in the interaction of peptide hormones with specific receptors in the membrane. In this connection, the question arose whether on energetic grounds the monomeric form of the Warner model of the ACTH nonadecapeptide could be considered as a likely conformation at the receptor site in the responsive cell. The answer was yes, provided that one assumed that the receptor site contained a flexible peptide component, complementary to the hydrophobic face of the peptide hormone. Utilizing and extending Koshland's concept (23), it was not difficult to envisage how in the presence of hormone, both receptor and peptide might undergo successive configurational changes as one component interacts, group by group, with the complementary component to produce a two-disc system (interlocked through hydrophobic faces). In such a system, all the non-polar side chains (except for edge groups) would be buried in the center; the groups exposed to water would be the polar carbonyl oxygens and $\alpha$-NH groups of the peptide bonds. This is an interesting solution to the energetic problem; two peptide configurations, inherently unstable when the units are isolated, in effect become a stable system when the

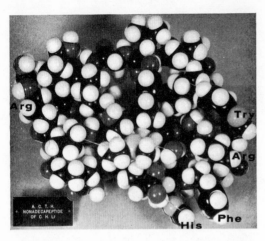

FIG. 3. This figure represents the hydrophobic surface, where certain edge groups are identified: His (6), Phe (7), Arg (8), Try (9) and Arg (17) to provide orientation on this face of the model.

units are locked together through the collective effect of a number of weak forces.

PACKING OF HEXAGONAL DISCS AS HEXAMERS

With this background, the question can now be posed whether the fundamental protein matrix of the membrane involves the packing of identical hexagonal units in a regular manner together with some pentagonal units. In this connection Warner's (53) application of the hexagonal principle to the protein coat of the TMV virus assumes special interest. Warner postulated a hexagonal conformation for the protein subunit (whose amino acid sequence is known) and then proceeded to consider theoretically how hexagonal subunit discs must be packed to form a protein coat for the TMV virus and conform to the available physical data bearing on this problem. It

should be noted that the subunit conformation and packing arrangement suggested by Warner for the protein coat of the TMV virus is very different from the generally accepted model (3), which assumes a helical conformation of the protein subunits packed in a helical array. Important as this point may be, the question of which conformation for the TMV virus is to be preferred does not concern us here. The important point for this discussion is that in the conceptual design utilized by Warner for locking hexagonal disc subunits together, certain principles emerge which we feel may be of fundamental interest to the elucidation of key problems of membrane function.

Let us therefore re-examine Warner's studies on the protein of the TMV virus from the point of view of membrane organization, independent of whether it applies in the TMV case. Figure 4*A* shows Warner's schematic arrangement of six peptide subunits, locked together through hydrophobic surfaces to form a hexameric A-protein unit. Warner then postulated that these A-protein units are "cemented" together at the hydrophilic surface by two water layers to form the protein coat illustrated in Fig. 4*B*. Two fundamental assumptions were made here by Warner: a) the distance between the hydrophilic surfaces of the two peptide subunits interlocked at the hydrophobic surfaces is about 6.9 A (from center to center of the carbonyl oxygens of the two surfaces); b) the hydrophilic surfaces of adjacent A-protein units are separated by a space of 4.9 A containing two second-neighbor water oxygen layers. In effect Warner postulated that the two water layers which play a structural role in his model are highly ordered and arranged hexagonally in an icelike lattice; it is apparent that this idea has significance for our previous discussion of the state of water in membrane systems.

The overlap pattern which results from the six-subunit arrangement of Warner's model of the A-protein unit (Fig. 4*A*) is shown in Fig. 5. It will be seen that a central hole or channel arises where the individual hexagonal discs do not overlap. The amino acid residues at the

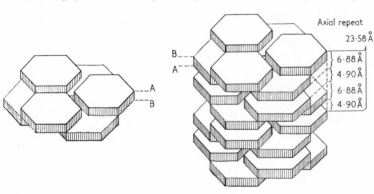

A——Hydrophilic surface
B----Hydrophobic surface

FIG. 4. The principles used by Warner to pack hexagonal protein subunits of the TMV virus are shown. *A* is a schematic A-protein unit composed of six protein subunits, arranged three on three, via interactions of their hydrophobic surfaces. *B* schematically illustrates how a protein coat for viral RNA might be formed by axial layering of the hexameric A-protein units.

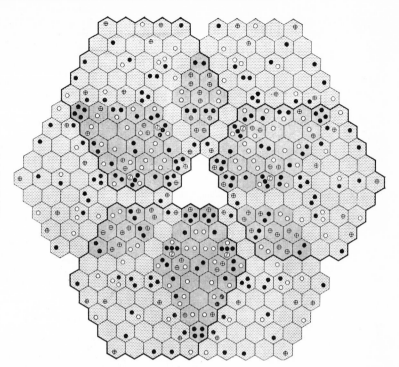

FIG. 5. Illustration of the overlap pattern achieved in the A-
protein unit (Fig. 4a). The three
upper subunits are outlined in
black; ●, aliphatic hydroxyl side
chains; ⊕, carboxyl side chain;
○, amide side chain; S, sulhydryl
group.

edges of this hole comprise a total of 12 carboxyl groups[2]
and 24 hydroxyl groups which are quite uniformly distributed around the edge; there are no cationic side
chains (arginyl, lysyl, or histidyl) at the edge of this hole.
Warner's arrangement gives rise to a channel lined with
carboxyl groups, some of which are COO⁻; the hydroxy
groups at the edge represent hydrogen-bonding sites
available to water. In effect, Warner's hexameric arrangement of three on three creates an aqueous channel
lined with hydrogen-bonded water, possessing COO⁻
sites for binding cations. Such a channel has obvious implications for the problem of ion selectivity in biological
membranes. It is permselective for cations and would exclude anions; depending upon the specific dimensions of
the channel and the nature of the amino acid residues at
the edge, the possibility of selectivity, as between cations,
can be envisaged. As one continues to use hexagons to
fill up the two-layered disc system, new channels emerge,
and the side chains at the edge comprise hydroxyl groups
and basic groups of amino acids (primarily arginine) to
produce an aqueous channel permselective for anions.

The implications for membrane structure and function
that arise out of Warner's design for a protein coat of the
TMV virus may represent trivial coincidences. I do

[2] Some of these 12 carboxyl groups may be replaced by car-
boxyamide groups if the slight modifications of the TMV sequence
proposed by Anderer and Handschuh (1) are verified in future
work.

not think this is the case; Warner's concept, suitably
translated, provides a basis for a fresh look at membrane
structure in terms of hexagonal protein subunits arranged primarily as hexamers, with a few pentamers.
These ideas may or may not apply to the proteins of the
membrane in its totality (of enzymes, pumps, contractile
elements, and other specialized units in transduction).
They may illustrate the basic molecular organization of
the protein envelopes of the membrane, and help us to
approach certain aspects of membrane function.

MODEL OF MEMBRANE WITH HEXAGONAL
PROTEIN SUBUNITS

Let us accept the basic features of the unit membrane
thesis as a basis for discussion and fill in the protein layers
primarily with hexagonal peptide subunits locked together as hexamers, as in the TMV model of Warner.
Important as the problem of extrinsic coatings of mucopolysaccharides or glycoproteins at the outer membrane
surface may be for the arrangement of water molecules at
the surface, in the absence of definitive chemical evidence
this aspect of the problem will not be considered here.
Using this model, let us now envisage the nature of membrane changes associated with the classical problem of
depolarization in nerve. Figure 6 is a representation of a
model of a membrane region in resting state, impermeable to sodium ion but not to potassium. The protein

phase of the membrane model is built of two layers of peptide-antipeptide units, each interlocked disc system being 6.9 A thick and separated by two water layers in a hexagonal icelike arrangement, hydrogen-bonded via second-neighbor relations to the carbonyl oxygens of the peptide hydrophilic surface. In this arrangement the outer protein layer is about 19 A thick, which is about the right order of magnitude for a plasma membrane of 85–100 A. If one wished to decrease the thickness of the protein layer, removal of one layer of interlocked hexameric discs would reduce the protein layer to 6.9 instead of 18.7 A. From the overlap design pattern in the TMV model of Warner, we now envisage channels edged with hydroxyl groups and either positively or negatively charged side chains. These charged aqueous channels are filled with ordered water, some water layers being tightly hydrogen-bonded to the edges, other water molecules being more mobile but still restricted in mobility. The effective dimensions of the channel would depend upon the number and arrangement of the mobile water molecules in the water channel. In such channels selectivity between cations would depend upon the size and shape of the hydrated ion. The potassium ion has about one or two water molecules in its immediate hydration shell, whereas sodium has at least six; $K^+$ is a smaller hydrated ion but likewise has a different shape. It is not difficult to envisage how a cationic channel of this type might be selectively available for potassium but not for sodium ion. We will arrange the cationic and anionic channels of the locked subunits of each hexameric layer in staggered relation, so that the cationic channel of the first set is above an anionic channel in the next layer. The protein layer in turn is associated with a conventional mixed lipid bilayer via two water layers in an ordered icelike arrangement. Warner and I have found that the carbonyl oxygens of the ester bonds of triglyceride can be fitted perfectly into the hexagonal water structure, these oxygens replacing the oxygen in water. It would be necessary to arrange the polar groups of the phospholipids so that they likewise fit the ordered water layers. Warner and I have studied structural models of several typical phospholipids and there appear to be no special difficulties in arranging the polar groups in this fashion. The lipid layer illustrated shows extended hydrocarbon chains partially interdigitated. It is of course possible to pack the hydrocarbon chains more or less tightly.

Finally, we come to the innermost protein layer of the membrane, which we know in principle must be different than the outermost protein layer in important respects, but about which we know very little indeed. The required asymmetry might well be related to extrinsic coatings of polysaccharide at the outer surface, but there are other possibilities, e.g., a different type of subunit structure or protein organization in the inner face of the membrane, etc. The question of asymmetry need not concern us at this juncture; for purposes of illustration, we consider the inner protein layer of the lipoprotein matrix to likewise consist of locked hexagonal units.

In effect, we have drawn in Fig. 6 a lattice arrange-

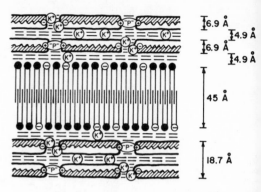

FIG. 6. Schematic representation of the resting membrane where the basic features of the unit-membrane concept are retained and the protein layers are represented as a system of interlocked hexagonal discs cemented together by water layers in an icelike arrangement to form a precisely ordered lattice system. The individual hexagonal subunits are shown as interlocked through hydrophobic surfaces to form disc units held together by two layers of water in an icelike state, this type of water being represented as (——). The aqueous channels in the protein layer of the membrane possess fixed charge sites, and are shown in a staggered relationship; most of the water in the aqueous channels has an icelike structure. The bilayer arrangement of the mixed lipids, involving interdigitation of fatty acid tails, is assumed to be dependent upon the icelike layers of water, which fix the hydrophilic portion of lipid molecules in position in relation to the hydrophilic surfaces of the neighboring protein subunits. Potassium is shown as the principal counterion for fixed negative sites in the resting membrane, phosphate as the counterion for fixed positive sites; but other ions possibly involved are not shown. In this model, selectivity for potassium over sodium ion depends upon the organization of the membrane units to form a precise lattice.

ment whose ordered stability depends on a set of interlocking weak forces acting in concert; the arrangement of water in a hexagonal icelike structure between protein layers depends upon a variety of weak forces (hydrophobic and hydrogen bonding) locking the hexagonal subunits together. The conformation of the locked peptide subunits depends in part upon the water structure. At some points, the interlocked hexagonal units may be crosslinked by disulfide bonds which provide covalent bonds for giving the structure stability. The ordered lipid bilayer depends in turn upon the hexagonal, icelike water structure in alignment with the hydrophilic surfaces of peptide subunits, and this in turn influences the arrangement of the inner protein layer. It is apparent that in this model, wherein fixed charges on protein channels are staggered and where the bulk of the water of the system is highly ordered at hydrophilic surfaces, there are considerable restrictions to the free diffusion of water-soluble permeant species. Our maze-like arrangement of charges in effect constitutes a formidable barrier to the translocation of any charged species, be they cations or anions. It is not difficult to visualize selective translocation of sugars and other nonelectrolytes in a system of this type.

Assuming appropriate dimensions, it is now possible

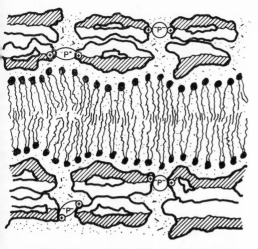

FIG. 7. Schematic representation of the depolarized membrane, where the arrangement of protein subunits, lipids, and of water no longer provide a precisely ordered lattice. For purposes of illustration, the hypothetical changes in the various structural components of the membrane are highly exaggerated. The protein subunits have changed from hexagonal discs to a more globular helical form, the lipid bilayer to a more random micellar arrangement, and the icelike water structures to less ordered water structures. In consequence, the fixed negative sites in the depolarized region of the membrane no longer exhibit high selectivity for potassium over sodium. Mobile water molecules are represented as small dots (·), thus become available, provide aqueous channels which permit relatively free diffusion of cations with the electrochemical gradient. The phosphate cross links between neighboring fixed positive sites are shown as undisturbed, to indicate that the membrane structure does not break down completely; other links which maintain membrane structure and which provide the basis for reversal to the resting membrane state are not illustrated.

to envisage how potassium ions are available to act selectively as the principal counterions at the fixed negative sites in the protein channels (divalent ions, perhaps $Mg^{++}$ or $Ca^{++}$ serving to lock negative sites together at critical points). The fixed positive sites likewise require a counterion, and we can use phosphate or chloride in this regard. The hydrated sodium ion may be too large to penetrate the cationic aqueous channels pictured that contain highly ordered water or the hexagonal icelike layers cementing the subunits together. Such an ordered lattice system thus resembles a potassium electrode, where the permeability of potassium is low but where conductance is high. It is apparent that the schematic model of Fig. 6 is a possible molecular representation of the long-pore theory which attempts to explain how a membrane with low potassium permeability nevertheless exhibits high conductance (24); it also is a representation of the classic molecular sieve theory of Boyle and Conway (2), in which ion selectivity in passive permeability processes was related to the relative dimensions of pores and hydrated ions, but takes edge-effects into account.

Let us now disturb the system at a local point near the outmost surface of the protein layer. At this point in our discussion, we are not concerned with the precise mechanism of how the local perturbation is initiated, be it by a) the opening of a strategic S—S bond which bridges two hexagonal subunits together, by the injection of electrons into the system so that the reaction $S{-}S + 2e^- + 2H^+ \rightarrow 2SH$ is enabled to proceed, or by b) the introduction of a molecular species which either disturbs the complementary interactions of paired hexagonal units so that a conformational change occurs or modifies the water structure of an aqueous channel. In all cases the initiating excitation produces a local change in the associated water structures. If, as we have assumed, the icelike arrangement of the water layers contributes to the conformational stability of the locked neighboring hexagonal peptide units, we can expect that as water structures are changed locally, configurational changes occur in neighboring hexagonal units so that in effect a local perturbation in water structures is enabled to spread through the outer protein layers of the membrane and also to involve the ordered water layers which maintain the lipid phase as a bimolecular leaflet, eventually influencing the inner protein layer. Figure 7 is a schematic representation of the depolarized membrane, where the conformation change in the hexagonal protein subunits is shown as a change in molecular configuration toward a more globular form, perhaps as a tendency for development of a partial helix (for purposes of illustration, the configuration change is very much exaggerated), and where the lipid phase is illustrated in a micellar arrangement. It is apparent that in this state, the precise ordered lattice arrangements envisaged in the resting membrane no longer apply—the water in the aqueous channels is less organized in relation to the peptide surfaces, more mobile, and increasingly available to serve as solvent for ionic diffusion. Although there are still fixed charged sites, their arrangement is no longer precise, and the modified water serves to create new channels so that sodium and potassium can diffuse rather freely into and out of the cell, with the electrochemical gradient. Our representation implies that all pieces of the membrane must fit together if the precise lattice is to be maintained, and that a localized change in a single component, which may be minor, produces widespread changes in the other components so that it disturbs the arrangement of the system of the whole, which no longer has the property of a precisely-ordered lattice.

We have already implied that if non-polar groups (whether from peptide or steroid hormones or other biological activators of cell function) were fitted into appropriate sites of the aqueous channels, the hydrocarbon character of these groups would tend to disturb local water structure. Whether a collection of appropriate non-polar groups could serve to create cages of water clathrates as Klotz (21) has suggested, or whether alternative modes of disturbance in the local water structure are envisaged (18, 42), such effects could be widespread through the type of membrane system envisaged. These considerations take on special significance in relation to the hydrate microcrystal theory of anesthesia advanced by Pauling (32) and Miller (28). To explain the anesthetic effects of rare gases like xenon, argon, and nonhydrogen-bonding anesthetics, the concept was developed that these agents act in membrane systems by forming stable clathrate cages of water (pentagonal dodecahedra, etc.) which interfere with nerve conduction.

Richards has pointed out (33) that the formation of complete clathrate cages around a non-polar group at a planar or convex surface of a protein in aqueous solution is difficult to envisage in more than two-dimensional order—the stability of clathrates is dependent upon extended order in three dimensions. In the aqueous regions of the membrane model we have presented, limited to a few water layers, the stability of two-dimensional lattices around the non-polar side chains of proteins can be markedly enhanced, since there is no "bulk solvent" to bombard the clathrate cage. The possibility that the suggested propagation mechanism of changing water structures in the membrane involves the formation and breaking of clathrates, as peptide units undergo conformational change and present non-polar groups to aqueous regions, emerges as an attractive idea. Phase transitions in membrane water would then involve the following shifts:

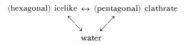

(hexagonal) icelike ↔ (pentagonal) clathrate

water

CONCLUSION

This presentation has considered the structure of water in relation to the problem of molecular organization of biological membranes. We suggested that the solution of the problem of organized water in the membrane was inextricably linked to the conformations of the structural protein of the fundamental lipoprotein matrix of the membrane. The need for a new structural concept of protein and peptide conformation adequate to deal with water-insoluble structural proteins and to form hexamers (and pentamers) arranged in geodesic patterns was suggested. The hexagonal concept of Warner—an idea in peptide and protein structure developed primarily on chemical structural grounds—was examined as a possible basis for forming the protein coat of a membrane and for approaching certain problems of membrane structure and function. We have tried to show how, starting with this principle of peptide conformation, it is possible to build a model which provides a unifying configuration for bringing together a variety of ideas, developed by others, dealing with selected aspects of membrane structure and function.

The conceptual configuration presented about membrane structure may be incorrect regarding specific detail and perhaps in basic principle. But we emphasize that if we are ever to understand the membrane at a molecular level in terms of both structure and function, we must clearly recognize that our primary difficulty may be the absence of a holistic concept sufficiently powerful to bridge the individual findings and atomistic concepts of the diverse disciplines involved in this problem.

The model of the cell membrane presented, initially developed at a work session of the Neurosciences Research Program dealing with membrane structure and function, resulted from stimulating discussions with Drs. H. Fernández-Morán, D. Robertson, A. Katchalsky, D. Green, and F. O. Schmitt. Later discussions, particularly with Drs. D. Warner and H. Fernández-Morán, clarified many of the issues involved; their special assistance is gratefully acknowledged. If the concept presented here should prove to have merit, in very large part this is due to the criticism and encouragement received from all of these individuals; the author retains exclusive rights to all of the inadequacies and deficiencies of the model presented.

REFERENCES

1. ANDERER, E. F., AND D. HANDSCHUH. *Naturforsch* 17b: 336, 1962.
2. BOYLE, P. J., AND E. J. CONWAY. *J. Physiol., London* 100: 1, 1941.
3. CASPAR, D. L. D. *Advan. Protein Chem.* 18: 37, 1963.
4. CASPAR, D. L. D., AND A. KLUG. *Cold Spring Harbor Symp. Quant. Biol.* 27: 1, 1962.
5. CRICK, F. H. C., AND J. D. WATSON. *Nature* 177: 473, 1956.
6. CRIDDLE, R. S., R. M. BOCK, D. E. GREEN, AND H. TISDALE. *Biochem.* 1: 327, 1962.
7. DAVSON, H., AND J. DANIELLI. *J. Cell. Comp. Physiol.* 5: 495, 1935.
8. DAVSON, H., AND J. DANIELLI. *Permeability of Natural Membranes* (2nd ed.). Cambridge: Cambridge Univ. Press, 1952, p. 111.
9. EIGEN, M., AND L. DE MAEYER. In: *The Structure of Electrolytic Solutions,* edited by W. J. Hamer. New York: Wiley, 1959, p. 64.
10. FAWCETT, D. W. *Circulation* 26: 105, 1962.
11. FERNÁNDEZ-MORÁN, H. In: *Metabolism of Nervous Tissue,* edited by D. Richter. London: Pergamon, 1957, p. 1.
12. FERNÁNDEZ-MORÁN, H. In: *Biophysical Science—A Study Program,* edited by J. L. Oncley. New York: Wiley, 1959, p. 319.
13. FERNÁNDEZ-MORÁN, H. *Circulation* 26: 1039, 1962.
14. FERNÁNDEZ-MORÁN, H. *J. Roy. Microscop. Soc.* 83: 183, 1964.
15. FERNÁNDEZ-MORÁN, H., T. ODA, P. V. BLAIR, AND D. E. GREEN. *J. Cell Biol.* 22: 63, 1964.
16. FINEAN, J. B. *J. Biochem. Biophys. Cytol.* 3: 95, 1957.
16a. GEREN, B. B. *Exptl. Cell Res.* 7: 588, 1954.
17. GREEN, D. E., AND S. FLEISCHER. In: *Horizons in Biochemistry,* edited by M. Kasha and B. Pullman. New York: Academic, 1962, p. 381.
18. KAUZMANN, W. *Advan. Protein Chem.* 14: 1, 1959.
19. KAVENAU, J. L. *Nature* 198: 525, 1963.
20. KLEINZELLER, A., AND A. KOTYK (editors). *Symposium on Membrane Transport and Metabolism* (Prague, Czechoslovakia, 1960). New York: Academic, 1961.
21. KLOTZ, I. M. *Brookhaven Symposium in Biology* Number 25. Upton, New York: Brookhaven National Laboratory, 1960.
22. KLOTZ, I. M. In: *Horizons in Biochemistry,* edited by M. Kasha and B. Pullman. New York: Academic, 1962, p. 523.
23. KOSHLAND, D. E., JR. In: *Horizons in Biochemistry,* edited by M. Kasha and B. Pullman. New York: Academic, 1962, p. 265.
24. LEA, E. J. A. *J. Theoret. Biol.* 5: 102, 1963.
25. LI, C. H. *Recent Progr. Hormone Res.* 18: 1, 1962.
26. LOCKE, M. (editor). *Cellular Membranes in Development.* New York: Academic, 1964.
27. LUZZATI, E., AND F. HUSSON. *J. Cell Biol.* 12: 207, 1962.

28. MILLER, S. L. *Proc. Nat. Acad. Sci., U.S.* 47: 1515, 1961.
29. MUELLER, P., D. O. RUDIN, H. TI TIEN, AND W. WESCOTT. *Circulation* 26: 1167, 1962.
30. MUELLER, P., D. O. RUDIN, H. TI TIEN, AND W. WESCOTT. *J. Phys. Chem.* 67: 534, 1963.
31. PALADE, G. *Proc. Nat. Acad. Sci., U.S.* 52: 613, 1964.
32. PAULING, L. *Science* 134: 15, 1961.
33. RICHARDS, F. M. *Ann. Rev. Biochem.* 32: 269, 1963.
34. RICHARDSON, S. H., H. O. HULTIN, AND D. E. GREEN. *Proc. Nat. Acad. Sci., U.S.* 50: 82, 1963.
35. ROBERTSON, J. D. *J. Physiol., London* 140: 58P, 1957.
36. ROBERTSON, J. D. *Biochem. Soc. Symp., Cambridge, Eng.* 16: 3, 1959.
37. ROBERTSON, J. D. *Progr. Biophys.* 10: 343, 1960.
38. ROBERTSON, J. D. *Res. Publ., Assoc. Res. Nervous Mental Disease* 40: 94, 1962.
39. ROBERTSON, J. D. *J. Cell. Biol.* 19: 201, 1963.
40. ROBERTSON, J. D. In: *Cellular Membranes in Development*, edited by M. Locke. New York: Academic, 1964, p. 24.

41. ROBINOW, C. F. In: *The Cell*, edited by J. Brachet and A. E. Mirsky. New York: Academic, 1960, vol. 4, p. 45.
42. SCHERAGA, H. A. *J. Phys. Chem.* 65: 1071, 1961.
43. SCHMIDT, W. J. *Kolloidzscht.* 84: 137, 1938.
44. SCHMITT, F. O. *Res. Publ. Assoc. Res. Nervous Mental Disease* 28: 247, 1950.
45. SCHMITT, F. O., R. S. BEAR, AND G. L. CLARK. *Radiology* 25: 131, 1935.
46. SCHMITT, F. O., R. S. BEAR, AND K. L. PALMER. *J. Cell. Comp. Physiol.* 18: 31, 1941.
47. SCHMITT, F. O., R. S. BEAR, AND E. PONDER. *J. Cell. Comp. Physiol.* 9: 89, 1936.
48. STOECKENIUS, W. *J. Cell. Biol.* 12: 221, 1962.
49. Symposium on the Plasma Membrane. *Circulation* 26: 1038, 1962.
50. THOMPSON, T. E. In: *Cellular Membranes in Development*, edited by M. Locke. New York: Academic, 1964, p. 83.
51. WARNER, D. T. *Nature* 190: 120, 1961.
52. WARNER, D. T. *J. Theoret. Biol.* 1: 514, 1961.
53. WARNER, D. T. *J. Theoret. Biol.* 6: 118, 1964.

**311**